VISUAL
ENCYCLOPEDIA OF
space

Saturn

Dried-up channels on Mars

Total solar eclipse

Chandra X-ray Telescope

Lagoon nebula

Ariane launch vehicle

VISUAL
E N C Y C L O P E D I A   O F
space

BASIC
REFRACTOR
TELESCOPE

CONSULTANTS

DAVID HUGHES AND ROBIN KERROD

Sandy Creek

DK London
Editor Niki Foreman
Senior Designer Spencer Holbrook
Project Art Editor Philip Letsu
Managing Editor Linda Esposito
Managing Art Editor Diane Thistlethwaite
DTP Designer Siu Chan
Production Controller Luca Bazzoli
Picture Researcher Myriam Megharbi

DK Delhi
Senior Editor Dipali Singh
Project Editor Aekta Jerath
Editor Larissa Sayers
Designers Romi Chakraborty, Arunesh Talapatra
DTP Designer Balwant Singh
Manager Aparna Sharma

Consultant Prof. David W. Hughes and Robin Kerrod

Sandy Creek
122 Fifth Avenue
New York, NY 10011

ISBN 978-1-4351-2399-1

A Cataloging-in-Publication record for this book
is available from the Library of Congress.

Color reproduction by Colourscan, Singapore
Printed and bound in Singapore by Star Standard

Lot 1 3 5 7 9 10 8 6 4 2

CONTENTS

INTRODUCTION 8
How To Use This Book 8

UNIVERSE 10
What Is the Universe? 12
Scale of the Universe 14
Distances in the Universe 16
Expanding Universe 18
Image: Distant Galaxies 20
Life Story of the Universe 22
Big Bang 24
First Three Minutes 26
Echoes of the Big Bang 28

SOLAR SYSTEM 30
What Is the Solar System? 32
Birth of the Solar System 34
Image: Planetary Birthplace 36
The Sun 38
Inside the Sun 40
Sun's Surface 42
Sun's Atmosphere 44

Eclipses of the Sun 46
Solar Energy and
Influence 48
Earth 50
Earth's Surface 52
Earth's Atmosphere 54
Life on Earth 56
The Moon 58
Moon's Surface 60
Near Side of the Moon 62
Far Side of the Moon 64
Lunar Influences 66
Exploring the Moon 68
Other Solar Systems 70
Image: Saturn Close-Up 72
Mercury 74
Mercury's Surface 76
Venus 78
Venusian Atmosphere 80
Venusian Surface 82

Mars 84
Surface of Mars 86
Image: Martian Mountains 88
Jupiter 90
Jupiter's Atmosphere 92
Jupiter's Moons 94
Saturn 96
Saturn's Rings 98

Image: Saturn's Rings 100
Saturn's Moons 102
Uranus 104
Neptune 106
Pluto 108

COMETS AND ASTEROIDS 110

Minor Members 112
Comets 114
Exploring Comets 116
Image: Comet Close-Up 118
Meteors 120
Meteorites 122
Asteroids 124
Impacts 126

STARS 128

What Is a Star? 130
Life Cycle of a Star 132
Where Stars are Born 134
Image: Orion Nebula 136
Properties of Stars 138
Stellar Classification 140
Brightness 142
Variable Stars 144
How Far Are the Stars? 146
Measure of the Stars 148
Constellations 150
Cataloging Stars 152
Clusters and Doubles 154
Image: A Starbust Region 156
Globular Clusters 158
Red Giants 160
Planetary Nebulas 162
Image: Dying Star 164

Supernovas 166
Neutron Stars 168
Black Holes 170
Inside a Black Hole 172

GALAXIES 174

What Is a Galaxy? 176
Colliding Galaxies 178
Image: Galactic Collision Course 180
Active Galaxies 182

The Milky Way 184
Structure of the Milky Way 186
Interstellar Medium 188
Our Local Neighborhood 190
The Perseus Arm 192
The Sagittarius Arm 194
Heart of the Milky Way 196
Magellanic Clouds 198
Image: 30 Doradus 200
Local Group 202
Clusters and Superclusters 204

OBSERVING SPACE 206

Above Our Heads 208
Stargazing 210
Special Effects 212
Optical Telescopes 214
Radio Telescopes 216
Observatories 218
Observatory Telescopes 220

New Designs 222
Unusual Telescopes 224
Analyzing Light 226
Information from Space 228
Images of Space 230
Image: Supernova Remnant 232
Infrared Astronomy 234
Ultraviolet Astronomy 236
X-Ray Astronomy 238
Gamma-Ray Astronomy 240

EXPLORING SPACE 242

Telescopes in Space 244
Rockets 246
Rocket Fuels 248
Space Launchers 250
Launch Centers 252
Image: Blastoff 254
Countdown 256

SATELLITES AND PROBES 258

Hubble Space Telescope 260
Satellites and Orbits 262
Communications Satellites 264
Navigation Satellites 266
Meteorology Satellites 268
Earth Resources Satellites 270
Space Debris 272
Flybys and Orbiters 274
Landers 276
Probes to the Planets 278
Search for Life on Mars 280
Missions to Mars 282

SPACE TRAVEL 284

Flying to Space 286
Space Shuttle 288
Working in Space 290
Living in Space 292
Image: Spacewalk 294
Science in Space 296
International Space Station 298
Space Missions I 300
Space Missions II 302
Spaceplanes 304
Interplanetary Travel 306
Futuristic Starships 308

Image: Interstellar Tornadoes 338
Scorpius 340
Taurus 342
Ursa Major 344
Polar Star Maps 346
Northern Hemisphere Star Maps 350
June to November

Northern Hemisphere Star Maps 354
December to May

Southern Hemisphere Star Maps 358
September to February

Southern Hemisphere Star Maps 362
March to August

Timeline 366
Biographies 374
Glossary 388
Index 392
Acknowledgments 399

REFERENCE 310

The Northern Sky 312
The Southern Sky 314
Constellations Guide 316
Andromeda and Aquarius 324
Carina 326
Centaurus and Crux 328
Cygnus 330
Dorado and Draco 332
Orion 334
Sagittarius 336

CONTENTS

HOW TO USE THIS BOOK

These pages show you how to use the *Visual Encyclopedia of Space*. The book is divided into ten sections dealing with every aspect of space, from how the universe was formed to space travel. A reference section follows, with a comprehensive constellation guide, a timeline, and biographies.

HEADING AND INTRODUCTION
Every spread has a subject heading. This is followed by the introduction, which outlines the subject and gives a clear idea of what each page is about.

"At a Glance" box

Caption

PLANETS AT A GLANCE
These boxes give information on the individual characteristics of each planet, making it easy to compare features.

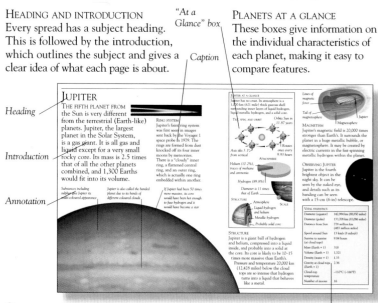

Heading

JUPITER
THE FIFTH PLANET FROM the Sun is very different from the terrestrial (Earth-like) planets. Jupiter, the largest planet in the Solar System, is a gas giant. It is all gas and liquid except for a very small rocky core. Its mass is 2.5 times that of all the other planets combined, and 1,300 Earths would fit into its volume.

RING SYSTEM
Jupiter's faint ring system was first seen in images sent back by the Voyager 1 space probe in 1979. The rings are formed from dust knocked off its four inner moons by meteorites. There is a "cloudy" inner ring, a flattened central ring, and an outer ring, which is actually one ring embedded within another.

Introduction

Annotation

Substances including sulphur give Jupiter its stain-coloured appearance

Jupiter is also called the banded planet due to its bands of different coloured clouds

If Jupiter had been 50 times more massive, its core would have been hot enough to fuse hydrogen and it would have become a star

JUPITER AT A GLANCE
Jupiter has no crust. Its atmosphere is a 1,000-km (621-mile) thick gaseous shell surrounding inner layers of liquid hydrogen, liquid metallic hydrogen, and a solid core.

THE SPIN AND ORBIT
Axis tilts 3.1° from vertical

Orbits Sun in 11.87 years

1 Rotates once every 9.93 hours

ATMOSPHERE
Helium (10.2%), traces of methane and ammonia

Hydrogen (89.8%)

Diameter is 11 times that of Earth

STRUCTURE
Atmosphere
Liquid hydrogen and helium
Metallic hydrogen
Probably solid core

SCALE

STRUCTURE
Jupiter is a giant ball of hydrogen and helium, compressed into a liquid inside, and probably into a solid at the core. Its core is likely to be 10–15 times more massive than Earth's. Pressure and temperature 20,000 km (12,428 miles) below the cloud tops are so intense that hydrogen turns into a liquid that behaves like a metal.

Lines of magnetic force

Tail of magnetosphere

Jupiter

MAGNETISM
Jupiter's magnetic field is 20,000 times stronger than Earth's. It surrounds the planet in a huge metallic bubble, or magnetosphere. It may be created by electric currents in the fast-spinning metallic hydrogen within the planet.

OBSERVING JUPITER
Jupiter is the fourth brightest object in the night sky. It can be seen by the naked eye, and details such as its banding can be seen with a 15-cm (6-in) telescope.

VITAL STATISTICS

Diameter (equator)	142,984 km (88,850 miles)
Diameter (poles)	133,708 km (83,080 miles)
Distance from Sun	778 million km (483 million miles)
Speed around Sun	13 km/s (8 miles/s)
Sunrise to sunrise (at cloud tops)	9.84 hours
Mass (Earth = 1)	318
Volume (Earth = 1)	1,321
Density (water = 1)	1.33
Gravity at cloud tops (Earth = 1)	2.36
Cloud-top temperature	–110°C (–166°F)
Number of moons	16

"Vital Statistics" box

CAPTIONS
Each illustration in the book is accompanied by a detailed, explanatory caption that expands on the points in the introduction.

VITAL STATISTICS BOXES
Many spreads have "Vital Statistics" boxes, which give important measurements about the feature.

BIOGRAPHIES

The biographies in the reference section of the book provide further information about famous astronomers and scientists.

Stunning double-page image

Detailed maps showing constellations, stars, and other night-sky features

CONSTELLATIONS

An extensive constellation section includes star maps and sky guides to assist in stargazing.

ANDROMEDA
DEPICTING A GREEK PRINCESS who was rescued by Perseus, Andromeda contains the nearest major galaxy to us, M31—the Andromeda Galaxy—which is the most distant object visible to the naked eye.

AQUARIUS
THIS CONSTELLATION REPRESENTS a youth pouring water from a jar. The "Water Jar" is a group of stars.

FULL-SPREAD IMAGES

Each section is interspersed with full-spread images, showing fantastic aspects of space and the technology we use to explore it.

Picture illustrates features of interest

WHAT IS A STAR?

A STAR IS an enormous spinning ball of hot and luminous gas. Most stars contain two main gases – hydrogen and helium. These gases are held together by gravity, and at the core they are very densely packed. Within the core, immense amounts of energy are produced.

CORE FUSION
A star produces energy by nuclear fusion. Within the core, hydrogen nuclei (protons) collide and fuse to form two deuterium (heavy hydrogen) and then two forms of helium. During fusion, energy is given off. This type of reaction, which is found in most stars, is called the proton-proton chain.

ANNOTATION

Pictures often have extra information around them, which picks out features. This text appears in italics and uses leader lines to point to details.

Fact box

DATA BOXES

On some spreads, data boxes give facts, figures, and general data about key topics featured on the page.

FACT BOXES

Data box

Many pages have fact boxes. The information in these is related to the main topic on the page.

INDEX

There is an index at the back of the book that alphabetically lists every subject. By referring to the index, information on particular topics can be found quickly.

UNIVERSE

WHAT IS THE UNIVERSE?

THE UNIVERSE IS EVERYTHING that exists. From planet Earth beneath our feet to the farthest stars, everything is a part of the universe. The universe is so large that it contains countless billions of stars. However, most of it consists of nothing but empty space.

Galaxies

Galaxy containing billions of stars

Quasar—the brilliant center of a distant galaxy

Supernova— the death of a large star

Comet—a dirty snowball

LOOKING TO THE SKIES

From Earth, we can look into space and study the universe. In every direction we look, there are stars. There are more stars in the universe than any other type of object—stars in enormous groups called galaxies, and stars at different stages of their lives, including at least one star that has planets. Despite the huge size of the universe, we know of only one place where life exists—planet Earth.

UNIVERSE FACTS

• There are at least 100 billion galaxies in the universe; large ones contain more than 100 billion stars.

• The most distant galaxies we can detect are 76,000 million million million miles (123,000 million million million km) away.

HORSEHEAD IN SPACE

Looking like a chess knight, the Horsehead Nebula is a gigantic cloud of dark-colored dust. It is visible because the dust blocks out light from behind the nebula, so that we see it in silhouette. The Milky Way Galaxy contains many similar clouds that block our view of different regions.

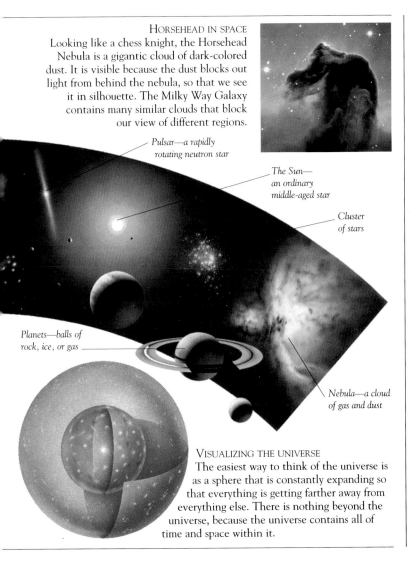

Pulsar—a rapidly rotating neutron star

The Sun— an ordinary middle-aged star

Cluster of stars

Planets—balls of rock, ice, or gas

Nebula—a cloud of gas and dust

VISUALIZING THE UNIVERSE

The easiest way to think of the universe is as a sphere that is constantly expanding so that everything is getting farther away from everything else. There is nothing beyond the universe, because the universe contains all of time and space within it.

SCALE OF THE UNIVERSE

DISTANCES IN THE UNIVERSE are so great that light is used as a unit of measurement. Light travels at about 186,000 miles per second (300,000 km/s), and a light-year (ly) is the distance light travels in one year. A galaxy can measure thousands of light-years across and be millions of light-years distant.

GALAXY NGC 4603

STUDYING DISTANT STARS
The Hubble Space Telescope is used to study and photograph the stars in distant galaxies, which can be seen if the galaxies are closer than 100 light-years. Studies such as these are essential in determining the age, size, and fate of the universe.

SCALE OF SIZES
The human world, the world of everyday experience, is dwarfed by the scale of the universe. Earth is one of nine planets orbiting the Sun, which is one of about 200 billion stars in the Milky Way Galaxy.

The Sun is one of over 200 billion stars in the Milky Way Galaxy

Earth is the third of nine planets orbiting the Sun

More than 6.5 billion people live on Earth

The human scale is the familiar one of everyday objects

Clusters of galaxies are grouped into superclusters

Galaxies group into clusters of many thousands

Most of the universe consists of the empty space between objects

THE BEGINNING
The universe began with a tremendous explosion called the Big Bang. The universe is still expanding with the force of the Big Bang.

DISTANCES IN THE UNIVERSE

WITHIN THE MILKY WAY, astronomers use radar to measure the distance to planets, and parallax to measure the distances of nearby stars. Beyond the Milky Way, the distance to nearby galaxies can be found by comparing their stars to similar stars in the Milky Way, and then using the distances to these galaxies to find how far away other galaxies lie.

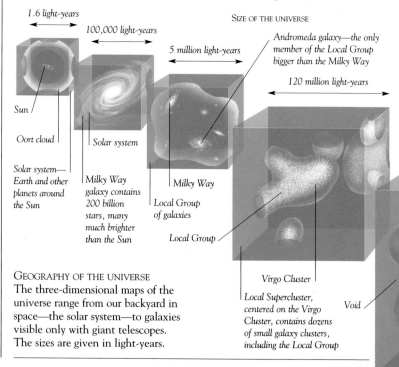

1.6 light-years

100,000 light-years

5 million light-years

SIZE OF THE UNIVERSE

Andromeda galaxy—the only member of the Local Group bigger than the Milky Way

120 million light-years

Sun

Oort cloud

Solar system

Solar system—
Earth and other
planets around
the Sun

Milky Way
galaxy contains
200 billion
stars, many
much brighter
than the Sun

Milky Way

Local Group
of galaxies

Local Group

Virgo Cluster

Local Supercluster,
centered on the Virgo
Cluster, contains dozens
of small galaxy clusters,
including the Local Group

Void

GEOGRAPHY OF THE UNIVERSE
The three-dimensional maps of the universe range from our backyard in space—the solar system—to galaxies visible only with giant telescopes. The sizes are given in light-years.

CEPHEID STANDARD CANDLES

Cepheid variables are a type of star that appears to brighten and dim with great regularity. This cycle, or variation in luminosity, is longer if the star is more luminous. If two stars generate the same amount of light but one is dimmer, it must lie farther away. Astronomers use Cepheid variables to measure distance. They find the luminosity (the energy emitted in unit time) of a Cepheid from the length of its cycle, and then compare this with its apparent brightness to measure the distance to the galaxy in which it lies— once the luminosity is known, the Cepheid can be used as a standard candle.

Cepheid star

Brightness doubled

"Light curve"

Brightness

Time

Brighter Cepheid

Brightness quadrupled

Light curve has longer period

Brightness

Time

Nearby universe contains superclusters of galaxies, which are strung together in vast filaments that can stretch across hundreds of millions of light-years. They are separated by huge voids containing very few galaxies

1 billion light-years

Local Supercluster

Galaxy filament

DISTANCES FROM SUPERNOVAS

Supernovas are exploding stars so brilliant that astronomers can spot them in galaxies billions of light-years away. Astronomers identify different kinds of supernovas from the way their light brightens, then fades. Type 1a supernovas always reach the same maximum luminosity, so they form ideal standard candles— though they appear only once or twice a century in an average galaxy.

EXPANDING UNIVERSE

In every direction, distant clusters of galaxies are rushing away from us—the farther away a cluster lies, the faster it is speeding away. Clusters are moving away from each other just as raisins in a cake move apart when it is baked. This expansion is very useful to astronomers—once they have measured the rate of expansion for nearby galaxies, they can use a galaxy's speed to find its distance.

EXPANSION OF SPACE
Although the universe is expanding, it is not expanding *into* anything. Instead, space itself is stretching, and carrying clusters of galaxies with it.

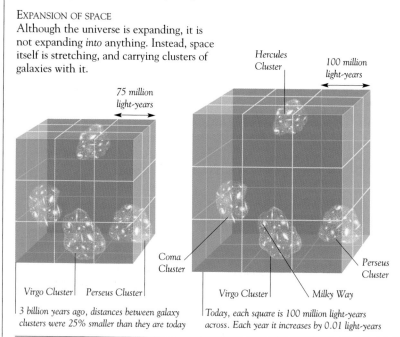

Hercules Cluster

100 million light-years

75 million light-years

Coma Cluster

Virgo Cluster

Perseus Cluster

Milky Way

Virgo Cluster | Perseus Cluster

Perseus Cluster

3 billion years ago, distances between galaxy clusters were 25% smaller than they are today

Today, each square is 100 million light-years across. Each year it increases by 0.01 light-years

Space outside gravitational well is free to expand

Space within gravitational well does not expand

Gravity of single galaxy

Combined gravity of whole cluster

SPACE AROUND A CLUSTER

In a two-dimensional view of space, massive objects can be thought of as making dents, called gravitational wells.

Coma Cluster

Hercules Cluster

115 million light-years

Space between the galaxy clusters grows

Virgo Cluster

Perseus Cluster

2 billion years in the future, galaxy clusters will be 15% farther apart than they are today

Dark lines formed by elements in galaxy absorbing light

Hubble's law states that a galaxy's speed depends on its distance

Increasing redshift and speed

Increasing distance

REDSHIFTING GALAXIES

If a galaxy is moving away, the dark lines in its spectrum are shifted toward the red (an effect called redshift). The more the lines are redshifted, the higher the galaxy's speed.

2dF spectrometer on the Anglo-Australian telescope can take spectra of up to 400 distant galaxies at one time

MEASURING REDSHIFTS

Huge telescopes have been built to collect light from distant galaxies, which can be used to reveal their redshifts and their distances. Sensitive electronic spectrometers, which measure the redshifts of many galaxies simultaneously, have also been developed.

LIFE STORY OF THE UNIVERSE

All matter, energy, space, and time were created in the Big Bang around 14 billion years ago. At first the universe was minute and blisteringly hot, but as it expanded and cooled, atomic particles joined to form hydrogen and helium. Over billions of years, these gases have produced galaxies, stars, planets, and us.

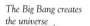

The Big Bang creates the universe

The universe keeps expanding

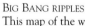

The universe will slowly cool as it gets ever larger and less dense

WHAT HAPPENS NEXT?

The universe has been expanding since the Big Bang, and will probably go on expanding forever. Recent observations indicate that the expansion is speeding up as the universe gets older and bigger.

BIG BANG RIPPLES

This map of the whole sky is based on tiny variations in the temperature of space. Red is warmer than average and blue is colder. These tiny variations are faint traces of the Big Bang explosion. The information for the map was obtained by the Cosmic Background Explorer Satellite (COBE).

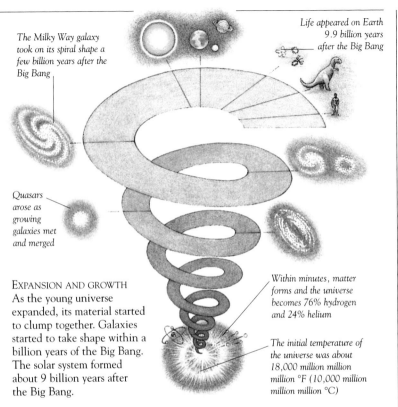

The Milky Way galaxy took on its spiral shape a few billion years after the Big Bang

Life appeared on Earth 9.9 billion years after the Big Bang

Quasars arose as growing galaxies met and merged

EXPANSION AND GROWTH
As the young universe expanded, its material started to clump together. Galaxies started to take shape within a billion years of the Big Bang. The solar system formed about 9 billion years after the Big Bang.

Within minutes, matter forms and the universe becomes 76% hydrogen and 24% helium

The initial temperature of the universe was about 18,000 million million million °F (10,000 million million million °C)

UNIVERSE: COOLING DATA	
Time after Big Bang	**Temperature**
10^{-6} seconds	1.8×10^{13}°F (10^{13}°C)
3 minutes	1.8×10^{8}°F (10^{8}°C)
300,000 years	18,000°F (10,000°C)
1 million years	5,400°F (3,000°C)
1 billion years	−275°F (−170°C)
14 billion years	−454°F (−270°C)

UNIVERSE FACTS
• Scientists can trace the life story of the universe back to what is called the Planck time, 10^{-43} seconds after the Big Bang.
• 10^{-43} means a decimal point followed by 42 zeros and then a one.

BIG BANG

THE BIG BANG occurred some 14 billion years ago. It was the beginning of everything—time, space, and the building blocks of all matter. At first, the universe was hot and dense. Then it began to expand and cool, and it is still expanding and cooling today.

EXPANSION REVERSED
If the expanding motion of the galaxies we see today is reversed, it leads back to an instant around 14 billion years ago when they all occupied a single point. This was the origin of the Big Bang.

Earliest possible date for Big Bang: 15 billion years ago

Most likely date for Big Bang: 14 billion years ago

Latest possible date for Big Bang: 11 billion years ago

Young, densely packed galaxies

Fueled by the strong force, the universe suddenly inflates

Just after creation, the universe is infinitely hot and expands slowly

The universe today

Increasing time

Big Bang

FUNDAMENTAL FORCES

Four forces control the universe. Electromagnetism rules electricity and magnetism; the weak force governs how the stars shine; the strong force glues together the nuclei in atoms; and gravity keeps the planets and stars in orbit. The forces were once united in a single superforce, but as the universe expanded and cooled, they split off, one by one.

Superforce

Gravity

Strong force

Weak force

Electromagnetic force

Matter and antimatter particles have the same mass, and are equal and opposite to each other

The force of inflation works like antigravity, driving everything apart

The temperature drops rapidly to absolute zero, then rises again

INFLATION

Conditions in the early universe turned energy into equal amounts of matter and antimatter—just 2 lb (1 kg) of material. Moments later, the universe blew up, growing a hundred trillion quintillion quintillion times in a fraction of a second (cosmic inflation). This released huge amounts of energy, creating more matter and shaping the fundamental forces.

VIRTUAL PARTICLES

Energy from the Big Bang created virtual particle pairs—one of matter and one of antimatter—that almost immediately annihilated each other.

SCALE OF INFLATION

In a fraction of a second, the universe grew from smaller than an atom to bigger than a galaxy.

Virtual particle pairs are of two types— heavy quarks (red) and light leptons (green)

Weak electromagnetic forces, separating after inflation, gave particles and antiparticles the energy to exist on their own

Photons are the particles that carry light and the electromagnetic force

UNIVERSE

25

FIRST THREE MINUTES

THE HOT EARLY UNIVERSE contained subatomic particles of matter and antimatter. Most of these particles wiped each other out, but matter finally triumphed. As the universe expanded and cooled, construction began. By the end of its third minute, the building blocks of all matter had been created— the nuclei of the first three elements: hydrogen, helium, and lithium.

DARK MATTER
Invisible, dark matter far exceeds visible matter, and probably consists of numerous WIMPS and neutrinos.

Particles and antiparticles destroy each other

Exotic particles include X bosons, Higgs bosons, and WIMPS

Quarks (red) and leptons (green) are released during inflation

Forces are carried between particles by W and Z bosons, gluons, photons, and gravitons

MATURING UNIVERSE
The early universe had short-lived particles like quarks, leptons, and WIMPS zooming around at temperatures of 18,000 trillion trillion °F (10,000 trillion trillion °C). Within three minutes, the temperature had dropped to less than 1.8 billion °F (1 billion°C) and the universe was much calmer, with fewer, more stable particles.

SEARCHING FOR ANTIMATTER
An antimatter galaxy would look just like a normal one, except around its edge, where there would be flashes of energy as matter and antimatter met and annihilated each other. So far, none have been detected.

PROTONS AND NEUTRONS

As the universe cooled, gluons pulled quarks together in threes to form protons and neutrons. Some neutrons decayed into protons. The remaining neutrons bonded with protons to form the nuclei of atoms. By the end of the first three minutes, there were no neutrons left.

Protons

Neutron in helium nucleus

Neutron

Free protons (hydrogen nuclei)

Photons carry radiation

Leptons still move freely

Quarks locked up in protons and neutrons

COSMOS COMPOSITION

The first elements created were probably hydrogen (77%), helium (23%), and lithium (0.000,000,1%).

EARLY UNIVERSE PARTICLES

Many subatomic particles from the early universe no longer exist, or have changed into other particles. The most important early particles are listed below.

- X boson: very heavy particle predicted by theory but as yet undetected.

- Higgs boson: a very heavy particle proposed by British physicist Peter Higgs.

- WIMP: weakly interacting massive particle, thought to make up most of the universe's dark matter.

- W and Z bosons: particles similar to photons—but with mass— that carry the weak force.

- Quark: building block of protons and neutrons, found in six varieties.

- Lepton: particle sensitive to the weak force—electrons are the lightest type of lepton.

- Neutrinos: low-mass, very common particles found in three types.

- Gluon: transmits the strong force that joins quarks together.

- Photon: massless particle carrying radiation and electromagnetism. This is the most common particle.

- Graviton: particle thought to carry gravitational force.

ECHOES OF THE BIG BANG

FOR A QUARTER of a million years, the ingredients of space stayed the same, but were diluted as the universe expanded. Most of the energy was in the form of radiation, but the early cosmos was foggy, so light could not travel far. Then the fog cleared suddenly and space became transparent.

Time →

At three minutes, matter consists of atomic nuclei, electrons, and dark matter particles

As the universe cools, heavier leptons decay into electrons. Atomic nuclei and electrons soon dominate

Dark matter in the universe, unaffected by radiation, begins to clump together under gravity

This division—"last scattering surface"—formed 300,000 years after the Big Bang. It separates the opaque from the transparent universe. Background radiation comes from this "surface"

Photons travel only short distances between collisions

Helium nucleus

Hydrogen nucleus

Electrons

PHOTON SCATTERING

In the early universe, photons of light kept interacting with atomic nuclei and electrons, so none got anywhere. Photons would bounce off one particle, only to collide with another. Light could never travel far in a straight line and, as a result, the universe was opaque.

COOLING UNIVERSE

At three minutes, the universe was filled with high-energy gamma radiation. As the universe expanded and cooled, the radiation lost energy, turning into X-rays, light, and heat. Electrons slowed down, combining with atomic nuclei to form the first atoms. These atoms did not interact with radiation, so light was able to travel in straight lines over long distances, and the universe became transparent.

28

AFTERGLOW

In 1965, physicists Arno Penzias and Robert Wilson discovered a weak radio signal coming from every direction in the sky. This signal was equivalent to that emitted by an object at –454°F (–270°C)—three degrees above absolute zero. The only possible source for this radiation was the dying heat of the Big Bang, cooled by the expansion of the universe.

COBE BACKGROUND RADIATION MAP

Hydrogen atoms

Helium atom

Photons travel longer distances— collisions are rarer

Temperature differences caused by dark-matter clumps show up in the background radiation

Galaxies begin to form as dark matter attracts hydrogen and helium clouds

FORMATION OF ATOMS

Up to 300,000 years after the Big Bang, the temperature had fallen to 5,430°F (3,000°C). The electrons had slowed down and could be pulled into orbit around the nuclei of hydrogen and helium, forming the first atoms.

Radiation from the "last scattering surface" continues to cool, turning from light and heat to radio waves

29

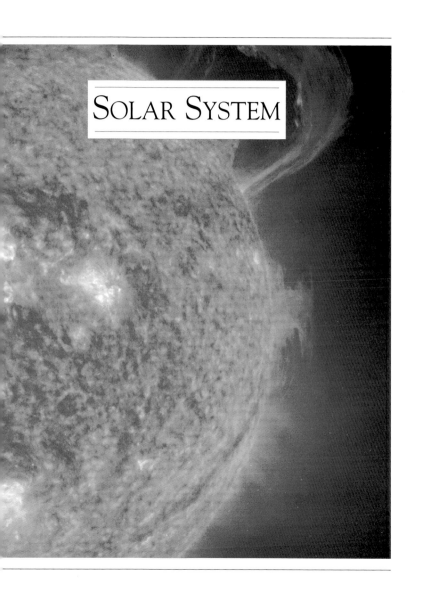

SOLAR SYSTEM

SOLAR SYSTEM

WHAT IS THE SOLAR SYSTEM?

THE SOLAR SYSTEM consists of the Sun and the many objects that orbit around it—nine planets, over 150 moons, and countless asteroids and comets. The system occupies a disk-shaped volume of space more than 7.5 billion miles (12 billion km) across. At the center is the Sun, which contains more than 99 percent of the solar system's mass.

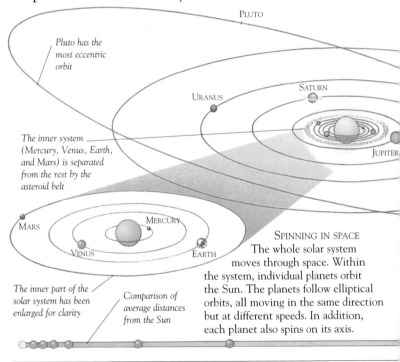

Pluto has the most eccentric orbit

The inner system (Mercury, Venus, Earth, and Mars) is separated from the rest by the asteroid belt

The inner part of the solar system has been enlarged for clarity

Comparison of average distances from the Sun

SPINNING IN SPACE
The whole solar system moves through space. Within the system, individual planets orbit the Sun. The planets follow elliptical orbits, all moving in the same direction but at different speeds. In addition, each planet also spins on its axis.

32

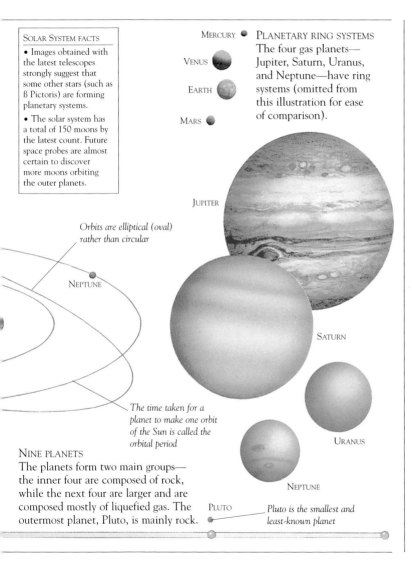

SOLAR SYSTEM FACTS

• Images obtained with the latest telescopes strongly suggest that some other stars (such as ß Pictoris) are forming planetary systems.

• The solar system has a total of 150 moons by the latest count. Future space probes are almost certain to discover more moons orbiting the outer planets.

MERCURY

VENUS

EARTH

MARS

PLANETARY RING SYSTEMS
The four gas planets—Jupiter, Saturn, Uranus, and Neptune—have ring systems (omitted from this illustration for ease of comparison).

JUPITER

Orbits are elliptical (oval) rather than circular

NEPTUNE

SATURN

The time taken for a planet to make one orbit of the Sun is called the orbital period

URANUS

NEPTUNE

NINE PLANETS
The planets form two main groups—the inner four are composed of rock, while the next four are larger and are composed mostly of liquefied gas. The outermost planet, Pluto, is mainly rock.

PLUTO

Pluto is the smallest and least-known planet

BIRTH OF THE SOLAR SYSTEM

It is widely believed that the solar system was born out of a vast, spinning cloud of gas and dust— the solar nebula. The process began 4.6 billion years ago with the Sun's birth. The planets and other objects formed from unused material. When the solar system was nearly complete, 500 million years later, just 0.002 percent of the solar nebula's original mass remained. The rest had fallen into the Sun or been blown out into space.

1 A giant, spinning cloud of gas and dust collected in space to form the solar nebula

Sun   Disk

2 The Sun formed as the solar nebula contracted, leaving a spinning outer disk of material

Dust and gas particles in the disk clumped together to form larger, grainlike particles

Grains collided to form ever-larger, rocky particles, eventually producing planetesimals

SUPERNOVA SHOCK WAVE
A massive star may explode as a supernova at the end of its life. In some supernovas, the star's core collapses in on itself, causing a powerful shock wave. The contraction of the solar nebula may have been triggered by such a shock wave.

Gravity pulls the star's core in with force, sending out a shock wave

SOLAR NEBULA
As the vast cloud spun, its center became denser and hotter, and the Sun was born. Rocky and metallic material near the Sun came together to form the inner planets. In the cooler, outer regions, snow combined with rock, metal, and gas to form the outer planets.

BIRTH OF THE PLANETS

The planets began to form about 4.6 billion years ago. Apart from Pluto, each planet came together from an initial, ring-shaped mass of material around the Sun. (Pluto was created from the leftovers.) As the planets formed, tiny particles stuck together to make grain-sized lumps, then pebbles and boulders, and eventually larger bodies called planetesimals. When they were a few miles (kilometers) across, the planetesimals' gravity was strong enough to attract more and more material.

Sun

Sun pulls material off large cloud

Passing cloud of gas and dust

CAPTURE THEORY

This alternative theory suggests that part of a cloud of gas and dust, passing close to the Sun, was captured by the Sun's gravity. This then split into mini-clouds that contracted and formed the planets.

3 *The newborn Sun blew off excess material. Rings of material formed around it; in these rings, planetesimals were born*

Rocky planets, such as Mercury, were molten when young. They developed a metallic core

Solar system debris consisted mainly of asteroids and comets

Rock and metal between Mars and Jupiter formed the asteroid belt

4 *Planetesimals joined to form larger bodies called protoplanets. These came together to form the rocky planets*

Rings produced planets

5 *Protoplanets also formed in the outer regions of the disk. As they grew larger, their gravity attracted vast amounts of gas, creating the gas giants*

Gas giants, such as Saturn, first formed a solid core and then captured a huge atmosphere

6 *Pluto formed from material not used in the gas giants. The remaining material formed the Oort cloud of comets*

37

THE SUN

LIKE OTHER STARS, the Sun is a huge ball of spinning gas. Nuclear reactions take place at its core, giving off energy. The Sun is the only star close enough to be studied in detail. Its surface features, such as sunspots and prominences, can be observed from Earth. Satellites and space probes are able to get a closer view and obtain even more information.

ECLIPSE OF THE SUN
During an eclipse, the outer layer of the Sun—the corona—becomes visible. Normally the corona is hidden by glare.

YEAR 1   YEAR 4   YEAR 7   YEAR 10   YEAR 12

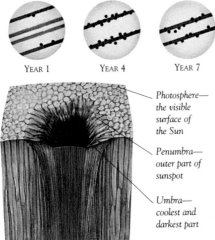

Photosphere—the visible surface of the Sun

Penumbra—outer part of sunspot

Umbra—coolest and darkest part

COOL AND DARK
Sunspots—dark patches on the surface—are regions of cooler gas caused by disturbances in the Sun's magnetic field. Sunspots follow an 11-year cycle that begins with the Sun being relatively spot-free. The spots appear at high latitude and gradually increase in number, moving toward the Sun's equator during the cycle.

SOLAR DATA	
Avg. distance from Earth	92,955,807 miles (149,597,870 km)
Distance from center of galaxy	25,000 light-years
Diameter (at equator)	864,976 miles (1,391,980 km)
Rotation period (at equator)	25.04 Earth days
Mass (Earth = 1)	330,000
Gravity (Earth = 1)	27.9
Avg. density (water = 1)	1.41
Absolute magnitude	4.83

SOLAR FACTS

• Never look directly at the Sun. Even with sunglasses, camera film, or smoked glass, you risk damaging your eyesight.

• The safe way is to project the Sun's image on to a piece of paper using a hand lens.

THE SUN: EXTERNAL AND INTERNAL FEATURES
(for details see pp.40–41)

Chromosphere

Photosphere temperature about 9,900°F (5,500°C)

Core temperature 27 million°F (15 million°C)

Corona

Sunspot

Radiative zone

Convective zone

INSIDE THE SUN

OUR NEAREST STAR, the Sun, is a huge globe of hot gas that is 109 times the diameter of Earth, and 745 times greater in mass than all the other bodies in the solar system put together. It has been blazing for 4.6 billion years and will continue to shine for about the same amount of time again.

The core is the center where nuclear reactions occur

THE SUN'S STRUCTURE

The Sun's core is so hot—27 million°F (15 million°C)—that atoms of gas are ripped apart, leaving just their bare nuclei, or centers. The energy travels through the radiative and convective zones to its photosphere, where it leaves the Sun.

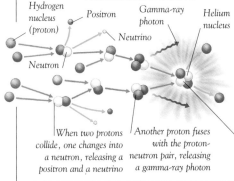

NUCLEAR FUSION OF HYDROGEN

Hydrogen nucleus (proton)

Positron

Gamma-ray photon

Helium nucleus

Neutrino

Neutron

When two protons collide, one changes into a neutron, releasing a positron and a neutrino

Another proton fuses with the proton-neutron pair, releasing a gamma-ray photon

NUCLEAR REACTIONS

At the Sun's core, energy is produced when four hydrogen nuclei (protons) fuse to make one helium nucleus.

The two groups collide, forming a helium nucleus and releasing two photons

40

The radiative zone is where energy leaves the core in streams of photons

Photosphere—the Sun's visible surface

SOLAR NEUTRINOS

Neutrinos produced by nuclear reactions in the Sun's core travel out into space. Most of these pass through Earth, but a few can be detected by neutrino telescopes. The Sudbury Observatory lies 1.2 miles (2 km) underground to protect it from cosmic rays.

SUDBURY NEUTRINO OBSERVATORY, ONTARIO, CANADA

Area where the Sun's surface is falling

Area where the Sun's surface is rising

SOLAR OSCILLATIONS

The Sun's surface moves up and down in complex patterns of vibrations, or solar oscillations. Most are caused by sound waves generated in the convective zone and trapped inside the Sun. Studying them tells us about the Sun's internal structure.

COMPUTERIZED IMAGE OF SOLAR OSCILLATION PATTERNS

The convective zone is where energy is carried by convection cells

Beyond the photosphere is the solar atmosphere, with the corona extending millions of miles (kilometers) into space

VITAL STATISTICS	
Escape speed from surface	384 mps (618 km/s)
Rate of conversion (hydrogen to helium)	675 million tons/s (615 million metric tons/s)
Time taken for light to reach Earth	8 minutes 19 seconds
Luminosity	390 quintillion megawatts
Surface temperature	9,900°F (5,500°C)
Core temperature	28 million°F (16 million°C)
Age	4.6 billion years
Remaining life	5×10^9 years

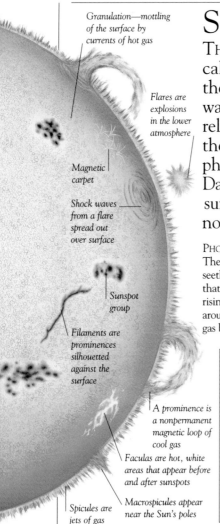

Granulation—mottling of the surface by currents of hot gas

Flares are explosions in the lower atmosphere

Magnetic carpet

Shock waves from a flare spread out over surface

Sunspot group

Filaments are prominences silhouetted against the surface

A prominence is a nonpermanent magnetic loop of cool gas

Faculas are hot, white areas that appear before and after sunspots

Spicules are jets of gas

Macrospicules appear near the Sun's poles

SUN'S SURFACE

THE VISIBLE DISK OF THE SUN is called the photosphere. After thousands of years working its way up from the core, the energy released by nuclear reactions inside the Sun finally bursts from the photosphere in a blaze of light. Dark markings on the Sun's surface—sunspots—were first noticed by Galileo 400 years ago.

PHOTOSPHERE
The photosphere is not solid like Earth's surface, but a seething sea of glowing gas 300 miles (500 km) thick that marks the tops of currents of hot, opaque gas rising from the Sun's interior. Its temperature averages around 9,930°F (5,500°C). At the photosphere, the gas becomes transparent, allowing light to escape.

SUNSPOTS
Sunspots (dark blotches) are shallow depressions in the photosphere where strong magnetic fields stop currents of hot gas from reaching the Sun's surface. They range from small spots, known as pores, to large clusters called sunspot groups. They last from a few hours to many weeks. They are cooler than their surroundings, so they appear darker.

Sunspot

MAGNETIC SUNSPOTS

Sunspots occur in areas of violent magnetic activity called active regions. The magnetic fields inside the Sun are wound up and twisted by the different speeds at which the Sun's surface rotates. Churning gas currents in the photosphere cause loops of magnetism to break through the surface and form sunspots. One end of each loop is a north magnetic pole, while the other end is a south magnetic pole.

Yellow areas are south magnetic poles

Blue areas are north magnetic poles

A magnetogram is a map of the Sun's magnetic fields

MAGNETOGRAM OF A SUNSPOT GROUP

Tower telescopes

TIEDE OBSERVATORY, TENERIFE, CANARY ISLANDS

SOLAR TELESCOPES

A tower telescope tracks the Sun with a moving mirror (a heliostat) on top of a tower. The heliostat reflects light down a vertical shaft to measuring instruments at ground level. In a vacuum tower telescope, air is removed to stop the Sun's heat from stirring up air currents that may distort the image.

35 days
33 days
31 days
29 days
27 days
25 days

27 days

ROTATION SPEED

The Sun is a globe of gas, so it does not all rotate at the same speed, as a solid object would. The Sun's equator makes one rotation roughly every 25 days, while areas near the poles turn once every 35 days. The way the Sun's surface oscillates, or vibrates, suggests that the inner part of the Sun spins like a solid ball, with a rotation period of 27 days.

SUN'S ATMOSPHERE

THE SUN'S THIN ATMOSPHERE consists of two main regions—the chromosphere and the corona. These regions are often rocked by enormous eruptions and explosions called prominences and flares. The corona is far hotter than the photosphere. As a result, hundreds of tons of the Sun's atmosphere evaporate into space every second.

PROMINENCES
These are vast loops or arches of gas extending from the chromosphere up into the corona. The gas may splatter down into the photosphere as coronal rain, or erupt into space.

This ultraviolet image of the chromosphere was taken by the SOHO spacecraft

Chromosphere can be seen as a blotchy pink ring around the edge of the Moon during a total eclipse

Hot hydrogen gas makes the chromosphere look pink in visible light

CHROMOSPHERE
The chromosphere is a layer of hydrogen and helium gas above the photosphere, about 3,100 miles (5,000 km) thick. Its temperature is about 7,230°F (4,000°C) at the bottom, near the photosphere, and 900,000°F (500,000°C) at the top. Brushlike jets of gas—spicules—project from the chromosphere into the corona above.

TOTAL ECLIPSE OF THE SUN

During a total eclipse, the dark disk of the Moon blots out the Sun, revealing the outer reaches of the solar atmosphere

SOLAR WIND

Made up of coronal electrons and protons, and the magnetic fields and electric currents generated, the solar wind passes Earth at 185 to 500 mps (300 to 800 km/s). Earth's magnetic field deflects most of it and is squeezed into a long tail by the wind.

AURORA SEEN FROM SPACE

Auroras are displays of colored lights over Earth's magnetic poles. They occur when solar wind particles, trapped by Earth's magnetic field, collide with air molecules in the upper atmosphere.

Density of corona is less than a trillionth the density of Earth's atmosphere

The photosphere appears as a dark disk because it is not hot enough to produce X-rays

Dark patches are coronal holes—low-density regions from which high-speed streams of particles flow into the solar wind

The eclipse reveals the corona as a milky-white halo, often displaying wisps, loops, and streamers

CORONA

The corona is the outermost region of the Sun's atmosphere, extending millions of miles (kilometers) into space. Even though temperatures can rise to more than 5.4 million°F (3 million °C), the corona is very faint because the gas is extremely thin. Bubbles containing billions of tons of gas sometimes erupt from the corona.

45

ECLIPSES OF THE SUN

IN ITS 27-DAY ORBIT OF EARTH, the Moon sometimes passes directly in front of the Sun, causing a solar eclipse. Between two and five solar eclipses are visible from somewhere on Earth each year. Partial eclipses—when only a portion of the Sun is covered by the Moon—are visible over a wide area. Total eclipses—when the Sun is completely hidden—are seen from a far narrower region of Earth's surface.

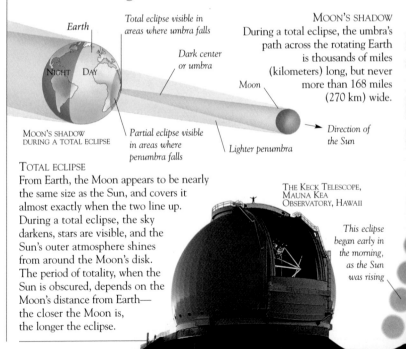

Earth

Total eclipse visible in areas where umbra falls

Dark center or umbra

Moon

NIGHT   DAY

MOON'S SHADOW DURING A TOTAL ECLIPSE

Partial eclipse visible in areas where penumbra falls

Lighter penumbra

MOON'S SHADOW
During a total eclipse, the umbra's path across the rotating Earth is thousands of miles (kilometers) long, but never more than 168 miles (270 km) wide.

Direction of the Sun

TOTAL ECLIPSE

From Earth, the Moon appears to be nearly the same size as the Sun, and covers it almost exactly when the two line up. During a total eclipse, the sky darkens, stars are visible, and the Sun's outer atmosphere shines from around the Moon's disk. The period of totality, when the Sun is obscured, depends on the Moon's distance from Earth—the closer the Moon is, the longer the eclipse.

THE KECK TELESCOPE,
MAUNA KEA
OBSERVATORY, HAWAII

This eclipse began early in the morning, as the Sun was rising

SOLAR SYSTEM

46

Direction
of Sun

Umbra

Penumbra

ANNULAR ECLIPSE

During an annular eclipse, the Moon is at its farthest from Earth and is not big enough in the sky to cover the Sun completely. When the Moon is exactly in front of the Sun, the Sun's photosphere is still visible around its edges, like a ring of fire. Annular eclipses can last for more than 12 minutes.

In the partial phase of the eclipse, the Sun looks as though a bite has been taken out of it

Umbra does not reach Earth

A total eclipse can last up to 7.5 minutes when the Earth and Moon are closest to each other, but it is usually much briefer

Annular eclipse visible in area beneath tip of umbra

Day Night

Earth

MOON'S SHADOW DURING
AN ANNULAR ECLIPSE

In the few minutes of totality, the Sun is completely hidden by the disk of the Moon

ECLIPSE EFFECTS

For a few seconds just before or after totality, the disappearing or emerging Sun shines between the mountains at the edge of the Moon's disk. Sometimes this produces a brilliant spot of light—the diamond ring. At other times, an arc of bright points similar to a string of pearls—Baily's beads—is visible.

As an eclipse proceeds, the Moon covers more and more of the Sun

Warning: Never look directly at the Sun during an eclipse. It should only be viewed through special filters or a projector

TIME-LAPSE
PHOTOGRAPH OF
TOTAL ECLIPSE

The last bright sliver of the Sun's disk shines like a diamond in a ring formed by the chromosphere

SOLAR ENERGY AND INFLUENCE

AT ITS CORE, the Sun converts hydrogen to helium at a rate of 660 million tons (600 million metric tons) every second. The energy produced eventually reaches the surface and travels through space.

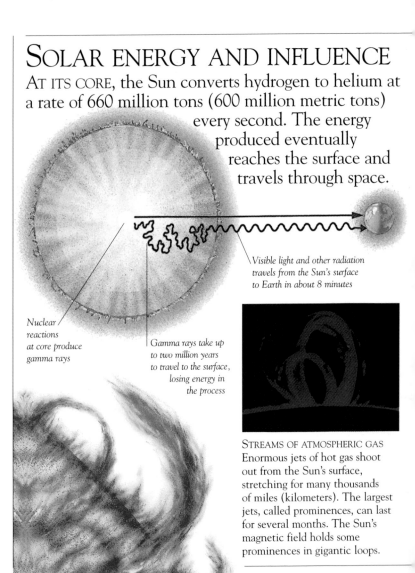

Nuclear reactions at core produce gamma rays

Gamma rays take up to two million years to travel to the surface, losing energy in the process

Visible light and other radiation travels from the Sun's surface to Earth in about 8 minutes

STREAMS OF ATMOSPHERIC GAS
Enormous jets of hot gas shoot out from the Sun's surface, stretching for many thousands of miles (kilometers). The largest jets, called prominences, can last for several months. The Sun's magnetic field holds some prominences in gigantic loops.

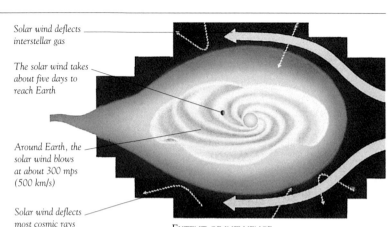

Solar wind deflects interstellar gas

The solar wind takes about five days to reach Earth

Around Earth, the solar wind blows at about 300 mps (500 km/s)

Solar wind deflects most cosmic rays

EXTENT OF INFLUENCE

The Sun influences an enormous volume of space around it. Gases streaming from the corona become the high-speed solar wind. The solar wind carries a magnetic field from the Sun. As the Sun rotates, the field takes on a spiral shape. The volume of space swept by the solar wind is called the heliosphere.

ULYSSES
SOLAR PROBE

Sensors located on hinged boom

TO THE SOLAR POLES

Earth's orbit in the Sun's equatorial plane means that the Sun's poles cannot be studied from Earth. The Ulysses probe was launched in 1990 to study these hard-to-observe regions.

SOLAR ENERGY FACTS

• The Sun coverts hydrogen to helium, losing 5,300 tons (4,900 metric tons) of its mass every second.

• The amount of the Sun's energy reaching Earth's surface (known as the solar constant) is equivalent to 1.15 kW (kilowatts) per square yard (1.37 kW per square meter) per second.

49

EARTH

THE THIRD PLANET FROM THE SUN, Earth, combines many features of the other planets with some that are all its own. It has craters as on Mercury, volcanoes as on Venus and Mars, and swirling weather systems as on Jupiter and Neptune. But it is the only planet with both liquid water and frozen ice that has an atmosphere rich in oxygen, and on which life exists.

VITAL STATISTICS	
Diameter	7,930 miles (12,756 km)
Avg. distance from Sun	92,955,807 miles (149,597,870 km)
Orbital speed around Sun	17.3 mps (27.8 km/s)
Sunrise to sunrise	24 hours
Mass	5.9742 x 10²⁴ kg
Volume	1.087 x 10²¹ m³
Avg. density (water = 1)	5.52
Surface gravity	9.78 m/s²
Avg. surface temperature	59°F (15°C)
Number of moons	1

BLUE PLANET

From space, Earth is blue in color. This is due to the vast expanses of water on its surface. It is the only planet with a surface temperature between 32°F (0°C) and 212°F (100°C), where water can be liquid at the surface.

Oceans and seas cover 71% of Earth's surface

Clouds condense from water vapor that evaporates from oceans

EARTH AT A GLANCE

Earth is the largest of the rocky planets. It is the only planet with a crust split into moving plates, oxygen in its atmosphere, and liquid water and life on its surface.

TILT, SPIN AND ORBIT

Orbits the Sun in 365.25 days

Axis tilts from the vertical by 23.5°

Spins on its axis once every 23.93 hours

ATMOSPHERE

Argon, water vapor and trace gases (1%)

Oxygen (20.9%)

Nitrogen (78.1%)

SCALE

STRUCTURE

Crust

Mantle of silicate rock

Outer core (liquid iron)

Inner core (solid iron)

Earth is about four times the size of the Moon

Rain from clouds returns water to the oceans to complete the water cycle

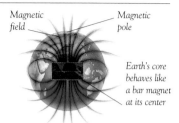

Magnetic field

Magnetic pole

Earth's core behaves like a bar magnet at its center

EARTH AS A MAGNET

Earth's magnetism is caused by swirling currents of molten iron at its core. For its size, Earth has the strongest magnetic field of any planet. Over time, the magnetism changes direction, causing the magnetic poles to wander.

Magnetic field lines

Magnetosphere

Van Allen belts trap particles from solar wind

Solar wind

Earth

MAGNETOSPHERE

Earth is surrounded by a "magnetic bubble" or magnetosphere that protects it from the effects of the solar wind—electrified particles that sweep outward from the Sun at high speeds. Some particles are trapped in the Van Allen belts—regions of radiation—close to Earth, while others stream to the magnetic poles, causing auroras.

51

EARTH'S SURFACE

EARTH'S SURFACE IS SHAPED by unique geological forces. The crust (outer shell) is split into huge sections called plates, which float on a partially molten layer of rock, and are always on the move. As they collide or drift apart, the surface rocks are continually destroyed and renewed.

250 million years ago, all the continents are a single land mass, Pangaea

200 million years ago, Pangaea splits into Laurasia and Gondwanaland

135 million years ago, Gondwanaland splits into Africa and South America

60 million years ago, the North Atlantic splits into Europe and North America

DRIFTING CONTINENTS

Carried on top of the moving plates, the continents gradually drift over Earth's surface about as fast as a fingernail grows. In the process, continents split apart. India, Africa, Australia, and Antarctica were once part of a single continent. India smashed into Asia, causing the mighty Himalayas to be pushed up.

PLATE TECTONICS

Earth's surface is shaped by plate tectonics—the forces caused by the moving plates. There are eight large plates and many smaller ones. Some consist only of ocean floor, while others include continents. The edges of the plates are marked by long cracks, winding ridges, strings of volcanoes, and earthquake zones.

RING OF FIRE

ALEUTIAN TRENCH

EURASIAN PLATE

HIMALAYA

HAWAII

PACIFIC PLATE

PHILIPPINE PLATE

MARIANA TRENCH

INDO-AUSTRALIAN PLATE

TONGA TRENCH

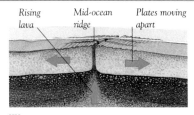

Rising lava | Mid-ocean ridge | Plates moving apart

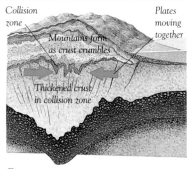

Collision zone — Mountains form as crust crumbles | Plates moving together — Thickened crust in collision zone

WHERE PLATES MOVE APART

Where two plates move apart, lava wells up to form a mountain range called a mid-ocean ridge, which is part of the ocean floor. The Mid-Atlantic Ridge is the longest mountain range on Earth. Its highest peaks are islands such as Iceland, Ascension Island, and Tristan da Cunha.

COLLIDING CONTINENTS

When continents collide, mountains are pushed up. The Alps are the result of the African Plate pushing northward into the Eurasian Plate.

Pacific Ocean floor forced under South America

WHERE PLATES MEET

The Andes are part of a volcanic chain—the Ring of Fire—circling the Pacific Ocean. In a process called subduction, South America is riding up over the Nazca Plate, causing ocean floor rocks to melt and erupt as volcanos.

53

EARTH'S ATMOSPHERE

EARTH IS SURROUNDED by a thin layer of gas called the atmosphere, which keeps the planet at a comfortable temperature and protects the surface from dangerous radiation. Heated unevenly by the Sun and spun by Earth, it has ever-changing, swirling patterns, and is the most complex atmosphere in the solar system.

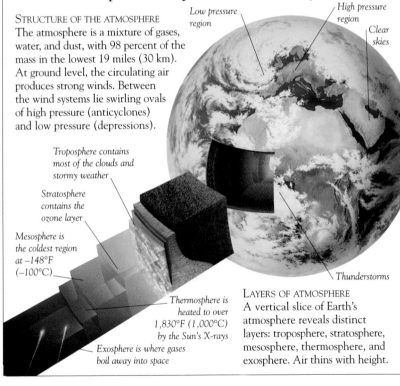

STRUCTURE OF THE ATMOSPHERE
The atmosphere is a mixture of gases, water, and dust, with 98 percent of the mass in the lowest 19 miles (30 km). At ground level, the circulating air produces strong winds. Between the wind systems lie swirling ovals of high pressure (anticyclones) and low pressure (depressions).

Low pressure region

High pressure region

Clear skies

Troposphere contains most of the clouds and stormy weather

Stratosphere contains the ozone layer

Mesosphere is the coldest region at −148°F (−100°C)

Thermosphere is heated to over 1,830°F (1,000°C) by the Sun's X-rays

Exosphere is where gases boil away into space

Thunderstorms

LAYERS OF ATMOSPHERE
A vertical slice of Earth's atmosphere reveals distinct layers: troposphere, stratosphere, mesosphere, thermosphere, and exosphere. Air thins with height.

GREENHOUSE EFFECT

Without the atmosphere, Earth would be 54°F (30°C) colder. Like a greenhouse, the air traps some of the heat generated by sunlight.

Some heat escapes Earth's atmosphere

Gases in the atmosphere

Sunlight

Heat from Earth

Heat radiated back to Earth

OZONE HOLE

The ozone layer protects Earth from the Sun's harmful ultraviolet rays. This layer has thinned above both poles.

THE WORLD'S TEMPERATURE IN THE TROPOSPHERE (RED IS HOTTER)

CHANGING CLIMATE

Earth warms up by 0.04°F (0.02°C) per year, probably due to extra carbon dioxide, released by burning coal and oil, and the destruction of rain forests, enhancing the greenhouse effect.

Earth's rotation

Winds in the Northern Hemisphere are twisted to the right by Earth's rotation

North Pole

Sea-level winds

Cold polar air sinks and spreads to warmer areas

Polar easterlies

Equator

Westerlies

High altitude winds

WIND CIRCULATION

At the equator, warm air rises, moves north and south, then descends and flows back at sea level. At each pole, cold air sinks and spreads. Then it warms up and rises to flow back at high altitude. Caught between these circulating currents, air at middle latitudes circulates the opposite way.

Northeast trade winds

Southeast trade winds

Westerlies

Southern Hemisphere winds are twisted to the left by Earth's rotation

South Pole

Life on Earth

IN 1990, THE GALILEO space probe swept past Earth and recorded a green covering over the land, a corrosive gas in the atmosphere, and some radio signals. The green covering was biological material absorbing sunlight, and in the process, releasing the corrosive gas oxygen. Earth has one special quality: it is the only place where life is known to exist.

EVOLUTION OF LIFE
Earth is home to more than a million species of living things, ranging from bacteria to giant trees and mammals. All have come about by the process of evolution—changes in successive generations as species adapt to their surroundings and to competitors.

2 Large shallow pools concentrated chemicals to make the first cells 4 billion years ago

3 Dinosaurs and giant tree ferns flourished 200 million years ago

4 Today, life is still evolving but is threatened by destructive human activity

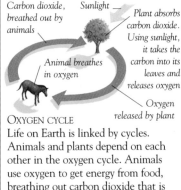

Carbon dioxide, breathed out by animals

Sunlight

Plant absorbs carbon dioxide. Using sunlight, it takes the carbon into its leaves and releases oxygen

Animal breathes in oxygen

Oxygen released by plant

OXYGEN CYCLE
Life on Earth is linked by cycles. Animals and plants depend on each other in the oxygen cycle. Animals use oxygen to get energy from food, breathing out carbon dioxide that is converted back to oxygen by plants.

SOLAR SYSTEM

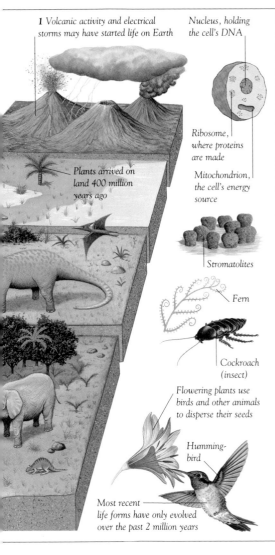

1 *Volcanic activity and electrical storms may have started life on Earth*

Plants arrived on land 400 million years ago

Nucleus, holding the cell's DNA

Ribosome, where proteins are made

Mitochondrion, the cell's energy source

Stromatolites

Fern

Cockroach (insect)

Flowering plants use birds and other animals to disperse their seeds

Humming-bird

Most recent life forms have only evolved over the past 2 million years

LIVING CELLS

All life is made up of microscopic cells. Some organisms consist of a single cell, while the human body has 100 billion cells. Cells differ in detail, depending on their function, but all have the same parts.

SINGLE CELLS

Many species consist of a single cell, such as bacteria and pond-dwelling algae. Sometimes single cells group together in colonies, such as stromatolites.

SIMPLE LIFE-FORMS

Some simpler life-forms have survived for millions of years. Ferns were the first plants on dry land. Mollusks in the sea and insects on land have stayed the same for 350 million years.

COMPLEX SYSTEMS

Many life forms have evolved to become more complex. Some plants use insects to pollinate them. Mammals and birds are warm-blooded, so they can endure temperature changes.

THE MOON

THE MOON IS THE CLOSEST celestial object to Earth. The pair waltz through space with the Moon spinning around Earth, as Earth orbits the Sun. The Moon is larger and brighter than any other object in the night sky. It has no light of its own but shines by reflecting sunlight. Three times a year, the Moon's face is eclipsed as it passes through Earth's shadow.

MOON AT A GLANCE

The Moon is a dusty, barren sphere of rock with no atmosphere or liquid water. It takes the same time to rotate on its axis as it does to orbit Earth.

TILT, SPIN, AND ORBIT — Orbits Earth in 27.32 days

Earth

Axis tilts from the vertical by 6.7° — Spins on its axis once every 27.32 days

STRUCTURE — Crust of granitelike rock

Rocky mantle

Probably solid inner core

SCALE

Moon is just over a quarter the diameter of Earth

VITAL STATISTICS	
Diameter	2,160 miles (3,476 km)
Avg. distance from Earth	238,866 miles (384,400 km)
Orbital speed around Earth	0.63 mps (1.02 km/s)
New moon to new moon	29.53 days
Mass (Earth =1)	0.0123
Volume (Earth = 1)	0.0202
Avg. density (water = 1)	3.34
Surface gravity (Earth = 1)	0.17
Avg. surface temperature	−4°F (−20°C)

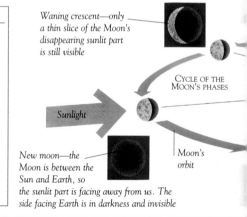

Waning crescent—only a thin slice of the Moon's disappearing sunlit part is still visible

CYCLE OF THE MOON'S PHASES

Sunlight

New moon—the Moon is between the Sun and Earth, so the sunlit part is facing away from us. The side facing Earth is in darkness and invisible

Moon's orbit

SOLAR SYSTEM

58

LUNAR ECLIPSES

When a full moon moves through Earth's shadow, a lunar eclipse occurs. In a total eclipse, the entire Moon is in the umbra, the central, darkest part of the shadow. In a partial eclipse, some of the Moon is in the umbra and the rest is in the penumbra—the paler, outer part.

HOW A LUNAR ECLIPSE OCCURS

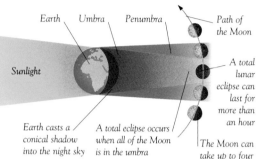

Earth   Umbra   Penumbra   Path of the Moon

Sunlight

A total lunar eclipse can last for more than an hour

Earth casts a conical shadow into the night sky

A total eclipse occurs when all of the Moon is in the umbra

The Moon can take up to four hours to pass through Earth's shadow completely

PHASES OF THE MOON

Just like Earth, one half of the Moon is always bathed in sunlight, while the other lies in darkness. As the Moon circles Earth, its shape seems to change as we see varying phases of its sunlit part. The phases follow a cycle, from new moon, when the dark side is facing us, to full moon, when we see all of the sunlit part.

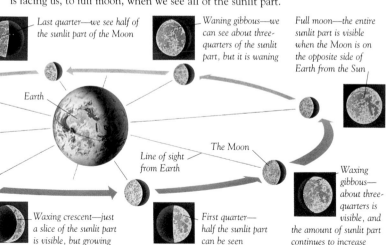

Last quarter—we see half of the sunlit part of the Moon

Waning gibbous—we can see about three-quarters of the sunlit part, but it is waning

Full moon—the entire sunlit part is visible when the Moon is on the opposite side of Earth from the Sun

Earth

Line of sight from Earth

The Moon

Waxing gibbous— about three-quarters is visible, and the amount of sunlit part continues to increase

Waxing crescent—just a slice of the sunlit part is visible, but growing

First quarter— half the sunlit part can be seen

59

MOON'S SURFACE

FROM EARTH, THE MOON looks very gray, but the variations in its grayness tell us something about it. The lighter areas are older, higher land, covering about 85 percent of the Moon, while the darker areas are younger, lowland plains. Only 7 percent of the light falling on the Moon is reflected by its surface. By studying the surface, astronomers can date the different stages of the Moon's development.

Regolith is the surface layer of dust and rock created by meteorite bombardment

"Mare," which means sea in Latin, is the name given to a dark plain on the Moon

Craters are bowl-shaped scars left by meteorites. "Crater" comes from the Greek word for bowl

Highlands, above the level of the maria, were the first parts of the crust to cool and solidify

Mountain ranges are uplifted areas of crust that ring some of the maria and large craters

The largest craters, several hundred miles (kilometers) across, are called basins

The rocky crust is 40–60 miles (60–100 km) thick

LUNAR LANDSCAPE
Two distinctive landscape forms on the Moon are dark gray plains, or maria (singular: mare) and lighter highlands. Covered with craters, the highlands are the oldest parts of the crust. The smooth plains are large craters that were filled with lava, and are usually surrounded by mountains.

HISTORY OF THE MOON

This vast crater will eventually become the Mare Imbrium

Meteorites pound the Moon's crust

The Mare Imbrium is created as lava floods the crater basin

Lava erupts through fractures in the crust

Copernicus forms about 800 million years ago

Volcanic activity has all but ceased

FOUR BILLION YEARS AGO
During its first 750 million years, the Moon went through a period of devastating bombardment by meteorites. Their impact punctured the crust and formed craters all over the surface.

THREE BILLION YEARS AGO
About 3.7 billion years ago, bombardment slowed and intense volcanic activity followed as deep craters filled with lava welling up from 60 miles (100 km) below the surface. The lava solidified to form maria.

THE MOON TODAY
The lunar surface has changed little in the past 1.6 billion years, though a few young craters, such as Copernicus, stand out. Most of the original crust has been destroyed by cratering.

SURFACE TEMPERATURES
The Moon experiences extremes of temperature. The lunar surface is −292°F (−180°C) at its coldest, but reaches a searing maximum of 230°F (110°C). The Moon's lack of atmosphere means that there is nothing to regulate the surface temperature. When sunlit, its surface is fully heated, but when in shadow, the heat is lost.

SOLAR SYSTEM

NEAR SIDE OF THE MOON

THE DOMINANT FEATURES on the Moon's near side—the side that always faces Earth—are the dark maria, which early astronomers thought were seas. These lava-filled basins formed when molten rock seeped through the Moon's crust to fill depressions left by meteorite impacts. The surface is pockmarked by craters everywhere. All landings by spacecraft have been on the near side.

MONTES APENNINUS
One of the most impressive ranges of lunar mountains, the Montes Apenninus, along with the Montes Carpatus, Caucasus, Jura, and Alpes, make up the walls of the Mare Imbrium. This broken ring of mountains formed from a meteorite impact.

Aristarchus, a 23-mile- (37-km-) diameter crater, is the brightest point on the entire Moon

COPERNICUS
Copernicus is a lunar ray crater. It is 66 miles (107 km) in diameter and 2.4 miles (4 km) deep, with rays of bright rock fragments leading out from it. Analysis of ray material collected by the Apollo 12 crew showed it to be 850 million years old.

MARE FRIG

Plato

17   MONTES JURA   MARE IMBRIUM   Aristillus

Archimedes

13   Eratosthenes
OCEANUS   MONTES
PROCELLARUM   CARPATUS
Kepler

9   Encke
Hevelius   1   12   3
Grimaldi   14   Fra Mai
Flamsteed   7   Ptolemaeu

MARE NUBIUM

Gassendi   MARE
MARE   HUMORUM
ORIENTALE

Schickard   Longomontanus

Clavius

NEAR-SIDE FEATURES

The extensive maria, the darkest of the near-side features, lie between 1.2 and 3.1 miles (2 and 5 km) below the average surface level. The most recently formed features are the bright ray craters. The southern area—the roughest part of the near-side surface—is mainly high, cratered land with a handful of large, walled plains. Both polar regions are highland areas.

MARE CRISIUM

Separated from the main system of interlinked maria is the Mare Crisium, measuring 280 miles (450 km) by 350 miles (563 km). The smooth, lava-filled floor of this oval-shaped basin contains two significant craters—Picard and Peirce—as well as smaller ones.

Maria are usually referred to by their Latin names, such as Mare Crisium, which means Sea of Crises

HUMBOLDT CRATER

Named after the German statesman Wilhelm Humboldt, the Humboldt crater is surrounded by a high mountain wall. A blanket of ejecta—material thrown out at the time of a meteorite impact—covers the ground outside the walls. Inside the crater is a central peak, while a system of fractures runs across the floor.

Ansrtoteles
Eudoxus
Posidonius
Cleomedes
21
17
MARE SERENITATIS
MONTES HAEMUS
MARE TRANQUILLITATIS
MARE CRISIUM
24
20
16
MARE FECUNDITATIS
8
5
11
Theophilus
Ibateginus
16
Cyrillus
Mare Nectaris
Langrenus
Catharina
Fracastorius
rbach
Rupes Altai
Petavus
Piccolomini
Walter
Cyrillus,
Theophilus,
and Catharina
are a chain of
overlapping craters
Maurolycus
MARE AUSTRALE
Maginus

LANDING SITES

Marked on the map are the landing sites of the 16 space probes and 6 crewed craft that reached the Moon between 1959 and 1976.

[7] Ranger 7, 8, & 9	Surveyor 1, 3, 5, 6, & 7	
(13) Luna 2, 9, 13, 16, 17, 20, 21, & 24	Apollo 11, 12, 14, 15, 16, & 17	

FAR SIDE OF THE MOON

THE FAR SIDE OF THE MOON is always turned away from Earth. It was a mystery until 1959, when the space probe Luna 3 was able to send back the first photographs. The far side has few maria, because the lunar crust is thicker here than on the near side, making it difficult for lava to seep through into the impact basins left by colliding space rocks. The far side also has more craters.

MARE MOSCOVIENSE
One of the few maria lying entirely on the far side, the 172-mile- (277-km-) long Mare Moscoviense is smaller than large far-side crater basins such as Apollo. Its dark floor makes it stand out clearly against its surroundings.

Gagarin is a crater named after Yuri Gagarin, the first person to go into space

VAN DE GRAAFF
This irregularly shaped crater is about 145 miles (233 km) long and has several smaller craters inside it. Surprisingly, it is only 2.4 miles (4 km) deep. The basin has stronger magnetism and is more radioactive than the land surrounding it, which may be because volcanic rock lies buried under it.

Schwarzschild
D'Alembert
Campbell
Fabry
Fleming
MARE MOSCOVIENSE
Mendeleev
Mandel'shtam
Mare Smythii
Pasteur
Heaviside
Hilbert
Aitken
Roche
Leibnitz
Poincaré
Mare Australe
Planck
Schrödinger

FAR-SIDE FEATURES

The two prominent far-side maria are the Mare Orientale and Mare Moscoviense. Craters abound, but they are smaller and not as dark as those on the near side. The most noticeable craters are the circular depressions such as Hertzsprung, Apollo, and Korolev. Hertzsprung's outer ring has smaller craters.

Many far-side craters are named after scientists and philosophers. Joule is named after English physicist James Joule

Sommerfeld
Stebbins
Birkhoff
Rowland
Fowler
ckroft
Mach
Tsander
Landau
Joule
Fersman
Michelson
Galois
Oppenheimer
Minkowski
Mendel
Lemaitre
an
Krylov

MONTES CORDILLERA
MONTES ROOK
MARE ORIENTALE

The Apollo crater was named in honor of the Apollo missions to the Moon

POLAR REGIONS

The polar regions were the last parts of the Moon to be mapped. Mosaic maps, made by assembling the images sent back in 1994 by the space probe Clementine, suggest that some polar craters are permanently in shadow.

LUNAR SOUTH POLE

Schrödinger Crater

KOROLEV

Measuring 271 miles (437 km) across, the Korolev Crater is among the largest ringed formations on the far side of the Moon. Many smaller craters lie inside it. One of these, Krylov, has a central peak and measures about 31 miles (50 km) across.

Hertzsprung, a 367-mile (591-km) crater basin, is one of the major features on the far side

MARE ORIENTALE

This huge mare is the Moon's youngest and measures 200 miles (327 km) across. It straddles the far-side/near-side boundary and is surrounded by concentric rings of mountains about 560 miles (900 km) wide. Beyond them lies ejected material. Only the center of the impact basin filled with lava.

65

LUNAR INFLUENCES

ALTHOUGH THE MOON IS much smaller than Earth, it still has an influence on it. Just as Earth's gravity pulls on the Moon, the gravity of the Moon pulls on Earth, stretching it into a slight ovoid (egg shape). This barely affects the landmasses, but makes the oceans bulge on either side of Earth, producing tides along coastlines. The tides also affect the speed of Earth's spin and the distance between Earth and Moon.

TIDES

The oceans rise in a high tide and then fall back in a low tide twice each day. This tidal cycle lasts 24 hours and 50 minutes, because the Moon arrives above a given spot 50 minutes later each day. The actual height of the tides depends on the position of the Moon in its orbit and on local geography.

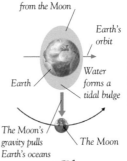

Tidal bulge also forms on side facing away from the Moon

Earth's orbit

Earth

Water forms a tidal bulge

The Moon's gravity pulls Earth's oceans

The Moon

Each coastal place experiences a high tide as Earth moves past a tidal bulge

Earth's spin

Low tides occur on either side of tidal bulges

The Moon's orbit

Tidal bulge is ahead of the Moon

CAUSES OF TIDES

Water on the side of Earth closest to the Moon feels the Moon's gravitational pull most strongly. Two bulges of tidal water form and follow the Moon as it orbits Earth. Earth's rotation causes the tidal bulges to be carried around slightly ahead of the Moon, rather than directly in line with it.

HIGH TIDE, SEVERN ESTUARY, ENGLAND

LOW TIDE, SEVERN ESTUARY, ENGLAND

66

SPRING AND NEAP TIDES

At full moon and new moon, the Sun's gravity and the Moon's tidal pull combine to make the highest high tides and the lowest low tides, called spring tides. When the Moon is at its first- and last-quarter phases, the Sun is at right angles to it. The Sun's gravity partly counteracts the Moon's tidal pull, resulting in neap tides—the lowest high tides and the highest low tides.

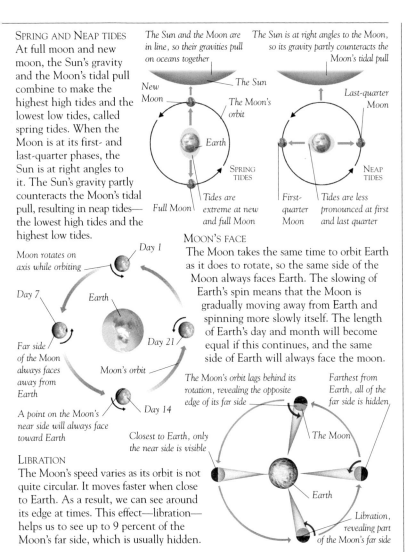

The Sun and the Moon are in line, so their gravities pull on oceans together

The Sun is at right angles to the Moon, so its gravity partly counteracts the Moon's tidal pull

The Sun

New Moon

The Moon's orbit

Earth

SPRING TIDES

Full Moon

Tides are extreme at new and full Moon

Last-quarter Moon

NEAP TIDES

First-quarter Moon

Tides are less pronounced at first and last quarter

Moon rotates on axis while orbiting

Day 1

Day 7

Earth

Far side of the Moon always faces away from Earth

Day 21

Day 14

Moon's orbit

A point on the Moon's near side will always face toward Earth

MOON'S FACE

The Moon takes the same time to orbit Earth as it does to rotate, so the same side of the Moon always faces Earth. The slowing of Earth's spin means that the Moon is gradually moving away from Earth and spinning more slowly itself. The length of Earth's day and month will become equal if this continues, and the same side of Earth will always face the moon.

The Moon's orbit lags behind its rotation, revealing the opposite edge of its far side

Farthest from Earth, all of the far side is hidden

The Moon

Closest to Earth, only the near side is visible

Earth

Libration, revealing part of the Moon's far side

LIBRATION

The Moon's speed varies as its orbit is not quite circular. It moves faster when close to Earth. As a result, we can see around its edge at times. This effect—libration—helps us to see up to 9 percent of the Moon's far side, which is usually hidden.

EXPLORING THE MOON

THE FIRST SPACECRAFT to leave Earth's gravity, Luna 1, was launched toward the Moon in 1959. Over the next decade, many probes, robots, and crewed craft were sent to investigate and land there. Scientists are now planning lunar bases, where astronauts will live and work for months at a time.

8 The Command Module enters the atmosphere 75 miles (120 km) above Earth

7 Approaching Earth, the Command Module separates from the Service Module

3 The rest of the rocket is discarded and the modules continue to the Moon

4 Lunar Module descends to the Moon

1 Liftoff from Cape Canaveral

6 The astronauts link up and the Lunar Module is abandoned

5 The Command and Service Modules orbit the Moon, waiting for the Lunar Module to return

9 Craft parachutes into the ocean

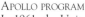

2 Saturn V's engines fire to send the Apollo craft to the Moon

Apollo 15's Jim Irwin

APOLLO PROGRAM
In 1961, the United States set up the Apollo program with the aim of sending astronauts to the Moon by the end of the decade. A powerful rocket, the Saturn V, was designed, built, and tested. In July 1969, Neil Armstrong and Buzz Aldrin touched down on the Moon. Their third crewmate, Mike Collins, remained in orbit in the Command and Service Module.

APOLLO SCIENTIFIC EXPERIMENTS

Astronauts left behind experiments and equipment to measure moonquakes, the soil temperature, the amount of dust in space, and the number of solar particles reaching the Moon.

CREWED APOLLO MOON LANDINGS

Mission	Date of landing	Landing site	Activity	Time outside vehicle
Apollo 11	Jul. 20, 1969	Mare Tranquillitatis	First astronaut on the Moon	2.5 hours
Apollo 12	Nov. 19, 1969	Oceanus Procellarum	First major scientific experiments set up	7.8 hours
Apollo 14	Feb. 5, 1971	Fra Mauro	First landing in lunar highlands	9.3 hours
Apollo 15	Jul. 30, 1971	Hadley-Apennines	First lunar rover excursions	18.6 hours
Apollo 16	Apr. 21, 1972	Descartes region	Explored highlands	20.2 hours
Apollo 17	Dec. 11, 1972	Taurus-Littrow	Longest and last stay on the Moon	22.1 hours

LUNOKHOD 1—A RADIO-CONTROLLED VEHICLE THAT TRUNDLED 6.2 MILES (10 KM) OVER THE MOON'S SURFACE IN 1970 AND 1971

Radio antenna

Lid with solar cells for power

The Lunar Module was the astronauts' home on the Moon. The upper part blasted off for the journey back to Earth

Cameras allowed scientists on Earth to direct the vehicle

Soil-testing equipment

Wheels gripped soft lunar soil

LUNAR PROBES

Besides the Apollo missions, many remote-controlled crafts, such as the US Ranger and Surveyor probes, also made the journey to the Moon. The Russian Luna probes were the first to land on its surface, followed by Lunokhod 1 and 2.

69

OTHER SOLAR SYSTEMS

IS OUR SOLAR SYSTEM UNIQUE? Until recently, astronomers could only guess whether there were extrasolar planets—those that orbit stars other than the Sun. Such planets are difficult to detect, being about one-billionth the brightness of their parent stars. But since 1995, sensitive instruments have discovered a number of extrasolar planets.

EXTRASOLAR ORBITS
The orbits of Earth and the first 10 extrasolar planets discovered can be compared as if they were all orbiting the same parent star. Most are closer to their parent stars than Earth is to the Sun, and have far more elliptical orbits.

ORBITS OF EARTH AND
EXTRASOLAR PLANETS,
AND AVERAGE DISTANCES
FROM PARENT STAR

47 Ursae Majoris,
199 million miles
(320 million km)

16 Cygni B,
155 million miles
(250 million km)

14 Herculis,
230 million miles (370 million km)

Earth,
93 million miles
(150 million km)

Rho Coronae Borealis,
21 million miles
(34 million km)

Gliese 876,
19 million miles
(31 million km)

70 Virginis,
40 million miles
(64 million km)

Upsilon Andromedae,
5.2 million miles
(8.5 million km)

51 Pegasi,
4.6 million miles
(7.5 million km)

STAR

55 Cancri,
10 million miles
(16 million km)

Tau Boötis,
4.2 million miles (6.9 million km)

FIRST 10 EXTRASOLAR PLANETS DISCOVERED				
Name of parent star	Distance of parent star from Sun (ly)	Year of discovery	Minimum mass (Earth = 1)	Time to orbit star in days
51 Pegasi	50	1995	150	4.2
55 Cancri	44	1996	270	14.6
47 Ursae Majoris	46	1996	890	1,090
Tau Boötis	49	1996	1,230	3.3
Upsilon Andromedae	54	1996	220	4.6
70 Virginis	59	1996	2,100	117
16 Cygni B	72	1996	480	804
Rho Coronae Borealis	55	1997	350	39.6
Gliese 876	15	1998	670	60.8
14 Herculis	55	1998	1,050	1,620

WHAT ARE OTHER PLANETS LIKE?
Most extrasolar planets that
have been detected are as big as,
or bigger than, Jupiter. They are
believed to be gas giants, and
most are close to their parent
stars, so they will also be very
hot. Astronomers have so far
discovered 134 extrasolar
planetary systems, containing a
total of 154 known planets.

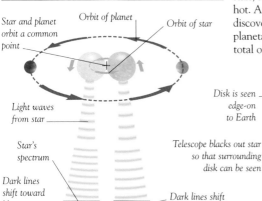

Star and planet orbit a common point

Orbit of planet

Orbit of star

Light waves from star

Star's spectrum

Dark lines shift toward blue

Dark lines shift toward red

Disk of gas and dust

Disk is seen edge-on to Earth

Telescope blacks out star so that surrounding disk can be seen

BETA PICTORIS
Astronomers have discovered
planets that are being formed
around newborn stars. It is
thought planets may be
forming in the swirling disk
of gas and dust around the
young star Beta Pictoris.

WOBBLING STARS
Extrasolar planets can be found by observing
how their gravity causes their parent stars to
wobble slightly. If the star's light is split into a
spectrum, the dark lines in the spectrum shift
to the blue end as the star wobbles toward us,
and to the red end as it wobbles away.

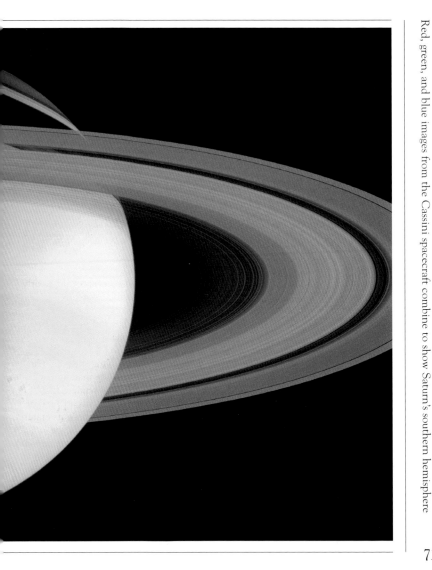

SATURN CLOSE-UP
Red, green, and blue images from the Cassini spacecraft combine to show Saturn's southern hemisphere

MERCURY

SCORCHED AND BLASTED by solar radiation, Mercury is the planet closest to the Sun. This dry, rocky world has an extremely thin atmosphere. Of all the planets in the solar system, it travels around the Sun the fastest, but spins slowly on its axis. From Earth, faint markings can be seen on its surface, and astronomers are puzzled as to why this small planet has such a vast iron core.

Red and hot areas, near the equator

FALSE-COLOR TEMPERATURE MAP OF MERCURY

Purple regions out of direct sunlight are coolest

SCARRED SURFACE

About 4 billion years ago, in the early history of the solar system, the young Mercury's surface was punctured by meteorite impacts. Lava flooded out from the interior to form extensive plains, giving the planet an appearance that, at first glance, resembles the Moon. With no wind or water to shape its crater-scarred landscape, Mercury has remained virtually unchanged since then.

Craters vary from a few yards (meters) to hundreds of miles (kilometers) across

Younger craters are surrounded by light-colored streaks of ejected material

Brontë crater

Craters are generally shallower than those on the Moon

In this image taken by the Mariner 10 space probe, ultraviolet light from the Sun causes the surface to look bleached

TEMPERATURE

Mercury, being closest to the Sun, has the greatest variation in day and night temperatures of any planet. The average surface temperature is 333°F (167°C). It can soar to 842°F (450°C) when it is closest to the Sun. At night, because the atmosphere is too thin to retain heat, temperatures fall to as low as –292°F (–180°C).

VITAL STATISTICS

Diameter	3,030 miles (4,880 km)
Avg. distance from Sun	36 million miles (58 million km)
Orbital speed around Sun	30 mps (48 km/s)
Sunrise to sunrise	176 days
Mass (Earth=1)	0.0553
Volume (Earth=1)	0.0560
Avg. density (water=1)	5.43
Surface gravity (Earth=1)	0.38
Avg. surface temperature	333°F (167°C)
Number of moons	0

MERCURY AT A GLANCE

A dense, fast-moving, rocky planet with a large metal core, Mercury has weak gravity and a thin atmosphere. It is the second-smallest planet, after Pluto.

TILT, SPIN, AND ORBIT

Orbits the Sun in 87.97 days

Axis of rotation is almost vertical

Spins on its axis once every 58.65 days

Potassium and other gases 1%   ATMOSPHERE
Helium 6%
Hydrogen 22%
Sodium 29%
Oxygen 42%

Crust of silicate rock

Rocky silicate mantle

Iron core

SCALE

Diameter is 2,237 miles (3,600 km) less than Earth's

STRUCTURE

North magnetic pole   Axis of spin

Magnetic field lines

Iron core

South magnetic pole

Magnetosphere—area of space affected by planet's magnetism

MAGNETIC CORE

Mercury is believed to have a solid iron core, surrounded by a layer of liquid iron and sulfur. The core produces the planet's magnetic field, which is about 1 percent as strong as Earth's.

MERCURY'S SURFACE

BECAUSE MERCURY IS CLOSE to the Sun, even a space-based observatory like the Hubble Space Telescope would get damaged by the Sun's rays if it tried to obtain views of it. In the 1970s, Mariner 10 used protective sunshields to produce detailed images of parts of its surface, but more than half is still unexplored.

Sobkou Planitia, a large lava plain formed after the Caloris impact

CALORIS BASIN
A crater about 800 miles (1,300 km) wide, Caloris Basin formed about 3.6 billion years ago when a space rock about 60 miles (100 km) across crashed into Mercury. There are similar, smaller impact craters on the crater floor.

Space rock strikes Mercury

Caloris Montes mountain chain was formed by the Caloris impact

IMPACT SHOCK WAVES
Mercury's crust and upper mantle were still cooling and compressing when the vast space rock that formed the Caloris Basin struck it. This made its surface buckle into ranges of hills and mountains.

Shock waves spread throughout planet

Shock waves converge and crumple surface opposite the impact site

Tolstoj, a huge, flooded crater in Mercury's southwestern quarter

CRATERED WORLD

Mercury's surface is covered with craters, including the Caloris Basin, ringed by the Caloris Montes. Beyond are rock-strewn areas, smooth lava-flooded plains, wrinkles, and ridges that formed as the planet cooled.

TRANSIT OF MERCURY

Mercury's path across our sky usually takes it just above or below the Sun. But every few years, when the Sun, Earth, and Mercury are aligned, a transit occurs and Mercury travels across the Sun's face. The planet appears as a black dot, and can take several hours to cross from one side of the Sun to the other.

Mercury

This part of Mercury and all of its opposite side were not photographed by Mariner 10 and remain unmapped

Petrarch is one of the younger craters on Mercury. Its smooth floor contains a few, more recent craters

DISCOVERY RUPES

This is a vast ridge that stretches about 310 miles (500 km) across Mercury's surface, towering up to 1.2 miles (2 km) above its surroundings. So far, 16 such features have been detected on Mercury.

SOUTH POLAR REGION

Mercury's polar regions include areas that are always shaded from the Sun's heat. Scientists, studying these regions by reflecting radar off them, believe there may be water ice at Mercury's poles, but other substances, such as sulfur, can produce similar results.

Craters cover about 60% of the known surface. The rest is mostly lava plains

Monteverdi
Stravinsky
Velázquez Holbein
Al-Hamadhāni
Praxiteles
Mussorgskij
Kuan Han-Ch'ing
Priust
Wren
Lennmioa
Le Po
Vivaldi
Giotto
Yeats
Handel
Polygnotus
Machaut
Titian
Homer
Renoir
Repin
Ibsen
Matisse
Chekhov
Unkei
Bramante
Schubert

VENUS

CALLED AN INFERIOR PLANET because it orbits closer to the Sun than Earth does, Venus is a sphere of rock similar in size to Earth. A dark, hostile world of volcanoes and suffocating atmosphere,

CLOUD-TOP VIEW OF VENUS

its average temperature is higher than that of any other planet. From Earth, we can only see cloud tops. Hidden under this thick blanket of gas is a landscape molded by volcanic eruption.

Venus is visible before sunrise at western elongation

Venus is lost in the Sun's glare at inferior conjunction

Venus

Earth

The Sun

Venus is visible after sunset at eastern conjunction

Venus is hidden behind the Sun at superior conjunction

ORBIT OF VENUS
The Venusian orbit sometimes passes between Earth and the Sun. During this inferior conjunction, it is hidden by the Sun's glare. It is brightest when the angle of elongation is about 39°, and it is visible after sunset or before sunrise.

VOLCANOES
The Venusian surface has long lava flows, volcanic craters, and dome- and shield-shaped volcanoes. There are 156 large volcanoes that are more than 60 miles (100 km) across, nearly 300 that are between 12 and 62 miles (20 and 100 km) across, and at least 500 clusters of smaller volcanoes.

Pancake dome volcanoes have flat tops and steep sides, like these in Alpha Regio

Eistla Regio, a spider-like Arachnoid volcano

VITAL STATISTICS	
Diameter	7,521 miles (12,104 km)
Avg. distance from Sun	67 million miles (108 million km)
Orbital speed around Sun	21.76 mps (35.02 km/s)
Sunrise to sunrise	117 days
Mass (Earth = 1)	0.82
Volume (Earth = 1)	0.86
Avg. density (water = 1)	5.2
Surface gravity (Earth = 1)	0.9
Avg. surface temperature	867°F (464°C)
Number of moons	0

VENUS AT A GLANCE

Venus is a rocky planet, with a structure and size similar to Earth's. Its atmosphere helps make it the hottest planet of all. It spins slowly, in the opposite direction of most planets.

TILT, SPIN, AND ORBIT

Orbits the Sun in 224.7 days

Axis tilts from the vertical by 2.7°

Spins on its axis once every 243 days

ATMOSPHERE

Nitrogen 3.5% and trace gases

Carbon dioxide 96.5%

SCALE

STRUCTURE

Iron and nickel core

Rocky mantle

Silicate crust

Venus is a little smaller than Earth

IMPACT CRATERS

More than 900 impact craters have been identified on Venus. About 60 percent are undamaged, a handful of the other 40 percent have been damaged by volcanic lava, and the rest have been altered by the cracking and movement of the planet's crust.

VENUSIAN PLAINS

Over three-quarters of Venus is covered by plains that were largely formed by volcanic processes. The plains are marked by volcanic and impact craters, lava flows, and features sculpted by the Venusian wind.

Belts of narrow ridges, a few hundred yards (meters) high, stretch across the plain

Lavinia Planitia is one of the main plains of Venus

79

VENUSIAN ATMOSPHERE

SOME FOUR BILLION YEARS AGO, Venus and Earth had similar atmospheres. Today, the Venusian atmosphere is mainly carbon dioxide, with sulfur dust and droplets of sulfuric acid from the many volcanic eruptions. It is also very thick, making Venus hot, gloomy, and suffocating.

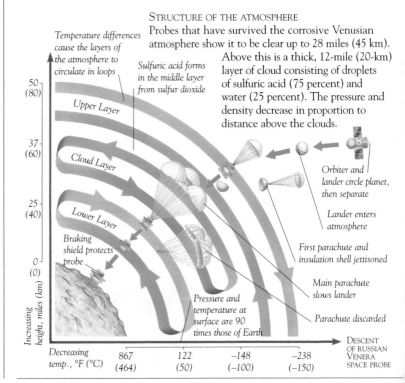

STRUCTURE OF THE ATMOSPHERE

Probes that have survived the corrosive Venusian atmosphere show it to be clear up to 28 miles (45 km). Above this is a thick, 12-mile (20-km) layer of cloud consisting of droplets of sulfuric acid (75 percent) and water (25 percent). The pressure and density decrease in proportion to distance above the clouds.

Temperature differences cause the layers of the atmosphere to circulate in loops

Sulfuric acid forms in the middle layer from sulfur dioxide

Upper Layer

Cloud Layer

Lower Layer

Braking shield protects probe

Orbiter and lander circle planet, then separate

Lander enters atmosphere

First parachute and insulation shell jettisoned

Main parachute slows lander

Parachute discarded

Pressure and temperature at surface are 90 times those of Earth

Increasing height, miles (km)

50 (80)

37 (60)

25 (40)

0 (0)

Decreasing temp., °F (°C)

| 867 (464) | 122 (50) | −148 (−100) | −238 (−150) |

DESCENT OF RUSSIAN VENERA SPACE PROBE

Hot gases from the equator spiral up to polar region

Orange shows the presence of sulfur dioxide

Bands show pattern of cloud-top movement

VENUS IN ULTRAVIOLET

The Pioneer Venus space probe took many ultraviolet pictures, which showed cloud patterns in the atmosphere that were studied to understand its winds.

CLOUD MOVEMENT

The Sun warms the gases in the Venusian atmosphere at the equator. These rise and move toward the cooler polar regions, and then sink to the lower cloud layer as they cool, moving back to the equator.

Thick sulfuric acid clouds

Sunlight

About 20% reaches surface

Infrared

Infrared

About 80% reflects away

Sunlight bounces off cloud tops

Clouds block out most of the sunlight

Carbon dioxide layer holds in heat

Only some of the infrared released by the ground escapes

Surface temperature, 864°F (462°C)– 870°F (466°C), is higher than if there were no atmosphere

GREENHOUSE EFFECT

The Venusian atmosphere traps only some of the Sun's heat. The infrared is absorbed by the carbon dioxide in the atmosphere, reflecting some of it back to the surface, while a small amount is radiated into space.

PHASES OF VENUS

We never see the full Venus, because when the whole of the sunlit side points toward Earth, Venus is obscured by the Sun. As it moves around the Sun and gets closer to Earth, it grows larger in Earth's sky, but we see less and less of its sunlit side.

VENUSIAN SURFACE

ALTHOUGH VENUS IS THE CLOSEST planet to Earth, it is only in the last 30 years that scientists have successfully pierced its cloud layers using radar techniques. The data collected by Earth-based instruments and orbiters has been combined to produce a global map of Venus. The orbiter Magellan added about 4,000 surface features to this map.

Ishtar Terra is an elevated plateau encircled by narrow mountain belts

Lakshmi Planum is a smooth volcanic plain dominated by two large shield volcanoes, Colette and Sacajawea

MAXWELL MONTES
A steep mountain range lies in the middle of Ishtar Terra, a highland region about the size of Australia. This is Maxwell Montes—the highest part of the Venusian surface, rising up to 39,400 ft (12,000 m).

ALPHA REGIO
This was the first feature to be identified on the Venusian surface using Earth-based radar. It is located in the southern hemisphere. It is an area of volcanic highland measuring about 800 miles (1,300 km) across. It includes low, domed hills, intersecting ridges, and troughs and valleys.

ISHTAR T
LAKSHMI PLANUM
Colette
VESTA RUPES
UT RUPES
Sacaja
SEDNA PLANITIA
Gula Mons
Sappho Patera
GUINEVERE PLANITIA
E I S T
PHOEBE REGIO
Navka Planitia
ALPHA REGIO
Innini Mons
Hathor Mons
Eve
LAVINIA PLANITIA

Lavinia Planitia, a lava plain

SURFACE FEATURES

Venus is a largely smooth planet, covered by rolling planes that rise or dip by no more than 2 miles (3 km). Lowland volcanic plains, or planitia, cover 85 percent of the surface. The remaining 15 percent consists of highland areas, named terra or regio.

Danu Montes, a 16,400-ft- (2,000-m-) high mountain

Waterfall-like flows of solidified lava

Tellus Tessera plateau rises about 6,600 ft (2,000 m) above the average ground level

Cleopatra

NIOBE PLANITIA
LEDA PLANITIA
TELLUS TESSERA
BELL REGIO
Pavlova
Hestia Rupes
OVDA REGIO
APHRODITE TERRA
AINO PLANITIA

Highlands rise about 13,100–16,500 ft (4,000–5,000 m)

LAKSHMI PLANUM

This is a high plateau rising about 2.5 miles (4 km), bounded by the mountain ranges Danu, Akna, Freyja, and Maxwell Montes. The eastern side has several lava flows.

MEAD CRATER

The largest impact crater on Venus, Mead crater has a diameter of 170 miles (280 km). Inside, the terrain is rough, with a hilly central region. Outside, material ejected on impact has been eroded by winds into narrow rock ridges separated by wind-eroded corridors.

APHRODITE TERRA

The most extensive highland region of Venus, Aphrodite Terra stretches for 3,700 miles (6,000 km). The western part shows little evidence of volcanic activity, but the eastern part is occupied by Atla Regio, a large volcanic rise with rifts and volcanic peaks.

MARS

NAMED AFTER THE ROMAN GOD OF WAR because of its dusty red appearance, Mars is also known as the Red Planet. Along with Mercury, Venus, and Earth, it is one of the four terrestrial, or Earth-like, planets of the inner solar system. It is one-and-a-half times more distant from the Sun than Earth is. In recent years, scientists have begun to study Mars in detail, and they may yet uncover fossils, or even show that primitive life exists.

The northern lowlands contain many fewer craters than the southern hemisphere. This indicates that the region has been smoothed off by volcanic lava flow and is younger, having been exposed to asteroidal bombardment for a lesser amount of time

The pale areas around the rims of impact craters are wind-blown dust deposits

Dark areas are thought to correspond to regions of fine-grained rock formed from solidified lava

SURFACE FEATURES

Much of the Red Planet's surface is a frozen, rock-strewn desert interrupted by dunes and craters. But Mars also has some of the most spectacular and diverse features of the solar system. Its volcanoes and canyons dwarf those found on Earth. The planet's red color comes from soil rich in iron oxide (rust).

MOONS AND THEIR ORBITS

The Martian moons, Phobos and Deimos, first observed in 1877, are small, lumpy satellites with a lower density than Mars, and both are heavily cratered. They may be asteroids captured by Martian gravity. They orbit Mars in an easterly direction. Phobos is 16 miles (26 km) in diameter and Deimos is 10 miles (16 km) at its widest.

Stickney, the largest crater on Phobos, is about 6 miles (10 km) across

Deimos orbits Mars in 30.3 hours at an altitude of 12,453 miles (20,040 km)

ATMOSPHERE

Mars has a thin atmosphere, mainly composed of carbon dioxide. At times, one-third of the atmosphere is frozen at the poles. Each day, solar winds carry away a little more of the atmosphere.

VITAL STATISTICS	
Diameter	4,222 miles (6,794 km)
Avg. distance from Sun	142 million miles (228 million km)
Orbital speed around Sun	15 mps (24.13 km/s)
Sunrise to sunrise	24.63 hours
Mass (Earth=1)	0.11
Volume (Earth=1)	0.15
Avg. density (water=1)	3.93
Surface gravity (Earth=1)	0.38
Avg. surface temperature	−81.4°F (−63°C)
Number of moons	2

MARS AT A GLANCE

Mars is a rocky planet with a small iron core. It is about half the size of Earth, with a similar rotation time. Its atmosphere is thin, and pressure at the surface is 1 percent of Earth's.

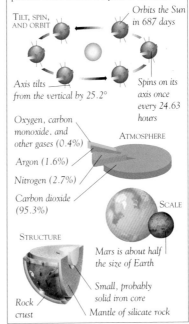

TILT, SPIN, AND ORBIT

Orbits the Sun in 687 days

Axis tilts from the vertical by 25.2°

Spins on its axis once every 24.63 hours

Oxygen, carbon monoxide, and other gases (0.4%)

Argon (1.6%)

Nitrogen (2.7%)

Carbon dioxide (95.3%)

ATMOSPHERE

SCALE

Mars is about half the size of Earth

STRUCTURE

Small, probably solid iron core

Rock crust

Mantle of silicate rock

SURFACE OF MARS

THE MARTIAN SURFACE IS cratered by
meteorite impacts and has no vegetation
and no water. It is probably made up
of one plate and lacks movement.
This explains the huge volcanoes
and volcanic flood plains, which
build up to great sizes because
molten rock continues to
pour from the same spot
for millions of years.

*This view shows
the northern ice cap
and the volcanoes
and canyons near
the equator*

LAND STRUCTURES

Highlands dominate the planet's southern
hemisphere, and vast lowland plains lie to
the north. There are long cliffs between
the two regions. In and around Tharsis Rise,
just north of the equator, there are huge
volcanoes, the Valles Marineris canyon
system, and many ridges and fractures.

Tharsis Rise extends 5,000 miles (8,000 km)

OLYMPUS MONS

The largest volcano
in the solar system,
Olympus Mons is situated
in Tharsis Rise. It is
78,740 ft (24,000 m) high
and 370 miles (600 km)
across. Its crater is 56
miles (90 km) across.

*Valles Marineris is
a vast canyon system
near Tharsis Rise*

Water-ice clouds sometimes develop, but dust and carbon dioxide clouds cause most of the planet's weather

Dark, low-reflective patches

Polar ice cap

ACIDALIA PLANITIA

Kasei Vallis

CHRYSE PLANITIA

LUNAE PLANUM

Coprates Chasma

Holden

LIS PLANUM

Lassell

Silpher

Lowell

Floods of lava have created smooth plains in the otherwise cratered southern highlands

SPOTTING SURFACE FEATURES
Some surface details on Mars can be distinguished with a relatively inexpensive 6-in (15-cm) telescope. The viewer can see polar ice caps and, occasionally, clouds. Some parts of the surface reflect less light and are seen as dark patches.

A Martian storm, in which wind speeds can rise to 185 mph (300 km/h), whips up dust storms that sometimes envelop the whole planet

POLAR ICE CAP
The north and south poles on Mars are capped with carbon dioxide ice, dust, and water ice. In the summer, the ice caps shrink as the frozen carbon dioxide evaporates, leaving behind mainly water ice. This picture, taken by the Viking Orbiter, shows the southern ice cap in summer, when it retreats to 250 miles (400 km) across.

MARTIAN MOUNTAINS
Northwest view of a 3-mile (5-km) section of Aureum Chaos, imaged by ESA's Mars Express spacecraft

JUPITER

THE FIFTH PLANET FROM the Sun is very different from the terrestrial (Earth-like) planets. Jupiter, the largest planet in the solar system, is a gas giant. It is all gas and liquid except for a very small rocky core. Its mass is 2.5 times that of all the other planets combined, and 1,300 Earths would fit into its volume.

RING SYSTEM
Jupiter's faint ring system was first seen in images sent to Earth by the Voyager 1 space probe in 1979. The rings are formed from dust knocked off its four inner moons by meteorites. There is a "cloudy" inner ring, a flattened central ring, and an outer ring, which is actually one ring embedded within another.

Substances including sulfur give Jupiter its multicolored appearance

Jupiter is also called the banded planet due to its bands of different-colored clouds

If Jupiter had been 50 times more massive, its core would have been hot enough to fuse hydrogen and it would have become a star

Lines of
magnetic
field

Tail of
magnetosphere

Jupiter

Magnetosphere

MAGNETISM
Jupiter's magnetic field is 20,000 times
stronger than Earth's. It surrounds the
planet in a huge magnetic bubble, or
magnetosphere. It most likely created
by electric currents in the fast-spinning
metallic hydrogen within the planet.

OBSERVING JUPITER
Jupiter is the fourth-
brightest object in the
night sky. It can easily
be seen by the naked
eye, and details such as
its banding can be seen
with a 6-in (15-cm) telescope.

STRUCTURE
Jupiter is a giant ball of hydrogen
and helium, compressed into a liquid
inside, and probably into a solid at
the core. Its core is likely to be 10–15
times more massive than Earth's.
Pressure and temperature 12,400
miles (20,000 km) below the
cloud tops are so intense that
hydrogen turns into a liquid
that behaves like a metal.

VITAL STATISTICS	
Diameter (equator)	88,850 miles (142,984 km)
Diameter (poles)	83,086 miles (133,708 km)
Distance from Sun	483 million miles (778 million km)
Speed around Sun	8 mps (13 km/s)
Sunrise to sunrise (at cloud tops)	9.84 hours
Mass (Earth = 1)	318
Volume (Earth = 1)	1,321
Density (water = 1)	1.33
Gravity at cloud tops (Earth = 1)	2.36
Cloud-top temperature	−166°F (−110°C)
Number of moons	60

JUPITER'S ATMOSPHERE

JUPITER'S ATMOSPHERE IS TURBULENT, with huge
swirling storm systems and giant super-bolts of
lightning. Its rapid rotation helps whip up winds,
measured by the Galileo probe at 400 mph
(650 km/h). Jupiter formed from the same
ancient gas cloud as the Sun, so scientists
study its deep atmosphere to understand
the solar system's earliest history.

CLOUD TOPS

Jupiter is a giant gas ball, compressed into a
liquid and then into a solid, with increasing
depth. It has no solid surface, so astronomers
often refer to properties
such as its temperature
at a certain level in the
atmosphere, where the
pressure is the same as Earth's
atmospheric pressure at sea level.

*North Temperate
Belt is bounded on
its southern edge
by red ovals*

*Violent winds give the North
Equatorial Belt a twisted look*

*Damp air in GRS rises and
is whipped into a spiral*

GREAT RED SPOT

A storm system three times the size of
Earth has raged in Jupiter's atmosphere
for more than 300 years. Known as
the Great Red Spot (GRS), it rotates
counterclockwise every six Earth days.

ZONES AND BELTS

Bright bands (zones) in the
atmosphere are areas of rising gas,
while dark bands (belts) are regions
of falling gas. The tops of the belts
are about 12 miles (20 km) lower
than the tops of the zones.

Charged particles from the moon Io strike Jupiter just below its poles

North Polar Region

CLOUD PROFILE
At the edge of Jupiter's 620-mile- (1,000-km-) thick atmosphere are three layers of cloud that reach down to a depth of about 50 miles (80 km).

Water ice appears about 19 miles (30 km) below the cloud tops

The hazy cloud tops are made of ammonia ice

About 12 miles (20 km) below the cloud tops are ammonium sulfide clouds

Increasing temperature and pressure lower in the atmosphere cause simple, colorless gases to react, forming complex colored molecules

Equatorial Zone

South Equatorial Belt

Bands are windstreams traveling in opposite directions at more than 370 mph (600 km/h)

One of the sites of impact

COMET IMPACT
In July 1994, 21 fragments of the comet Shoemaker-Levy 9 hit Jupiter at about 130,000 mph (210,000 km/h), sending 2,500-mile- (4,000-km-) wide fireballs 1,200 miles (2,000 km) into the atmosphere.

South Polar Region

93

JUPITER'S MOONS

JUPITER AND ITS 60 known moons are like a mini solar system. Some of the moons are rocky, some icy, and some may have had the conditions needed to foster primitive life. They may be asteroids or comets captured by Jupiter's gravity. The four largest moons were first investigated by the Italian astronomer Galileo in 1610. There may be many more moons yet undiscovered.

The volcanoes on Io can send up plumes of gas 155 miles (250 km) high

JUPITER'S MOONS				
Name	Diameter in miles (km)	Distance to Jupiter in miles (km)	Orbit in days	Year of discovery
Metis	25 (40)	79,514 (127,960)	0.29	1979
Adrastea	12 (20)	80,148 (128,980)	0.30	1979
Amalthea	124 (200)	112,660 (181,300)	0.50	1892
Thebe	62 (100)	137,889 (221,900)	0.67	1979
Io	2,264 (3,643)	261,982 (421,600)	1.77	1610
Europa	1,945 (3,130)	416,897 (670,900)	3.55	1610
Ganymede	3,274 (5,268)	664,898 (1,070,000)	7.15	1610
Callisto	2,986 (4,806)	1,170,096 (1,883,000)	16.69	1610
Leda	6 (10)	6,893,812 (11,094,000)	239	1974
Himalia	106 (170)	7,133,672 (11,480,000)	251	1904
Lysithea	15 (24)	7,282,808 (11,720,000)	259	1938
Elara	50 (80)	7,293,372 (11,737,000)	260	1905
Ananke	12 (20)	13,173,680 (21,200,000)	631	1951
Carme	19 (30)	14,043,640 (22,600,000)	692	1938
Pasiphae	22 (36)	14,602,900 (23,500,000)	735	1908
Sinope	17 (28)	14,727,180 (23,700,000)	758	1914

AMALTHEA

INNER MOONS

Jupiter's innermost moons, Metis and Adrastea, will eventually spiral into the planet. The largest of the non-Galilean moons is the potato-shaped Amalthea.

GANYMEDE

Jupiter's largest satellite is bigger than the planet Mercury. The space probe Galileo discovered that it had a magnetosphere of its own. It is thought to have a core of molten iron surrounded by a rocky mantle with an icy shell.

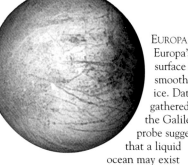

Ganymede's surface has faults similar to the San Andreas fault in California, where grooves have slipped sideways

IO

Io has a thin atmosphere of sulfur dioxide. The gravities of Jupiter, Europa, and Ganymede bend Io's crust back and forth, causing heat to be generated. As a result, Io is the most volcanically active body in the solar system.

CALLISTO

Callisto's surface is completely covered with craters, dating from the birth of Jupiter's system. Callisto consists of about 60 percent rock and iron and 40 percent ice and water. Scientists believe that it has a salty ocean beneath its icy crust.

EUROPA

Europa's surface is smooth ice. Data gathered by the Galileo probe suggests that a liquid ocean may exist beneath the ice and aquatic life may have arisen in the warmer parts of the ocean. A very thin atmosphere, composed of both molecular oxygen and hydrogen, has been detected.

SATURN

THE SECOND-LARGEST PLANET, Saturn is the easiest to recognize because of the bright rings around its equator. Like Jupiter, it is a large ball of gas and liquid topped by clouds. Nearly 10 times farther from the Sun than we are, it was the most distant planet known before the invention of the telescope.

Rings are made of particles and larger pieces of ice

BUTTERSCOTCH PLANET
Saturn, like Jupiter, has a surface of clouds, drawn out into bands by the planet's spin. The clouds are calmer and less colorful but also lower and colder at −220°F (−140°C) in the topmost layer. Above the clouds is a layer of haze, which gives Saturn its butterscotch color and makes it look smoother than Jupiter.

Saturn's cloud patterns are hidden by a haze of ammonia crystals

Saturn is nine times wider than Earth

Clouds form bright belts and dark zones

White clouds

Dark orange clouds

Blue clouds

ATMOSPHERE
Saturn has three main cloud layers and a haze above them. The clouds have the same gases as Jupiter's clouds, but the layers are farther apart because Saturn's gravity is weaker than Jupiter's.

A storm cloud broke out in 1990 and spread around the planet

STORMS ON SATURN
Every 30 years or so, during summer in the northern hemisphere, storms break out on Saturn, producing large white spots near the equator.

BULGING PLANET
Saturn spins every 10 hours 39 minutes at the equator, but takes nearly half an hour longer at the poles. Its low density and fast spin mean that Saturn's equator bulges more than any other planet.

At the equator, Saturn spins every 10 hours 39 minutes

Saturn's core spins every 10 hours 14 minutes

If we could find an ocean large enough, Saturn would float

PLANET DENSITY
Saturn is the least dense of the planets. Its average density is 70 percent that of water (its center is more dense than its surface), which means that it would float in water.

SATURN AT A GLANCE
Nine times the diameter of Earth, Saturn has a rocky center, with outer layers of liquid and gas. Bright rings of icy particles circle the planet's equator.

TILT, SPIN, AND ORBIT

Orbits the Sun in 29.46 years

The Sun

Axis tilts from the vertical by 26.7°

Spins on its axis once every 10.66 hours

ATMOSPHERE

Helium (15–20%) and trace gases

Hydrogen (80–85%)

Atmosphere

Liquid hydrogen and helium

Liquid metallic hydrogen and helium

Core of rock and ice

SCALE

STRUCTURE

Saturn is nine times wider than Earth

VITAL STATISTICS	
Avg. diameter	71,232 miles (114,632 km)
Avg. distance from the Sun	0.9 billion miles (1.4 billion km)
Orbital speed around the Sun	6 mps (10 km/s)
Sunrise to sunrise (at cloud tops)	10.23 hours
Mass (Earth=1)	95
Volume (Earth=1)	763.59
Avg. density (water=1)	0.69
Cloud-top temperature	–220°F (–140°C)
Number of known moons	46

97

SATURN'S RINGS

Four planets have rings—Jupiter, Saturn, Uranus, and Neptune—but Saturn's are the brightest. They are visible from Earth even through small telescopes. They consist of chunks of ice and rock, ranging from specks of dust to large icebergs, and are probably the remains of a failed satellite production process.

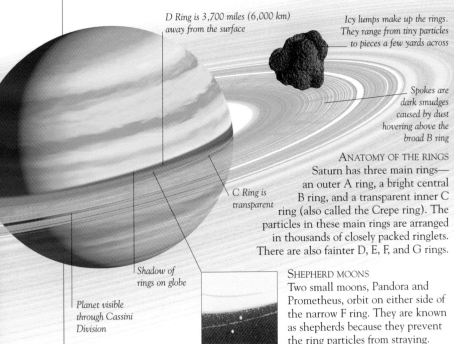

D Ring is 3,700 miles (6,000 km) away from the surface

Icy lumps make up the rings. They range from tiny particles to pieces a few yards across

Spokes are dark smudges caused by dust hovering above the broad B ring

ANATOMY OF THE RINGS

Saturn has three main rings—an outer A ring, a bright central B ring, and a transparent inner C ring (also called the Crepe ring). The particles in these main rings are arranged in thousands of closely packed ringlets. There are also fainter D, E, F, and G rings.

C Ring is transparent

Shadow of rings on globe

Planet visible through Cassini Division

SHEPHERD MOONS

Two small moons, Pandora and Prometheus, orbit on either side of the narrow F ring. They are known as shepherds because they prevent the ring particles from straying.

GLORIOUS RINGS

This view of Saturn cannot be seen from Earth. It was taken by Voyager 2 in 1981, looking back as it left the planet on its way to more distant Uranus and Neptune. The rings are lit up by sunlight shining through from behind. Saturn's globe shows through the inner part of the rings.

Each particle is a satellite of Saturn

Smaller particles are up to a few inches (centimeters) in size

Dust from the moon Enceladus may be found in the E ring, which is the farthest from Saturn

INNER RINGS

Ring B is the brightest and the broadest of the rings visible from Earth. The Cassini Division, 3,100 miles (5,000 km) wide, lies between the A and B rings. A narrower gap, the Encke Division, splits the A ring. The fainter G and E, farther from Saturn, are not shown here.

D ring
C ring
B ring
Cassini Division
A ring
Encke Division
F ring

CASSINI CLOSE-UP

The Cassini orbiter reached Saturn in July 2004. It will complete 74 orbits of Saturn, 44 close flybys of its moon Titan, and numerous flybys of the other icy moons.

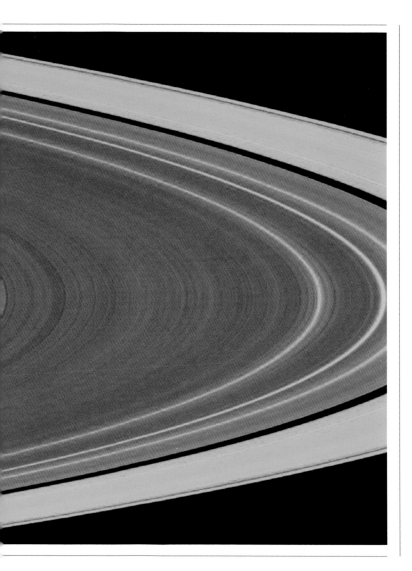

SATURN'S MOONS

SATURN HAS 49 KNOWN moons, most of which were discovered by the Cassini probe in 2004. Except for Titan, which is the largest, all of them have a low density and are thought to consist of a mixture of rock and frozen water. Some of them share the same orbits.

HUYGENS PROBE

This probe, built by the European Space Agency (ESA), was carried to Saturn as part of the Cassini mission. In January 2005, it parachuted to the surface of Titan to report on conditions beneath the moon's orange clouds.

Titan

Titan's density is increased by gravitational compression

DIONE

Dione is Saturn's fourth-largest moon and has a diameter of 695 miles (1,118 km). The Cassini space probe sent images of a heavily cratered surface, and the bright, wispy streaks first noticed by Voyager 2 were found to be bright ice cliffs created by tectonic fractures.

TITAN

Titan is Saturn's largest moon, the second-largest in the solar system. It is even larger and more massive than the planet Pluto. Its dense, fully developed atmosphere contains complex hydrocarbons, including benzene, and the surface pressure is one and a half times that of Earth's. Its surface temperature is about −292°F (−180°C).

Dione

VITAL STATISTICS				
Satellite	Diameter in miles (km)	Distance to Saturn in miles (km)	Orbit (days)	Year of discovery
Pan	12 (20)	83,008 (133,583)	0.57	1990
Atlas	21 (34)	85,530 (137,640)	0.60	1980
Prometheus	62 (100)	86,592 (139,350)	0.61	1980
Pandora	55 (88)	88,052 (141,700)	0.63	1980
Epimetheus	68 (110)	94,094 (151,422)	0.69	1966
Janus	119 (191)	94,125 (151,472)	0.69	1966
Mimas	247 (398)	115,282 (185,520)	0.94	1789
Enceladus	309 (498)	147,906 (238,020)	1.37	1789
Tethys	659 (1,060)	183,102 (294,660)	1.89	1684
Telesto	16 (25)	183,102 (294,660)	1.89	1980
Calypso	10 (16)	183,102 (294,660)	1.89	1980
Dione	696 (1,120)	234,516 (377,400)	2.74	1684
Helene	20 (32)	234,516 (377,400)	2.74	1980
Rhea	950 (1,528)	327,503 (527,040)	4.52	1672
Titan	3,200 (5,150)	759,258 (1,221,850)	15.95	1655
Hyperion	174 (280)	920,356 (1,481,100)	21.28	1848
Iapetus	892 (1,436)	2,212,992 (3,561,300)	79.33	1671
Phoebe	137 (220)	8,048,373 (12,952,000)	550.48	1898

Epimetheus

EPIMETHEUS AND JANUS

Janus and Epimetheus are two small moons with orbits only 31 miles (50 km) apart near the edge of Saturn's rings. Every four years, when the inner moon overtakes the outer, the two swap orbits, one moving farther away from Saturn and the other dropping closer, thus avoiding a collision. These two small moons may be halves of a former moon that broke apart.

Janus

ENCELADUS

Parts of this moon's icy surface are cratered, but other parts are so smooth they seem to have melted, wiping out any craters.

URANUS

URANUS, THE FIRST PLANET
discovered through a telescope,
was spotted in 1781. Its most
remarkable feature is that it
appears to lie on its side, so that
first one pole and then the
other points to the Sun as it
moves along its orbit. It has 27
known moons and faint rings.

Oberon is the second-largest and most distant moon. It is 946 miles (1,523 km) wide

Titania, at 980 miles (1,578 km) wide, is the largest moon of Uranus

STRUCTURE AND COMPOSITION
Like Jupiter and Saturn, Uranus is
covered in clouds, but its clouds are
almost featureless, apart from a few
brighter streaks, photographed by the
Voyager 2 space probe. The clouds
of Uranus consist of methane ice
crystals and appear blue-green.

The narrow rings are made up of particles about 3 ft (1 m) across

Bulge at the equator due to rapid rotation

RINGS
Uranus has 11 known
rings, which circle
the planet's equator.
These dark rings, and
the equator, appear
to be almost upright,
because Uranus is
tilted on its side. Two
tiny moons, Cordelia
and Ophelia, orbit on
either side of the
outermost ring
(the Epsilon ring).

VOYAGER 2 IMAGE
OF THE RINGS

Puck, the largest of the moons discovered by Voyager 2, is just 93 miles (150 km) across

VITAL STATISTICS	
Diameter	31,763 miles (51,118 km)
Avg. distance from Sun	1.8 billion miles (2.871 billion km)
Speed around Sun	4.2 mps (6.82 km/s)
Sunrise to sunrise	17.24 hours
Mass (Earth=1)	14.5
Volume (Earth=1)	63.1
Avg. density (water=1)	1.32
Gravity at cloud tops (Earth=1)	0.89
Cloud-top temperature	−323°F (−197°C)
Number of known moons	27

ARIEL AND UMBRIEL

These two moons are similar in size—
about 720 miles (1,160 km)—but look
very different. Ariel is the brightest of
the major moons, while Umbriel is the
darkest. Ariel has valleys on its
surface, caused by its crust cracking.
Uranus's moons are named after
characters from the writings of
William Shakespeare and
Alexander Pope.

Umbriel

Ariel

MIRANDA

Miranda, the
smallest of the five
main moons with
a diameter of 292
miles (470 km), has a
jumbled surface with a bright
"check mark" and grooves. One theory
for this is that Miranda broke apart and
then came together again.

URANUS AT A GLANCE

The extreme tilt of Uranus gives it unusually
long seasons. As the planet follows its 84-year
orbit around the Sun, each pole has 42 years
of continuous sunlight, followed by 42 years
of darkness.

TILT, SPIN,
AND ORBIT

Orbits the Sun
in 84 years

Axis
tilts from the
vertical by 98°.

Spins on its
axis once every 17.24 hours

Methane (2%)
and trace gases

ATMOSPHERE

Helium (15%)

Hydrogen (83%)

STRUCTURE

Atmosphere of hydrogen,
helium, and other gases

Mantle of
water, ice,
methane,
and
ammonia

SCALE

Core of
silicate rock

Uranus is about four
times the size of Earth

NEPTUNE

THE MOST DISTANT OF the four giant planets in the solar system, Neptune is 30 times farther from the Sun than Earth. It was discovered by Johann Galle in 1846, but its existence was predicted earlier, from the fact that its gravity was pulling Uranus off course. It has 13 known moons, and a faint set of rings. It is similar to Uranus in many ways.

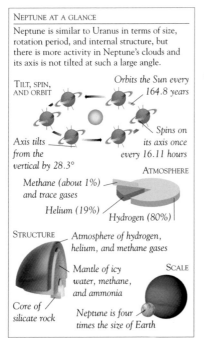

NEPTUNE AT A GLANCE

Neptune is similar to Uranus in terms of size, rotation period, and internal structure, but there is more activity in Neptune's clouds and its axis is not tilted at such a large angle.

TILT, SPIN, AND ORBIT

Orbits the Sun every 164.8 years

Axis tilts from the vertical by 28.3°

Spins on its axis once every 16.11 hours

ATMOSPHERE

Methane (about 1%) and trace gases

Helium (19%)

Hydrogen (80%)

STRUCTURE

Atmosphere of hydrogen, helium, and methane gases

Mantle of icy water, methane, and ammonia

SCALE

Core of silicate rock

Neptune is four times the size of Earth

At least four rings surround the planet

ATMOSPHERE

Methane gas high up in Neptune's atmosphere makes its clouds appear blue. Most of the gas in its atmosphere is helium and hydrogen. Its clouds are stormier than Uranus's because the inside of the planet is warmer, stirring up the gas to produce white and dark clouds that appear and disappear.

CLOUDS

Bright streaks of cloud, similar to cirrus clouds on Earth but made of methane, were photographed by Voyager 2.

The blue coloring is due to methane in the planet's atmosphere

GREAT DARK SPOT

A large oval cloud, about the size of Earth, was discovered by Voyager 2 in 1989, but had vanished when the Hubble Space Telescope looked at Neptune in 1994.

VITAL STATISTICS	
Diameter	30,779 miles (49,532 km)
Avg. distance from Sun	2.795 billion miles) (4.498 billion km
Orbital speed around Sun	3.4 mps (5.48 km/s)
Sunrise to sunrise	16.11 hours
Mass (Earth=1)	17.2
Volume (Earth=1)	57.74
Avg. density (water=1)	1.64
Gravity at cloud tops (Earth=1)	1.13
Cloud-top temperature	−328°F (−200°C)
Number of known moons	13

Triton is 1,681 miles (2,706 km) across

South polar ice cap on Triton

TRITON

Neptune's largest moon, Triton, is bigger than the planet Pluto. Triton was once a minor planet that was captured by Neptune's gravity. It has the coldest surface in the solar system, −391°F (−235°C), and is covered with frozen nitrogen and methane.

PLUTO

PLUTO IS THE SMALLEST planet of all, and the most distant from the Sun. Clyde Tombaugh discovered it in 1930. Its orbit is the least circular of all the planets. It is so small and unusual that some wonder if it is a true planet at all, or simply the largest of a family of icy bodies in the Kuiper belt.

Pluto's surface is covered in frozen nitrogen and methane

ANATOMY OF PLUTO
Pluto is just 1,413 miles (2,274 km) in diameter, smaller than Earth's Moon. It has bright markings that may be made by patches of ice on its otherwise dark reddish surface. There may also be craters.

The elliptical and angled Pluto orbit

Orbit of Uranus

Orbit of Neptune

Pluto's orbit is more tilted than other planets

UNUSUAL ORBIT
Pluto's orbit takes it from 2.7 to 4.6 billion miles (4.4 to 7.4 billion km) from the Sun. On each 248-year orbit, Pluto comes nearer to the Sun than Neptune. This lasts for about 20 years and brings it closer to Uranus than Neptune for that 20-year period.

MOST DISTANT PLANET
From Pluto, the Sun is a thousand times fainter than from Earth, but still much brighter than the stars. Pluto's temperature is about –364°F (–220°C), but when it is closest to the Sun, its surface warms up and some of the ice turns to gas and produces a thin atmosphere.

ARTIST'S IMPRESSION OF SUN FROM SURFACE OF PLUTO   *Sun*

Pluto's surface is dotted with impact craters

Surface covered by water ice and scarred with impact craters

Charon's density is less than Pluto's

PLUTO AT A GLANCE

Pluto is a tiny ball of ice and rock much smaller than Earth. The tilt of its axis is greater than that of Uranus. It is thought that a collision knocked off ice from Pluto to make Charon.

TILT, SPIN, AND ORBIT

Orbits the Sun every 247.68 years

Axis tilts from the vertical by 122°

Spins on its axis once every 6.39 days

STRUCTURE

Frozen methane on surface

Water ice

SCALE

Rocky core

Pluto is about one-fifth the size of Earth

DOUBLE WORLD

Pluto's moon, Charon, has a diameter of 714 miles (1,150 km)—over half of Pluto's. The two bodies are so similar in size that they are often thought of as a double planet.

VITAL STATISTICS	
Diameter	1,413 miles (2,274 km)
Avg. distance from Sun	3.6 billion miles (5.9 billion km)
Orbital speed around Sun	3 mps (4.75 km/s)
Sunrise to sunrise	6.39 days
Mass (Earth=1)	0.00251
Volume (Earth=1)	0.00658
Avg. density (water=1)	2.05
Surface gravity (Earth=1)	0.067
Surface temperature	−387°F (−223°C)
Number of moons	1

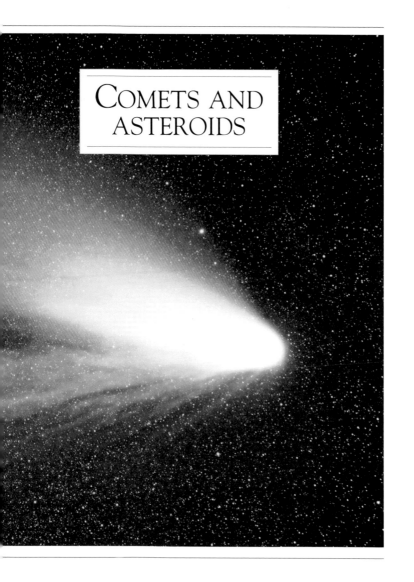

COMETS AND ASTEROIDS

MINOR MEMBERS

NEARLY ALL THE MASS of the solar system is found in the Sun, planets, and moons. The remaining tiny proportion of material is distributed among a huge number of small objects—the minor members. They are lumps of rock, or combinations of rock, dust, ice, and snow. The rocky bodies—asteroids—lie in the planetary region of the solar system, while most of the snow-and-dust objects—comets—form the Oort cloud on its outer edge.

OUTER SOLAR SYSTEM
The Oort cloud marks the outer edge of the solar system. The spherical cloud is made of orbiting comets that surround the planetary region of the solar system out to 0.8 light-years. Between the Oort cloud and the planets, a belt of cometlike objects orbits the Sun—the Kuiper belt.

The Oort cloud extends a fifth of the distance to the nearest star

KUIPER BELT
At least 70,000 objects with diameters of more than 60 miles (100 km) are believed to exist in the Kuiper belt, which stretches from the orbit of Neptune into the outer solar system. More than 80 of these cometlike objects have been found, although none have been seen close up.

ARTIST'S IMPRESSION OF KUIPER BELT OBJECT

The Oort cloud consists of about 10 trillion comets and is 1.6 light-years across

A comet on the edge of the Oort cloud takes 10 million years to orbit the Sun. Comets cannot permanently exist beyond the Oort cloud because the Sun's gravity is not strong enough here to stop them from being pulled away by a passing star

The combined mass of all the comets in the Oort cloud is equivalent to about three Earths

Kuiper belt

Kopff (long period)

Neptune's orbit

Uranus's orbit

Saturn's orbit

Neujmin 3 (short period)

Tempel-Tuttle (short period)

Hale-Bopp (long period)

Halley (short period)

PERIODIC COMETS
Comets only become visible when they leave the Oort cloud and travel toward the Sun. Some of them—periodic comets—follow regular paths. About 180 are short-period comets, which orbit the Sun in less than 200 years. Long-period comets may take thousands of years to return.

COMETS

A COMET is a "dirty snowball" composed of snow and dust. Billions of comets orbit the Sun at a distance of about one light-year. A few comets have orbits that take them closer to the Sun. As they near the Sun and are heated, the snow turns to gas and forms a long, bright tail.

HALLEY'S COMET
Most comets that approach the Sun are seen only once, but a few return periodically. Halley's comet travels out beyond Neptune and returns to the Sun about every 76 years.

ORBITING THE SUN
A periodic comet has an elliptical orbit that brings it close to the Sun. For most of its orbit, the comet has no tail. The tail only develops as the comet nears the Sun and its surface is heated. The tail gets longer and longer, and then disappears as the comet moves away from the Sun.

Tail develops as the comet approaches the Sun

SUN

Tail is longest near the Sun

For most of its orbit, a comet is a tailless, dirty snowball

Tail shrinks as comet moves away

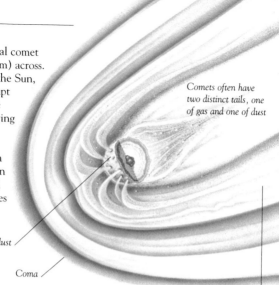

GLOWING GAS

The nucleus of a typical comet is about 0.6 miles (1 km) across. When it is heated by the Sun, jets of gas and dust erupt from the surface of the nucleus to form a glowing cloud called a coma, which surrounds the nucleus. The coma can be ten times larger than Earth. The comet's tail may be millions of miles (kilometers) long.

Comets often have two distinct tails, one of gas and one of dust

Nucleus made of dust and frozen gases

Coma

Dust reflects sunlight

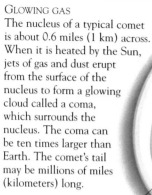

HEART OF A COMET

This photograph of the nucleus of Halley's comet was taken by the Giotto probe from a distance of about 1,000 miles (1,700 km). Bright gas jets can be seen on the comet's sunlit surface. Instruments aboard Giotto showed that the main constituent of the nucleus was water ice.

COMET FACT

• The planet Jupiter is so massive that its gravity can affect the orbit of comets. In 1992, Comet Shoemaker-Levy passed close to Jupiter and was broken into several fragments by gravitational forces. During July 1994, these fragments crashed into Jupiter, causing a series of huge explosions in Jupiter's atmosphere.

115

EXPLORING COMETS

BILLIONS OF COMETS exist at the edge of the solar system, forming the large Oort cloud. Comets are small, irregularly shaped lumps of snow and rocky dust orbiting the Sun. Occasionally, one leaves the Oort cloud and travels into the inner solar system. About 1,000 comets have been seen in Earth's sky, and another 60 to 80 are added to the list yearly.

COMET HALE-BOPP
About three times a century, a spectacular comet can be seen from Earth. Comet Hale-Bopp was clearly visible by eye during much of 1997.

ANATOMY OF A COMET
A comet's nucleus is a loose collection of snow and rocky dust. When it crosses the inner solar system, the Sun's heat turns the snow to gas and forms a glowing head—the coma. Solar wind and radiation also sweep away gas and dust from the nucleus into two tails—one gas, the other dust.

Coma can grow to 62,000 miles (100,000 km) across

Inside the coma, the nucleus of snow and dust (usually only a few miles [kilometers] in size) is too small to be seen

COMET-WATCHING WITH TELESCOPES

SPOTTING COMETS
Some comets are bright enough to see with the naked eye; others can only be seen using binoculars or a telescope. Comets look like fuzzy patches of light, and travel quickly. Their nightly progress can be observed and charted.

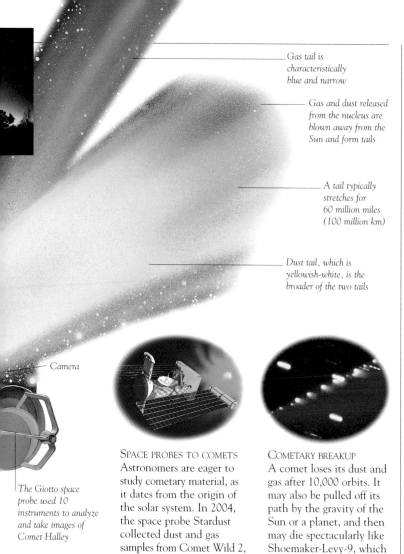

Gas tail is characteristically blue and narrow

Gas and dust released from the nucleus are blown away from the Sun and form tails

A tail typically stretches for 60 million miles (100 million km)

Dust tail, which is yellowish-white, is the broader of the two tails

Camera

The Giotto space probe used 10 instruments to analyze and take images of Comet Halley

SPACE PROBES TO COMETS
Astronomers are eager to study cometary material, as it dates from the origin of the solar system. In 2004, the space probe Stardust collected dust and gas samples from Comet Wild 2, after five years of travel.

COMETARY BREAKUP
A comet loses its dust and gas after 10,000 orbits. It may also be pulled off its path by the gravity of the Sun or a planet, and then may die spectacularly like Shoemaker-Levy-9, which crashed into Jupiter.

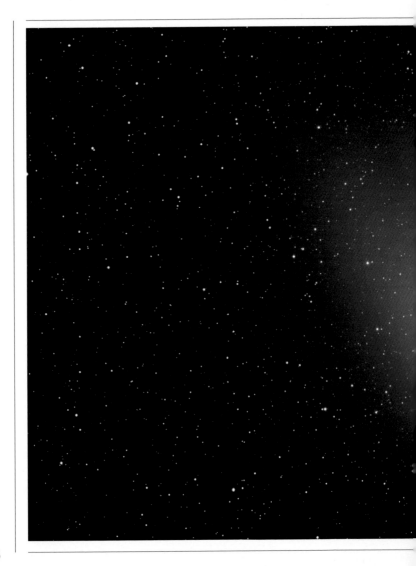

COMET CLOSE-UP
One-square-degree view of Comet NEAT, taken with the 35-inch (0.9-meter) Kitt Peak telescope

METEORS

EVERY NIGHT, BRIGHT STREAKS of light can be
seen in the sky. These meteors, or shooting stars,
are caused by pieces of rock and dust—meteoroids—
that are lost by comets or colliding asteroids. They
burn up as they travel through Earth's atmosphere.
Each year, Earth sweeps up 220,000 tons
(200,000 metric tons) of meteoroids that
appear as random meteors, or as
part of a meteor shower.

LIFE OF A METEOR
Comets lose material
when they travel close to
the Sun, and pieces of
asteroid break off when
asteroids collide. When a
meteoroid enters Earth's
atmosphere, it is heated by
friction and evaporates,
producing a trail of light—
a meteor—along its path.

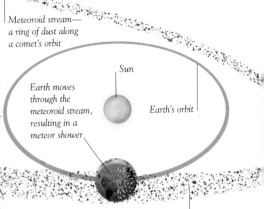

*Meteoroid stream—
a ring of dust along
a comet's orbit*

Sun

*Earth moves
through the
meteoroid stream,
resulting in a
meteor shower*

Earth's orbit

*A meteoroid
stream can take
dozens to
hundreds of
years to form*

LEONID SHOWER
This long-exposure photograph
shows the stars as short trails of
light. The longer trails in the
foreground are meteors that fell
as part of the Leonid meteor
shower in November 1966.

FIREBALLS AND BOLIDES
The brightest meteors are known as fireballs, and have a magnitude of at least –5, brighter than Venus. Fireballs that break up and explode are called bolides.

FROM METEOROID TO METEOR
The greater a meteoroid's speed, the faster and higher up it will burn out while traveling through Earth's atmosphere. The core of a massive one may survive the atmospheric friction and fall to the ground as a meteorite.

SINGLE METEOR
About 10 single meteors—that are not part of a shower and fall on their own—can be seen per hour, each lasting less than a second.

A meteoroid enters the atmosphere at 7–46 mps (11–74 km/s)

Meteors occur between 75 and 50 miles (120 and 80 km) above Earth

Meteors with magnitudes of 5 or brighter are visible to the naked eye

Fireballs occur lower in the atmosphere

Meteoroid breakups occur between 19 and 6 miles (30 and 10 km) above the ground

Very large rocks punch through the atmosphere, producing explosion craters

METEOR SHOWERS		
Name	Date	Constellation
Quadrantids	Jan. 1–6	Boötes
April Lyrids	Apr. 19–24	Lyra
Eta Aquarids	May 1–8	Aquarius
Delta Aquarids	Jul. 15–Aug. 15	Aquarius
Perseids	Jul. 25–Aug. 18	Perseus
Orionids	Oct. 16–27	Orion
Taurids	Oct. 20–Nov. 30	Taurus
Leonids	Nov. 15–20	Leo
Geminids	Dec. 7–15	Gemini

Aerogel used on aircraft

COLLECTING DUST
Aircraft with gel-coated panels cruise 12 miles (20 km) high. Fast-moving meteoroid particles slow down within the aerogel and become buried inside it to be studied later.

121

METEORITES

EACH YEAR ABOUT 3,000 space rocks, weighing more than 2 lb (1 kg) and too big to burn up in the atmosphere, land on Earth's surface. They are called meteorites. Most fall in the sea and are never discovered. Some meteorites are seen to fall on land and are quickly collected. Others are discovered centuries later. Many are never found.

METEORITE TYPES
Meteorites are usually made of materials commonly found on Earth, but in different proportions. They are believed to represent the solid material in the early solar system. Meteorites are divided into three types: iron, stony, and stony-iron.

Canyon Diablo meteorite, which collided with Earth 50,000 years ago

Meteorite consists of iron-nickel alloy

IRON METEORITE
The second most common meteorites consist mainly of iron-nickel metal with small amounts of other minerals. Most were originally molten and formed in the cores of asteroids.

METEORITE ORIGINS
Statistics indicate that 24,000 different meteorites have been discovered on Earth. Of these, 39 have come from the Moon, and 34 from Mars. Meteorites are also found on the Moon; most of these are believed to come from asteroids.

ASTRONAUT JACK SCHMITT INVESTIGATES THE SITE OF A METEORITE IMPACT ON THE MOON

STONY METEORITE
Most meteorites found on Earth are lumps of stone. About 20,000 of them have been collected. They can be subdivided into chondrites that contain "drops" of solidified rock, and achondrites that do not.

Dark fusion crust formed as meteorite fell through Earth's atmosphere

This 2.3-in (6-cm) stony-iron was found in Antarctica

Piece broken off reveals lighter original rock

Melted surface solidifies into a thin black crust

Molten rock flows away from direction of fall

ANATOMY OF A METEORITE
Friction with the atmosphere causes the outer surface of a falling space rock to heat up and melt. Some meteorites have a uniform outer surface, while others have a leading edge and a shielded surface.

STONY-IRON METEORITE
These are the rarest meteorites. Some were formed from molten iron-nickel and olivine, and others by impact and welding of metal and stony fragments.

Pale-green olivine crystals set in iron-nickel

SEARCHING FOR METEORITES
Scientists find about 400 meteorites a year by searching undisturbed areas of Earth, including Antarctica, the Sahara Desert, and parts of Australia. It is easy to spot the dark meteorite falls against the snow and ice.

NOTABLE METEORITES		
Name and site	Tons (metric tons)	Year of find
Iron meteorites:		
Hoba West, Namibia	66 (60)	1920
Ahnighito, Greenland	34 (30)	1895
Bacuberito, Mexico	30 (27)	1871
Mbosi, Tanzania	29 (26)	1930
Stone meteorites:		
Jilin, China	1.95 (1.77)	1976
Norton County, Kansas	1.1 (1)	1948
Long Island, Kansas	0.62 (0.56)	1891
Paragould, Arkansas	0.44 (0.4)	1930
Bjurbole, Finland	0.33 (0.3)	1899
Recent finds:		
Algeria NwA 3171 (Mars)	1.1 lb (0.5 kg)	2004
Dhofar 1180 Oman (Moon)	0.25 lb (0.115 kg)	2005

COMETS AND ASTEROIDS

123

ASTEROIDS

BILLIONS OF SPACE ROCKS—ASTEROIDS—orbit the Sun within the inner solar system. They are sometimes called minor planets because they have their own orbits around the Sun. Most are in the asteroid belt, or main belt, which lies between the orbits of Mars and Jupiter. Asteroids vary in size, shape, and color. Only one, Vesta, is large and bright enough to be seen with the naked eye.

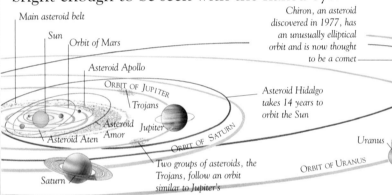

Main asteroid belt

Sun

Orbit of Mars

Asteroid Apollo

ORBIT OF JUPITER

Trojans

Asteroid Jupiter
Amor

Asteroid Aten

ORBIT OF SATURN

Saturn

Chiron, an asteroid discovered in 1977, has an unusually elliptical orbit and is now thought to be a comet

Asteroid Hidalgo takes 14 years to orbit the Sun

Uranus

ORBIT OF URANUS

Two groups of asteroids, the Trojans, follow an orbit similar to Jupiter's

ASTEROID BELT

The main belt contains billions of asteroids, all moving independently around the Sun. It stretches from about 158 million miles (254 million km) to 372 million miles (598 million km) from the Sun.

NEAR-EARTH ASTEROIDS

Some asteroids follow orbits that bring them close to Earth's orbit. These are members of the Apollo, Amor, and Aten groups, with each group following a particular orbit.

Ceres contains about one-third of the total mass of all asteroids

Vesta is the third largest asteroid

Psyche has an irregular shape

115 miles (185 km) wide

SIZES OF ASTEROIDS

The first asteroid discovered—Ceres—is also the biggest, with a diameter of 579 miles (932 km), and spherical in shape. However, Ceres is not typical. Most asteroids measure less than 185 miles (300 km) across, and are irregular in shape.

ORBIT OF PLUTO

Pluto

ORBIT OF NEPTUNE

Neptune

TYPES OF ASTEROIDS

There are three main types of asteroids: those made of rock, those made of metal, and those that are a mixture of the two. Gaspra is a rock asteroid, the first to be seen close up. It is about 12 miles (19 km) long, orbits the Sun every 3.3 years, and was photographed by the Galileo space probe in 1991.

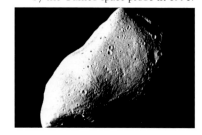

COLLISIONS BETWEEN ASTEROIDS

The main belt has changed over time. When the solar system was forming, over 600 rocky bodies larger than Ceres inhabited the belt. These protoplanets collided and broke up, and a large amount of material was lost. Remaining asteroid pieces collided and formed the present-day main belt. There are three types of collisions that still occur today.

When the impacting asteroid is less than 1/50,000th the mass of the larger body, a crater forms

When the impacting body is 1/50,000th the mass of the body it hits, the larger asteroid breaks up and forms a ball of rubble

When an asteroid is hit by an object more than 1/50,000th of its mass, it breaks up and forms a family of asteroids

Stream of dust forms

IMPACTS

WHEN A METEORITE COLLIDES with Earth, it can form an impact crater on its surface. Craters up to 600 miles (1,000 km) wide exist in very large numbers on moons and planets throughout the solar system. About 150 have been found on Earth, dating back to 4 billion years ago when the planet was young.

IMPACT ON MIMAS
The surface of Mimas, Saturn's moon, is full of impact craters. One of them, Herschel, covers an area that is a third of Mimas's diameter.

CRATERS ON EARTH
Impact craters are found on every continent on Earth, and are being formed all the time. They are most common in parts of Australia, Europe, and North America. This is not because more have fallen there, but because the surface of these areas has changed so little that craters have been preserved.

MANICOUAGAN CRATER
This huge crater, one of the largest in Canada, can even be seen by astronauts orbiting Earth. Two semicircular lakes form its outline.

METEOR CRATER
This 0.7-mile- (1.2-km-) wide crater in the Arizona Desert has been known since 1871. It was formed about 50,000 years ago when an iron meteorite about 100 ft (30 m) wide struck Earth.

HOW CRATERS ARE FORMED

All craters are formed in much the same way. An impacting meteorite blasts surface material from the point of impact and produces a crater. The size of the crater depends on the size of the original rock.

1 *Meteorite breaks up and burns up as it meets the friction of the atmosphere*

2 *Outer layer of rock is shattered as the meteorite impacts with Earth*

3 *Shock waves move through the surface as the meteorite burrows into Earth*

4 *An explosion, caused by heat and compression, blasts a crater in Earth's surface*

HENBURY CRATERS

A cluster of 11 craters in northern Australia includes the smallest craters on Earth. The craters are thought to have been formed by a meteorite that broke up in the atmosphere no more than 5,000 years ago. The smallest crater is 20 ft (6 m) across.

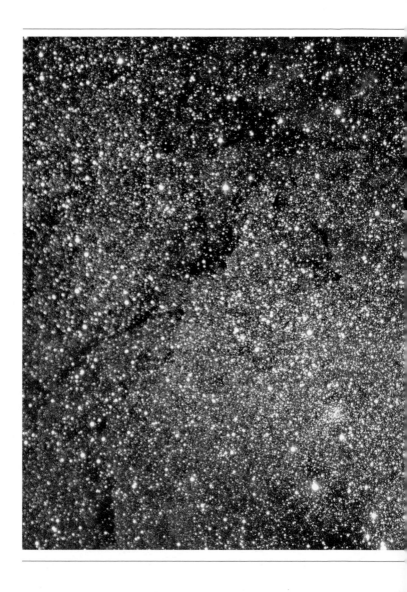

STARS

S T A R S

WHAT IS A STAR?

A STAR IS an enormous spinning ball of hot and luminous gas. Most stars contain two main gases—hydrogen and helium. These gases are held together by gravity, and at the core they are very densely packed. Within the core, immense amounts of energy are produced.

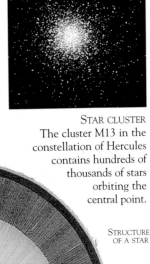

STAR CLUSTER
The cluster M13 in the constellation of Hercules contains hundreds of thousands of stars orbiting the central point.

Temperature and pressure increase toward the core

STRUCTURE OF A STAR

Energy is released at the surface as light and heat

Energy is produced by nuclear reactions in the core

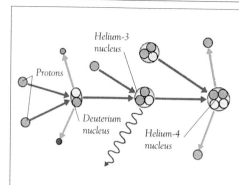

CORE FUSION

A star produces energy by nuclear fusion. Within the core, hydrogen nuclei (protons) collide and fuse to form first deuterium (heavy hydrogen) and then two forms of helium. During fusion, energy is given off. This type of reaction, which is found in most stars, is called the proton-proton chain.

Helium-3 nucleus

Protons

Deuterium nucleus

Helium-4 nucleus

VARYING SIZES

Stars differ greatly in the amount of gas they contain, and in their size. The largest stars are 1,000 times the diameter of the Sun, while white dwarf stars are just a fraction of its size—not much bigger than Earth.

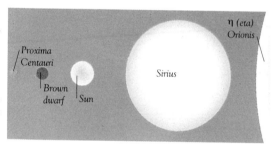

η (eta) Orionis

Proxima Centauri

Brown dwarf

Sun

Sirius

PROMINENT STARS: DATA	(see p 153 for more on Greek lettering)	
Name	**Designation**	**Distance**
Vega	α Lyrae	26 light-years
Pollux	β Geminorum	36 light-years
Capella	α Aurigae	45 light-years
Aldebaran	α Tauri	68 light-years
Regulus	α Leonis	84 light-years
Canopus	α Carinae	98 light-years
Spica	α Virginis	260 light-years
Betelgeuse	α Orionis	520 light-years
Polaris	α Ursa Minoris	700 light-years

STAR FACTS

• All the chemical elements that exist in the universe and are heavier than hydrogen, helium, and lithium were made by nuclear reactions inside stars 14 billion years ago.

• The mass of the Sun (1 solar mass) is used as a standard for measuring other stars.

LIFE CYCLE OF A STAR

A STAR'S LIFE CYCLE depends on its mass. Stars of the same mass as the Sun shine steadily for about 10 billion years. More massive stars convert their hydrogen more quickly, and have shorter lives. The Sun is halfway through its life. In about 5 billion years, it will expand to become a red giant star, and then collapse and end its life as a white dwarf star.

All stars converting hydrogen are called main sequence stars

STRUCTURE OF
A RED GIANT

Helium converted to carbon in core

Core temperature about 180 million°F (100 million °C)

Cooler outer layers glow red

RED GIANTS

When most of the hydrogen has been converted to helium, the star becomes a red giant—converting helium to carbon. The core heats up, causing the surface to expand and cool. A red giant may expand to more than 100 times its former size.

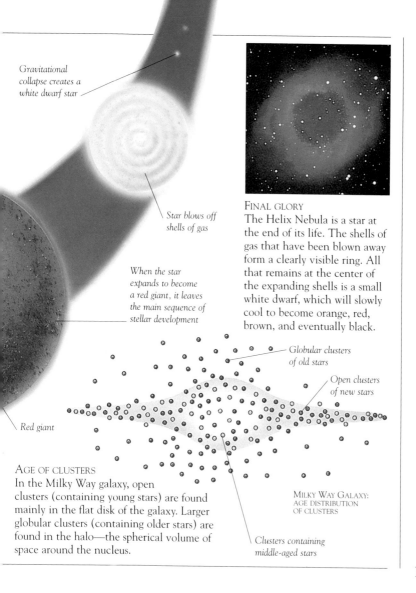

Gravitational collapse creates a white dwarf star

Star blows off shells of gas

When the star expands to become a red giant, it leaves the main sequence of stellar development

Red giant

FINAL GLORY

The Helix Nebula is a star at the end of its life. The shells of gas that have been blown away form a clearly visible ring. All that remains at the center of the expanding shells is a small white dwarf, which will slowly cool to become orange, red, brown, and eventually black.

Globular clusters of old stars

Open clusters of new stars

AGE OF CLUSTERS

In the Milky Way galaxy, open clusters (containing young stars) are found mainly in the flat disk of the galaxy. Larger globular clusters (containing older stars) are found in the halo—the spherical volume of space around the nucleus.

MILKY WAY GALAXY: AGE DISTRIBUTION OF CLUSTERS

Clusters containing middle-aged stars

133

WHERE STARS ARE BORN

STARS ARE BORN DEEP within dark molecular clouds of gas and dust. When newborn stars—protostars—light up, they heat this cloud with their radiation. The glowing cloud is called a nebula. The stars' gravitation causes the cloud to collapse, and eventually the whole cloud turns into stars.

Radiation from nearby stars disperses thinner parts of the cloud

Dense globules with protostars become detached as parts of the cloud disperse

HEART OF A NEBULA

The Orion Nebula, 1,500 light-years away, is the star-forming region closest to Earth. It is heated by UV radiation from a tiny cluster of young stars—the Trapezium. Many stars and protostars lie within it. The nebula is itself burning its way through a giant molecular cloud.

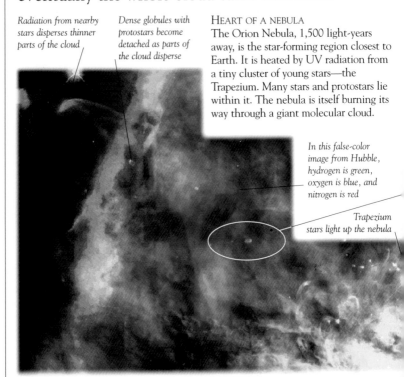

In this false-color image from Hubble, hydrogen is green, oxygen is blue, and nitrogen is red

Trapezium stars light up the nebula

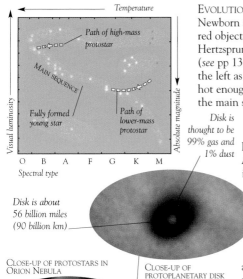

Path of high-mass protostar

MAIN SEQUENCE

Fully formed young star

Path of lower-mass protostar

O B A F G K M

Spectral type

Visual luminosity

Temperature

Absolute magnitude

Disk is thought to be 99% gas and 1% dust

Disk is about 56 billion miles (90 billion km)

CLOSE-UP OF PROTOSTARS IN ORION NEBULA

CLOSE-UP OF PROTOPLANETARY DISK

EVOLUTION OF YOUNG STARS
Newborn stars appear as glowing red objects on the right of the Hertzsprung-Russell diagram (*see* pp 138–139). They move to the left as they shrink and become hot enough to burn hydrogen on the main sequence.

PROTOPLANETARY DISK
A new star is being formed inside this small, dark disk of dust and gas. The protostar, which is only a few hundred thousand years old, has about one-fifth the mass of the Sun. The surrounding disk contains about seven times the mass of Earth.

PROTOSTAR GROUP
Astronomers have identified more than 150 protostars within the Orion Nebula. The five protostars in this group are surrounded by the swirling disks of dust and gas out of which they were formed. These disks are called protoplanetary disks, because planets may be forming inside them.

OBSERVING THE ORION NEBULA
Several star-forming regions are bright enough to be seen with binoculars, appearing as misty patches against the sky. The Orion Nebula is the brightest of all. It is visible to the naked eye between November and March, and is easy to find, since it forms part of Orion's Sword.

135

ORION NEBULA
A portion of Orion's dusty star nursery, located 1,500 light-years from Earth

STARS

PROPERTIES OF STARS

THERE ARE DIFFERENT STAR types that vary in size, age,
and mass. Some are white dwarfs the size of Earth and
some are supergiants big enough to engulf the solar
system. Some stars are only a few million years old,
while others are as ancient as the universe itself. To
sort out different star types, astronomers use a special
graph called a Hertzsprung-Russell (H-R) diagram.

LUMINOSITY AND ABSOLUTE MAGNITUDE
The total energy that a star radiates in a
second is called its luminosity.
Compared with the Sun, we find
stars with luminosities ranging from
100,000 times to 1/100,000 that of
the Sun. Luminosity also refers to a
star's absolute magnitude—the
magnitude the star would appear if
it were 10 parsecs (32.6 light-years)
from Earth.

A red giant has
about the same
mass as the Sun

The apparent brightness of
stars depends on the luminosity
and distance from Earth

About 10 low-mass,
hydrogen-burning
type M stars would
balance the Sun

Two white dwarfs
are heavier
than the Sun

Sun

Sun

Sun

MASSES COMPARED
The masses of stars are not usually measured
in pounds (kilograms) or tons, but in relation
to the mass of the Sun. The lightest stars are
less than one-tenth of a solar mass, while
the heaviest may be more than 50 solar
masses. Like pebbles on a beach, there are
uncountable small stars, but few big ones.

About 30 Suns are
needed to balance
a high-mass,
hydrogen-burning
type B star

Type B star

138

HERTZSPRUNG-RUSSELL DIAGRAM
Astronomers plot stars on a graph, with spectral type along the bottom and visual luminosity up the side. Absolute magnitude and temperature may also be given. Each star has a place on this H-R diagram, according to what point it has reached in its life. Most stars fall into a band called the main sequence, while others fall into groups called giants, supergiants, and white dwarfs.

Surface temperature in thousand °F (°C)

Visual luminosity (Sun = 1)

Absolute magnitude

SUPERGIANTS

MAIN SEQUENCE

RED GIANTS

WHITE DWARFS

O   B   A   F   G   K   M
Spectral type (see p 140)

AVERAGE SIZES OF STARS
Stars vary greatly in size, from supergiants 300 times the size of the Sun to neutron stars, and black holes that are very much smaller than Earth.

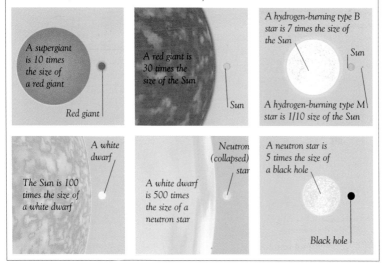

A supergiant is 10 times the size of a red giant

Red giant

A red giant is 30 times the size of the Sun

Sun

A hydrogen-burning type B star is 7 times the size of the Sun

Sun

A hydrogen-burning type M star is 1/10 size of the Sun

The Sun is 100 times the size of a white dwarf

A white dwarf

A white dwarf is 500 times the size of a neutron star

Neutron (collapsed) star

A neutron star is 5 times the size of a black hole

Black hole

STELLAR CLASSIFICATION

THE MASS OF A STAR affects its other properties—its color, temperature, and luminosity. By studying their properties, astronomers have been able to devise a system that enables them to classify all stars.

Type O		72,032–52,232°F (40,000–29,000°C)
Type B		50,432–17,492°F (28,000–9,700°C)
Type A		17,312–12,992°F (9,600–7,200°C)
Type F		12,812–10,472°F (7,100–5,800°C)
Type G		10,292–8,492°F (5,700–4700°C)
Type K		8,312–5,972°F (4,600–3,300°C)
Type M		5,792–3,812°F (3,200–2,100°C)

SPECTRAL TYPES

A star's color depends on its temperature—the hottest are blue-white and the coolest orange-red. Stars are classified into seven spectral types—O, B, A, F, G, K, and M—where O is the hottest and M the coolest. Each type has 10 subdivisions, 0 to 9, from hottest to coolest. The Sun is type G2.

Continuous spectrum	Distinctive absorption lines	Lines from several elements
PURE WHITE LIGHT	SODIUM LIGHT	SUNLIGHT

CHEMICAL LINES

Each star emits its own particular light. Splitting this light into a spectrum reveals the chemical elements that make up the star. The different elements are indicated by dark absorption lines that run across the spectrum. Sodium atoms absorb light only in the yellow part of the spectrum. Sunlight displays hundreds of absorption lines, but only the most prominent are shown here.

HERTZSPRUNG-RUSSELL (H-R) DIAGRAM OF STELLAR CLASSIFICATION

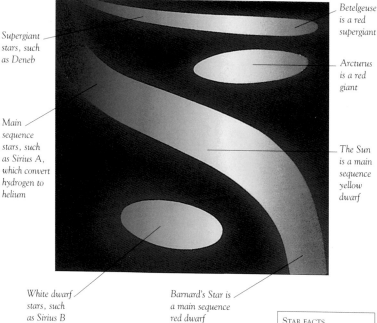

Supergiant stars, such as Deneb

Main sequence stars, such as Sirius A, which convert hydrogen to helium

White dwarf stars, such as Sirius B

Betelgeuse is a red supergiant

Arcturus is a red giant

The Sun is a main sequence yellow dwarf

Barnard's Star is a main sequence red dwarf

COLOR-CODED DIAGRAM

The H-R diagram plots a star's temperature against its luminosity (the amount of light it gives off). The brightest stars are at the top, and the dimmest are near the bottom. The hottest stars are to the left, and the coolest to the right. Most stars spend some part of their lives on the main sequence, which runs from top left to bottom right across the diagram. Brown dwarfs are the smallest stars on the main sequence, with giant stars above them, and white dwarf stars below.

STAR FACTS

• Hot, bright young stars are found in large groups known as OB associations.

• By the standards of space, the Sun is very small. Astronomers refer to it as a type G dwarf star.

• The smallest stars, cooler and fainter than red dwarfs, are known as brown dwarfs.

STARS

BRIGHTNESS

HOW BRIGHTLY A STAR shines in
the sky depends on its luminosity
(the amount of light energy it
produces), and on its distance
from Earth. Astronomers use two
different scales to measure a star's
magnitude (brightness). Absolute
magnitude compares stars from
a standard distance. Apparent
magnitude describes how bright a
star appears as viewed from Earth.

1
2
3
4
5
6

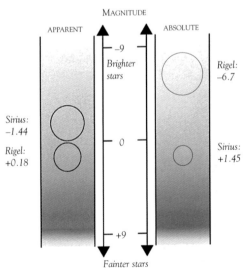

MAGNITUDE

APPARENT

ABSOLUTE

−9
Brighter
stars

Rigel:
−6.7

Sirius:
−1.44

Rigel:
+0.18

0

Sirius:
+1.45

+9

Fainter stars

OBSERVED BRIGHTNESS
On the scale of apparent
magnitude for stars
viewed with the naked
eye, brighter stars have
lower numerical values.

APPARENT VS ABSOLUTE
Sirius is the brightest star
in our sky (apparent
magnitude −1.46) and is
brighter than Rigel
(apparent magnitude
+0.12). However, in
reality, Rigel is by far the
more luminous star with
an absolute magnitude of
−7.1, as opposed to Sirius,
which has an absolute
magnitude of +1.4.

Calcium   Hydrogen   Hydrogen   Sodium   Hydrogen

SPECTRUM SHOWING DARK LINES OF 3 ELEMENTS

Wavelengths are longest at the red end

SPECTRAL ANALYSIS

Light consists of electromagnetic waves of varying lengths. In spectral analysis, a spectrograph splits the light from a star into its different wavelengths, producing a band of colors called a spectrum. Elements in the star's atmosphere absorb light at some wavelengths, producing dark absorption lines on the spectrum. Each element gives a different pattern of lines, so by studying the lines on the spectrum, astronomers can tell what a star is made of.

BRIGHTEST STARS

Name	Apparent magnitude	Spectral type	Distance in ly
Sirius	–1.4 (double star)	A0, white dwarf	8.6
Canopus	–0.6	F0	310
Alpha Centauri	–0.3 (triple star)	G2, K1, M5	4.4
Arcturus	0.0	K2	36.8
Vega	0.0	A0	25.3
Capella	0.1 (double star)	G2, G6	42.2
Rigel	0.2	B8	800
Procyon	0.4 (double star)	F5, white dwarf	11.4
Achernar	0.5	B3	144
Betelgeuse	0.5 (variable star)	M2	400

BRIGHTNESS FACTS

• With both scales of magnitude, each whole number step (e.g., from +3 to +4) means that the star is 2½ times brighter or fainter.

• The Sun's apparent magnitude is –26.7.

• The brightest planet is Venus, with a maximum apparent magnitude of –4.7.

THE COLOR OF HEAT

Anything that is hot will glow, whether it is a star or an iron bar—temperature determines its color, not what it is made of. As the temperature increases, it will glow red, then yellow and then white-hot, and ultimately takes on a bluish tinge.

VARIABLE STARS

STARS DO NOT ALWAYS shine constantly. Some vary in brightness and are called variable stars. Pulsating, eclipsing, and rotating variables have a regular pattern or period to their variation. Others, such as eruptive and cataclysmic variables, are more unpredictable. A star may vary because it gives out changing amounts of light, or because its light is obscured by shifting dust clouds or a companion star.

CONSTELLATION OF CYGNUS, DURING AND AFTER THE 1975 NOVA

CATACLYSMIC VARIABLES
Stars that burst into brilliance due to sudden, violent changes are called cataclysmic variables. They include novas and supernovas. A nova occurs when a white dwarf in a binary star (two-star) system pulls hydrogen gas off its companion. The gas builds up until there is a nuclear explosion.

ETA CARINAE
As an eruptive variable, Eta Carinae's brightness has fluctuated dramatically, from magnitude –0.8 in the mid-19th century, to below magnitude 6. It puffed out an obscuring cloud of dust—the Homunculus Nebula. The shifting dust and unstable outer layers account for the variations in brightness.

Homunculus Nebula envelops star in dust

Eta Carinae is a luminous supergiant, 100 times the mass of the Sun

Today, most of Eta Carinae's energy is in the form of infrared radiation

PULSATING VARIABLES

Toward the end of their lives, stars often pulsate, varying in brightness, temperature, and size. Mira stars are red giants that pulsate over a period of up to 1,000 days. Cepheid variables are yellow supergiants that pulsate in cycles of 1–50 days.

ECLIPSING VARIABLES

Some pairs of stars are so close to each other, they look like a single star. If their orbits are angled edge-on to Earth, each star periodically passes in front of the other and eclipses it, so that the total light reaching Earth is reduced and the star appears to fade.

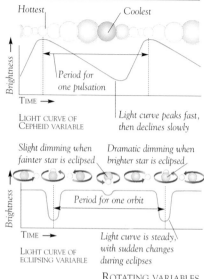

Hottest | Coolest

Brightness

Period for one pulsation

TIME →

LIGHT CURVE OF CEPHEID VARIABLE

Light curve peaks fast, then declines slowly

Slight dimming when fainter star is eclipsed

Dramatic dimming when brighter star is eclipsed

Brightness

Period for one orbit

TIME →

LIGHT CURVE OF ECLIPSING VARIABLE

Light curve is steady, with sudden changes during eclipses

ROTATING VARIABLES

Some stars vary in brightness due to spots on their surfaces. As the star rotates, different spots come into view and the star's brightness changes. AB Doradus, a cool dwarf star 65 light-years from the Sun, varies by 0.15 magnitudes in its 12.4-hour rotation.

Keyhole Nebula is a dark cloud of gas and dust silhouetted against the bright Carina Nebula

Carina Nebula, about 300 light-years across, includes the Keyhole Nebula

The Keyhole Nebula is about 9,000 light-years away

ETA CARINAE AND KEYHOLE NEBULA

Computerized images show half a rotation of the star

Star dims when dark spots come into view

The more spots and the larger their area, the dimmer the star

Spots may be up to 1,000 times bigger than sunspots

STARSPOTS ON AB DORADUS

HOW FAR ARE THE STARS?

ASTRONOMERS HAD LITTLE IDEA of the true size of the universe until 1838, when Friedrich Bessel used the parallax method to make the first successful measurement of the distance to a star. Our knowledge of stellar distances was revolutionized further by the Hipparcos survey satellite, which used parallax to pinpoint many thousands of stars.

Statue of Liberty in New York City

Eiffel Tower in Paris, France

NEAREST STAR
The Sun's nearest neighbor is Proxima Centauri, one of the three stars that make up the Alpha Centauri system. It is 4.2 light-years away. If the Sun were the size of a soccer ball, the distance to Proxima Centauri would be the same as the distance from Paris, France, to New York City.

ALPHA CENTAURI
4.4 LIGHT-YEARS AWAY

LIGHT-YEARS AND PARSECS
Distances are measured in light-years and parsecs. One light-year (ly) equals 5.9 trillion miles (9.5 trillion kilometers)—the distance light travels in a year. One parsec is 3.26 ly, the distance at which a star shows a parallax angle of one arc second.

NEAREST STARS AND STAR SYSTEMS			
Name of star or star system	Magnitude	Spectral type	Distance in ly
Alpha Centauri A, B, C	0.1, 1.4, 11.0	G2, K1, M5	4.4
Barnard's Star	9.5	M5	5.9
Lalande 21185	7.5	M2	8.3
Sirius A, B	–1.4, 8.5	A0, white dwarf	8.6
Ross 154	10.4	M4	9.7
Epsilon Eridani	3.7	K2	10.5
HD 217987	7.4	M2	10.7
Ross 128	11.1	M4	10.9
61 Cygni A, B	5.2, 6.1	K5, K7	11.4
Procyon	0.4, 10.7	F5, white dwarf	11.4

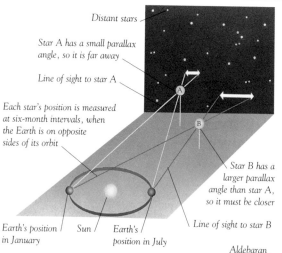

Distant stars

Star A has a small parallax angle, so it is far away

Line of sight to star A

Each star's position is measured at six-month intervals, when the Earth is on opposite sides of its orbit

Earth's position in January

Sun

Earth's position in July

Star B has a larger parallax angle than star A, so it must be closer

Line of sight to star B

PARALLAX METHOD

As Earth orbits the Sun, the stars that are closer seem to move from side to side against the background of more distant stars. The angle through which a star moves over a period of six months is called its parallax and is used to calculate the star's distance. The smaller the parallax, the farther the star.

INVERSE SQUARE LAW

A more distant star looks dimmer than a nearby one of a similar luminosity. This is because its light spreads out over a larger area before it reaches Earth, making it appear fainter. The inverse square law states that a star's apparent brightness decreases with the square of its distance.

The larger sphere has twice the radius of the smaller sphere

Star

Light from the star spreads over this area of the smaller sphere

When the light reaches the larger sphere, it is spread over 4 times the area (the square of the distance, or 2 x 2).

Aldebaran

Hyades

ALDEBARAN AND THE HYADES

Stars that seem close in the sky are not necessarily neighbors in space. The red giant Aldebaran appears to be a member of the Hyades star cluster in Taurus. In fact, Aldebaran is much closer to us than the cluster. It lies 65.1 light-years from the Sun, compared with 150 light-years for the Hyades cluster.

STARS

MEASURE OF THE STARS

SINCE IT TAKES SO LONG to travel any significant distance outside the solar system, we have to study the stars from afar. Astronomers can tell a star's brightness, color, and temperature by analyzing its light. By splitting starlight into its constituent colors, they can find out what stars are made of and how fast they are moving. With accurate measurements of position, astronomers can predict where stars will wander through the sky, thousands of years from now.

Coalsack Nebula

Hadar—magnitude 0.6, type B1

Alpha Centauri (triple star)— magnitude 0.1, 1.4, and 11.0, types G2, K1, and M5

PANORAMIC VIEW OF THE SOUTHERN MILKY WAY

STARRY SKY

The stars appear to our eyes as little more than twinkling points of light. Some are brighter than others, some are grouped in clusters, and here and there a red or blue star stands out. It may seem hard to believe, but everything we understand about the stars has been learned by studying starlight. We know that they are suns and that they are powered by nuclear energy. We know how they are born, how they live their lives, and how they die. Stars are classified according to their magnitude (luminosity) and color.

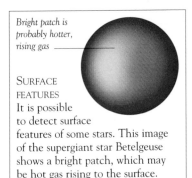

Bright patch is probably hotter, rising gas

SURFACE FEATURES

It is possible to detect surface features of some stars. This image of the supergiant star Betelgeuse shows a bright patch, which may be hot gas rising to the surface.

Mimosa—magnitude
1.3, type B0

Lambda Centauri—
magnitude 3.6, type A7

Open Cluster
NGC 3532

Carina
Nebula

Theta Carinae—
magnitude 2.8,
type B0

Lambda Muscae—
magnitude 3.6, type A7

Mu Muscae—
magnitude 4.8, type K4

Alpha Muscae—
magnitude 2.7, type B2

DOPPLER SHIFT

The wavelengths of dark lines in a star's spectrum are affected by the star's motion—this is the Doppler effect. Motion toward Earth shortens the wavelengths, shifting the lines toward the spectrum's blue end (blue shift). Motion away from Earth stretches the wavelengths and shifts the lines toward the red end (red shift). By measuring the changes in wavelength, astronomers can calculate the star's speed along the line of sight.

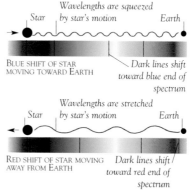

Wavelengths are squeezed
Star by star's motion Earth

BLUE SHIFT OF STAR
MOVING TOWARD EARTH
Dark lines shift
toward blue end of
spectrum

Wavelengths are stretched
Star by star's motion Earth

RED SHIFT OF STAR MOVING
AWAY FROM EARTH
Dark lines shift
toward red end of
spectrum

PROPER MOTION

Stars are so far away, we are not normally aware of their movement through space. Over time, however, this movement—called proper motion—changes the shapes of constellations dramatically. Astronomers can work out a constellation's past and future shape by accurately measuring the positions of its stars over several years.

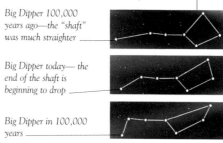

Big Dipper 100,000 years ago—the "shaft" was much straighter

Big Dipper today— the end of the shaft is beginning to drop

Big Dipper in 100,000 years

CONSTELLATIONS

SEEN FROM EARTH, the stars seem to form patterns in the sky. These patterns are known as constellations. The skies around Earth have been divided into 88 different constellations, each one of which is supposed to represent a mythological person, creature, or object.

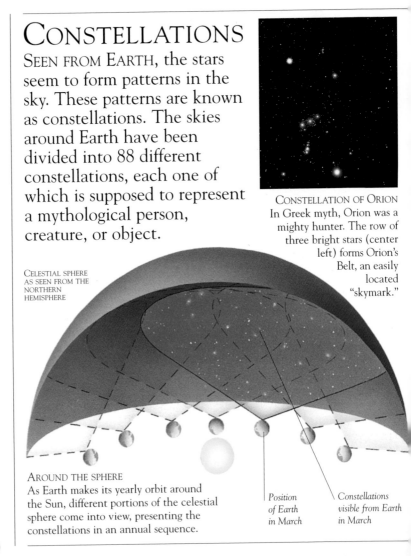

CONSTELLATION OF ORION
In Greek myth, Orion was a mighty hunter. The row of three bright stars (center left) forms Orion's Belt, an easily located "skymark."

CELESTIAL SPHERE AS SEEN FROM THE NORTHERN HEMISPHERE

AROUND THE SPHERE
As Earth makes its yearly orbit around the Sun, different portions of the celestial sphere come into view, presenting the constellations in an annual sequence.

Position of Earth in March

Constellations visible from Earth in March

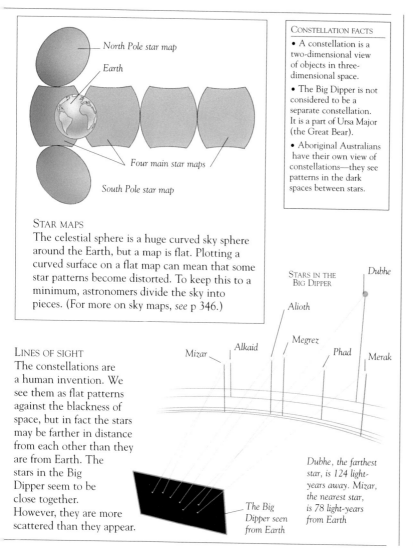

North Pole star map

Earth

Four main star maps

South Pole star map

STAR MAPS

The celestial sphere is a huge curved sky sphere around the Earth, but a map is flat. Plotting a curved surface on a flat map can mean that some star patterns become distorted. To keep this to a minimum, astronomers divide the sky into pieces. (For more on sky maps, *see* p 346.)

STARS IN THE BIG DIPPER

Dubhe

Alioth

Megrez

Mizar   Alkaid   Phad   Merak

LINES OF SIGHT

The constellations are a human invention. We see them as flat patterns against the blackness of space, but in fact the stars may be farther in distance from each other than they are from Earth. The stars in the Big Dipper seem to be close together. However, they are more scattered than they appear.

The Big Dipper seen from Earth

Dubhe, the farthest star, is 124 light-years away. Mizar, the nearest star, is 78 light-years from Earth

STARS

CATALOGING STARS

STARS ARE cataloged according
to the constellation in which
they appear. Within each
constellation, the individual
stars are identified by means
of letters or numbers. Other
objects are cataloged separately.

*The constellation
"figure" is drawn
around the stars*

ORION

ORION NEBULA
In Earth's sky, the Orion Nebula
appears as a faint, fuzzy patch
of light just below Orion's Belt.

POSSESSIVE NAMES
Constellations have been given Latin
names, and when referring to particular
stars, the possessive case of the Latin
name is used—stars in the constellation
of Orion are designated Orionis. (For
more on Orion and other constellations
see REFERENCE SECTION, p 312.)

MAPPING THE SKIES
The constellations fit
together to map the sky.
All the stars inside
a constellation's
boundaries belong to
that constellation,
even if they appear
to be unconnected to
the stars making up the
main "title" figure.

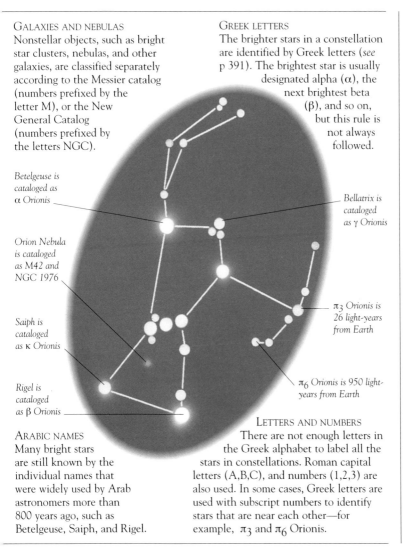

GALAXIES AND NEBULAS

Nonstellar objects, such as bright star clusters, nebulas, and other galaxies, are classified separately according to the Messier catalog (numbers prefixed by the letter M), or the New General Catalog (numbers prefixed by the letters NGC).

GREEK LETTERS

The brighter stars in a constellation are identified by Greek letters (*see* p 391). The brightest star is usually designated alpha (α), the next brightest beta (β), and so on, but this rule is not always followed.

Betelgeuse is cataloged as α Orionis

Bellatrix is cataloged as γ Orionis

Orion Nebula is cataloged as M42 and NGC 1976

π_3 Orionis is 26 light-years from Earth

Saiph is cataloged as κ Orionis

π_6 Orionis is 950 light-years from Earth

Rigel is cataloged as β Orionis

ARABIC NAMES

Many bright stars are still known by the individual names that were widely used by Arab astronomers more than 800 years ago, such as Betelgeuse, Saiph, and Rigel.

LETTERS AND NUMBERS

There are not enough letters in the Greek alphabet to label all the stars in constellations. Roman capital letters (A,B,C), and numbers (1,2,3) are also used. In some cases, Greek letters are used with subscript numbers to identify stars that are near each other—for example, π_3 and π_6 Orionis.

CLUSTERS AND DOUBLES

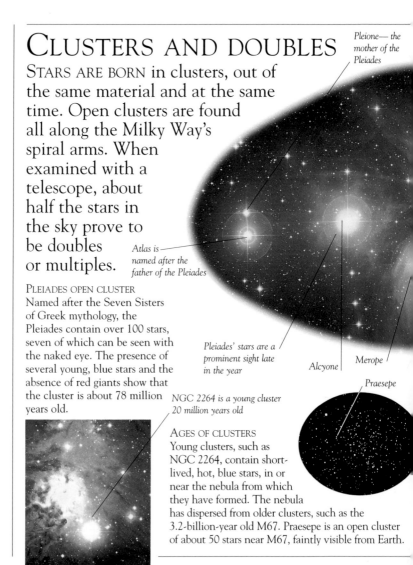

STARS ARE BORN in clusters, out of the same material and at the same time. Open clusters are found all along the Milky Way's spiral arms. When examined with a telescope, about half the stars in the sky prove to be doubles or multiples.

Pleione— the mother of the Pleiades

Atlas is named after the father of the Pleiades

PLEIADES OPEN CLUSTER
Named after the Seven Sisters of Greek mythology, the Pleiades contain over 100 stars, seven of which can be seen with the naked eye. The presence of several young, blue stars and the absence of red giants show that the cluster is about 78 million years old.

Pleiades' stars are a prominent sight late in the year

Alcyone *Merope*

Praesepe

NGC 2264 is a young cluster 20 million years old

AGES OF CLUSTERS
Young clusters, such as NGC 2264, contain short-lived, hot, blue stars, in or near the nebula from which they have formed. The nebula has dispersed from older clusters, such as the 3.2-billion-year old M67. Praesepe is an open cluster of about 50 stars near M67, faintly visible from Earth.

Asterope

Maia

Taygeta

Celaeno

Electra

Streaks in the dust clouds
are due to interstellar
magnetic fields

Clouds of dust around the
stars are lit up by starlight

In a double binary system,
each star orbits its companion,
and the two pairs orbit
the same balance point

OPEN CLUSTERS				
Name	Constellation	Age in millions of years	Distance in light-years	Number of bright stars
Double Cluster (h and chi Persei)	Perseus	3.2 + 5.6	7,400	150 + 200
Jewel Box	Crux	7.1	7,600	100
NGC 2264	Monoceros	20	2,400	40
Butterfly Cluster	Scorpius	51	2,000	80
M47	Puppis	78	1,600	30
Pleiades	Taurus	78	375	100
M41	Canis Major	190	2,300	100
Praesepe	Cancer	660	520	50
Hyades	Taurus	660	150	200
M67	Cancer	3,200	2,600	200

DOUBLE STARS

In optical pairs, two stars that are not really close look like a pair when they lie along the same line of sight. Two stars bound together by their gravities form a true binary system. They orbit a shared point of balance, determined by their masses. In visual binaries, two separate stars can be seen; in spectroscopic binaries, the stars are so close, they appear as one star; and in eclipsing binaries, the stars pass in front of each other, causing the brightness to change.

In a binary system with stars of equal mass, the balance point is in the middle

If one star in a binary system is more massive than the other, the balance point is closer to the heavier star

MULTIPLE STARS

Sometimes three or more stars are grouped in a multiple system. The stars are usually arranged in pairs, or as a pair orbited by a single star.

Shared balance point

Balance point of pair

155

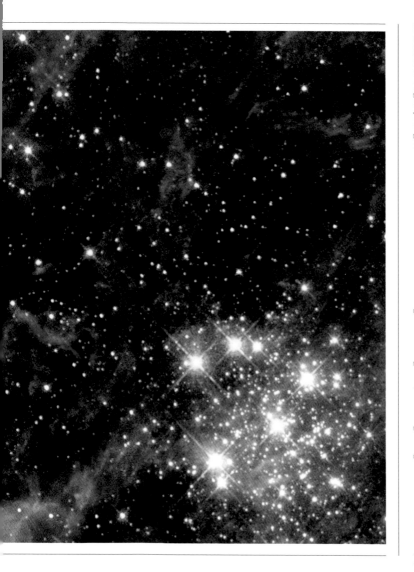

GLOBULAR CLUSTERS

GLOBULAR CLUSTERS are tight-knit
swarms of up to a million stars
that inhabit the lonely outer
reaches of the Milky Way.
Our galaxy may contain as
many as 200 of them.
Their stars are among the
oldest in the Milky Way
and help in determining
the age of the universe.

WHAT GLOBULARS LOOK LIKE
Globular clusters are bigger and brighter than
open clusters and contain about a thousand
times more stars, bound tightly by gravity. While
open clusters are irregular in shape, globulars are roughly
spherical and measure about 100 light-years in diameter.

IMPORTANT GLOBULAR CLUSTERS

Name	Constellation	Distance in light-years	Diameter in light-years
M4	Scorpius	7,000	50
M22	Sagittarius	10,000	70
47 Tucanae	Tucana	15,000	140
Omega Centauri	Centaurus	17,000	180
M13 (Great Cluster)	Hercules	23,000	110
M92	Hercules	25,000	85
M5	Serpens	25,000	130
M15	Pegasus	31,000	110
M3	Canes Venatici	32,000	150
M2	Aquarius	37,000	140

*47 Tucanae is the
second-brightest
globular cluster*

*At the core, about
1,000 stars are
packed into each
cubic light-year*

*Stars in the center of
a globular cluster are
packed about a million
times more densely than
the stars near the Sun*

47 TUCANAE
GLOBULAR CLUSTER

47 Tucanae measures 140 light-years across and has a mass of about a million Suns

R136, in the Tarantula Nebula in the Large Magellanic Cloud, may become a globular cluster in 100 million years

FORMATION OF GLOBULARS

Globulars are typically 10 billion years old. It was originally thought they were created as their parent galaxies first started to form, but the Hubble Space Telescope has found much younger globulars, especially in galaxies colliding with each other. Some of the globulars in the Milky Way may have been brought here by smaller galaxies that collided with it in the past. The giant open cluster R136 is so big that it may be in the process of becoming a globular.

Globulars probably contain many white dwarfs, but they are too faint to see

Most globulars move in long, elliptical orbits around the galactic center, journeying far out into the halo

A few globulars orbit close to the bulge

Most of the bright stars are giants

OMEGA CENTAURI

Three globular clusters can easily be seen with the naked eye—M13, 47 Tucanae, and Omega Centauri. Of these, Omega Centauri in the constellation of Centaurus is the brightest, being highly luminous and relatively close to Earth.

The Sun

Omega Centauri looks like a fuzzy, bright star

MAPPING GLOBULARS

While open clusters lie in the disk of the Milky Way, globulars occupy a spherical region around its central bulge. Distances to globulars are found using the RR Lyrae stars—a type of pulsating variable star—in the same cluster.

159

RED GIANTS

STARS DO NOT LIVE FOREVER. Their supply of hydrogen dwindles and the nuclear reactions in the core die down. The star balloons into a brilliant red giant, hundreds of times its former diameter, as its core begins to tap helium as a new energy source.

INSIDE A RED GIANT

With its hydrogen almost gone, a red giant's core shrinks to a tenth of its size. Enormous temperatures and pressures are generated, and helium—produced in the core when the star was on the main sequence—is fused into carbon and oxygen, producing energy.

Heavy-burning inner shell at 180 million°F (100 million°C)

INSIDE A RED GIANT STAR

Carbon and oxygen products of helium burning

Helium produced by main sequence hydrogen burning

Hydrogen continues to burn in a shell on the outside of the core

Enlarged view of core region

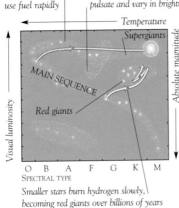

High-mass stars use fuel rapidly

Instability strip, where stars pulsate and vary in brightness

Temperature

Supergiants

MAIN SEQUENCE

Red giants

Visual luminosity

Absolute magnitude

O   B   A   F   G   K   M
SPECTRAL TYPE

Smaller stars burn hydrogen slowly, becoming red giants over billions of years

EVOLUTION OF GIANT STARS

When a star runs out of hydrogen, it swells and cools, moving away from the main sequence, and entering the giant phase. Lower-mass stars brighten dramatically and become red giants. High-mass stars remain about the same brightness but become supergiants. A giant star's color depends on its surface temperature—blue (hottest), white, yellow, or red.

Hotspots— where large currents of hot gas reach the surface

Sooty grains of dust condense in the outer atmosphere of the star, and can give rise to a new generation of stars

Convection cells carry heat from the core to the surface in rising and falling currents of hot gas. Some of the elements made in the core are carried to the surface as well

Sun is less than 10% the diameter of a typical red giant

GIANT STAR STATISTICS

Name	Magnitude	Spectral type	Distance in light-years
Canopus	−0.6	F0 White supergiant	310
Arcturus	0.0	K2 Orange giant	37
Capella	0.1	G6 & G2 Yellow giants	42
Rigel	0.2	B8 Blue supergiant	800
Betelgeuse	0.5	M2 Red supergiant	400
Hadar	0.6	B1 Blue giant	530
Aldebaran	0.9	K5 Red giant	65
Antares	1.1	M1 Red supergiant	500
Pollux	1.2	K0 Orange giant	129
Deneb	1.2	A2 White supergiant	1,500
Mimosa	1.2	B0 Blue giant	350
Gacrux	1.6	M4 Red giant	88

SIZES OF RED GIANTS

When a typical star first leaves the main sequence, it can swell up to 200 times the diameter of the Sun, eventually settling down to between 10 and 100 times the diameter of the Sun once helium starts burning. Supergiants may exceed 1,000 times the Sun's diameter.

Large red giant star at the center of the solar system could engulf Mercury, Venus, and Earth

Orbit of Earth

Orbit of Saturn

Orbit of Mars

Orbit of Jupiter

Sun

Typical supergiant at the center of the solar system could engulf the planets as far out as Mars and Jupiter

STELLAR WINDS

A giant star's outer atmosphere can drift into space across many light years as a stellar wind. The Toby Jug Nebula is a cloud of gas and dust that has been blown out by the giant star situated at its heart.

PLANETARY NEBULAS

WHEN A RED GIANT dies, it puffs off its outer layers in a planetary nebula—an expanding cloud that shines for tens of thousands of years. Stars with a mass up to eight times that of the Sun end their lives this way. The nebula gradually fades while the white dwarf at its heart slowly cools.

Outer lobes of older gas

CAT'S-EYE NEBULA

When a red giant has no helium left to burn, its core shrinks and the outer layers are blown away into space. The departing gas is lit up by the intensely hot core, creating a planetary nebula. These nebulas are quite rare, with only about 1,500 known in the Milky Way.

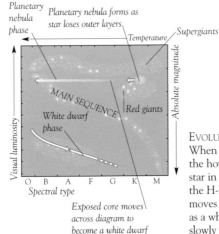

Planetary nebula phase

Planetary nebula forms as star loses outer layers

Temperature

Supergiants

Absolute magnitude

MAIN SEQUENCE

White dwarf phase

Red giants

Visual luminosity

O B A F G K M
Spectral type

Exposed core moves across diagram to become a white dwarf

CAT'S EYE
NEBULA

Green and blue areas are heavier elements, such as oxygen and nitrogen

The glowing nebula is made of gas blown off the star during its red giant phase. It is kept hot by the white dwarf in the middle

EVOLUTION OF WHITE DWARFS

When a red giant puffs off its outer layers, the hot core is seen as the bright central star in a planetary nebula, on the far left of the H-R diagram. As the core cools, it moves into the bottom left of the diagram as a white dwarf. With no more fuel, it slowly fades, moving down and to the right.

Inner shell of recently ejected gas

Red areas are hydrogen, which makes up most of the material in the nebula

NOTABLE PLANETARY NEBULAS

Name	Constellation	Distance in light-years	Size in light-years
Helix	Aquarius	450	1.0
Dumbbell	Vulpecula	1,000	1.5
Owl	Ursa Major	1,300	1.0
Bug	Scorpius	2,000	0.5
Ring	Lyra	2,000	1.5
Saturn	Aquarius	3,000	1.5
Clown	Gemini	3,000	0.5
Blinking Planetary	Cygnus	3,500	2.5
Little Dumbbell	Perseus	3,500	5.0
Cat's Eye	Draco	3,500	6.0

White dwarf at the center—the burned-out core of a red giant, which astronomers think may be part of a double star system

Less massive white dwarf is larger

More massive white dwarf is smaller and denser

CHANDRASEKHAR LIMIT

In 1930, Subrahmanyan Chandrasekhar showed that the mass of a white dwarf cannot exceed 1.4 times that of the Sun. If it does, it will collapse into a neutron star or black hole. The more massive the white dwarf, the smaller it is as it is crushed under its own gravity.

DENSITY OF A WHITE DWARF

White dwarf material is extremely dense—a million times more so than water. This means that the gravitational field around a white dwarf is intense. A person standing on a white dwarf would weigh about 660 tons (600 metric tons). A matchbox of white dwarf material would weigh as much as an elephant.

163

DYING STAR
A star's outer envelope is blasted into space as it transforms itself into a white dwarf.

SUPERNOVAS

THE MOST MASSIVE STARS end their lives in a huge explosion called a supernova. Supernovas are rare; only two or three are expected in our galaxy each century, and most will be hidden by interstellar dust. The last one seen in the Milky Way was in 1604, but many more have been found in other galaxies.

Hydrogen makes up most of star

Supergiant may be more than a thousand times the Sun's size

Dense core

COLLAPSE OF A STAR

When a very massive star uses up most of its available hydrogen, it becomes a supergiant. Unlike red giants, supergiants are hot and can use carbon and oxygen—made by helium-burning—as fuel to make heavier elements, like iron.

Other heavy elements

Iron at the center

Core has onionlike layers of elements. Nuclear fusion cannot create elements heavier than iron, which builds up at the core

Core reaches 1.4 solar masses and collapses in on itself

Subatomic neutrinos burst from iron at center

Outer layers of core collapse inward

Large companion star

White dwarf

Material being pulled from companion star

OTHER KINDS OF SUPERNOVAS

An exploding supergiant is a Type II supernova. A Type Ia supernova is even more powerful—a small, dense white dwarf star pulls gas from a larger companion, and increases its mass until it cannot support itself and collapses in a huge explosion.

STARS

Shock wave from the collapse creates an immense explosion. Heavy elements blown into space are incorporated into new stars

Outer layers of star are blasted out into space

Neutron star or black hole forms from the core

SUPERNOVA REMNANTS

There are about 150 known supernova remnants. They are extremely hot, and continue to expand and glow for thousands of years. This X-ray image shows the remnants of a supernova that exploded in Cassiopeia in 1572. It was named after Tycho Brahe, who studied it.

STELLAR REMAINS

The Vela supernova remnant is the remains of a star that exploded about 11,000 years ago. The center is about 1,500 light-years from the Sun. Expanding material collided with gas lying in space, heating it and making it glow. The red light comes from hydrogen and the blue from oxygen.

SUPERNOVA 1987A

The brightest supernova in Earth's skies for four centuries appeared on February 23, 1987 in the Large Magellanic Cloud—a satellite galaxy of the Milky Way. At magnitude 2.8, it was faint compared with those in distant galaxies.

NOTABLE SUPERNOVAS			
Year	Constellation	Magnitude	Distance in light-years
185	Centaurus	−8	9,800
386	Sagittarius	1.5	16,000
393	Scorpius	0	34,000
1006	Lupus	−9.5	3,500
1054	Taurus	−5	6,500
1181	Cassiopeia	0	8,800
1572	Cassiopeia	−4	7,500
1604	Ophiuchus	−3	12,500
1987	Dorado	2.8	160,000

NEUTRON STARS

A SUPERNOVA EXPLOSION MARKS the death of a star, but also its rebirth in another form. As the outer parts of the star are flung off, the core collapses into a tiny, superdense neutron star. Because of their intense magnetic and gravitational fields, neutron stars often become radio or X-ray pulsars. The Milky Way may be strewn with the dark remains of pulsars.

Ripples spread out from the pulsar as its radio beams heat the gas around them

Gas from the explosion, driven outward at 600 mps (1,000 km/s)

CRAB NEBULA
The best-known neutron star is at the heart of the Crab Nebula—the remains of a star that exploded as a supernova almost 1,000 years ago. Although most of the star's material has been flung over a region of space 15 light-years across, the collapsed core of the star remains. Spinning furiously 30 times a second, the neutron star is the powerhouse of the nebula, pouring out energy in the form of light, radio waves, and X-rays.

CRAB NEBULA

The central star is a pulsar, a spinning neutron star with a powerful magnetic field whose energy makes the nebula glow

Beams of radiation from the pulsar light up the surrounding gas

PULSARS

More than a thousand pulsars have been discovered since the first one was found in 1967. They are strongly magnetic, spinning neutron stars that send out rhythmic bursts of radio waves. The fastest pulses 642 times a second, while the slowest pulses every 8.51 seconds. Most lie in the Milky Way Galaxy. Magnetars are a recently discovered type of neutron star with an even stronger magnetic field, which may be linked to gamma-ray bursts from space.

STRUCTURE OF A PULSAR

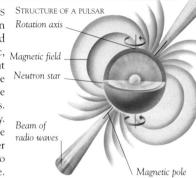

Rotation axis

Magnetic field

Neutron star

Beam of radio waves

Magnetic pole

Pulsar off / *(undetected)* *Pulsar on* / *(detected)* *Pulsar off* / *(undetected)*

HOW PULSARS WORK

A neutron star sends out a radio beam from each magnetic pole, which is detected each time it sweeps past Earth. It gradually radiates away its energy and slows down. Eventually it stops emitting radio waves and fades away.

Giant companion star

Stream of gas pulled from the companion star onto the neutron star

Neutron star

X-rays come from the bright hot spot at the poles of the neutron star

X-ray beam

BINARY PULSARS

Pulsars often orbit other stars, which may be a normal star, a white dwarf, or another neutron star. In binary pulsar systems with two neutron stars, the stars slowly spiral toward each other. They may eventually collide or even form a black hole.

Stars spiral in on each other over many orbits

Neutron stars

X-RAY BINARIES AND RECYCLED PULSARS

A neutron star in a binary system pulls gas from its normal companion star. An X-ray-emitting hot spot forms where the gas hits the surface. X-ray binaries may be recycled pulsars—old, dead pulsars, spun up again by gas from a companion red giant.

STARS

169

BLACK HOLES

THE MOST BIZARRE OBJECTS in the universe, black holes emit no visible light at all. Most are the end state of brilliant giant stars that go supernova. The supercompressed core that remains has such strong gravity that even light cannot escape, so it is black. Since nothing travels faster than light, whatever falls in is trapped forever—so it is also a hole in space.

Small, slow orbit of visible star shows it is close to the balance point of the system, and that it must be heavier than its invisible companion

Large, fast orbit of visible star shows it is farther from the balance point, and therefore lighter than its invisible companion

Streamer hits the gas orbiting the black hole, creating a bright hot spot

Neutron star

Balance point

Small orbit

Black hole

Companion star

WEIGHING A BLACK HOLE

When a star is in orbit with an invisible companion, the companion is weighed to see if it is a neutron star or black hole. The visible star's mass, visible by its color and brightness, is used to work out its companion's mass. Anything more than three solar masses is a black hole.

Dust ring feeding the accretion disk

Region of black hole

NGC 4261

SUPERMASSIVE BLACK HOLES

Some black holes were made by the collapse of huge gas clouds in the past. Their great gravity attracts dust and gas from space, forming massive accretion disks. They can appear dark, as in NGC 4261, or shine, as in quasars.

DETECTION

Black holes can be detected only if they are close to another star. The hole's powerful gravity pulls gas off its companion at high speeds. The gas pours down the black hole, forming a spiral vortex around it called an accretion disk. Friction makes the swirling gas hot, and it emits X-rays.

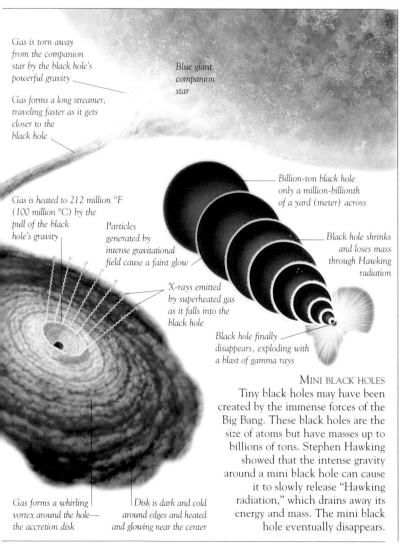

Gas is torn away from the companion star by the black hole's powerful gravity

Blue giant companion star

Gas forms a long streamer, traveling faster as it gets closer to the black hole

Billion-ton black hole only a million-billionth of a yard (meter) across

Gas is heated to 212 million °F (100 million °C) by the pull of the black hole's gravity

Particles generated by intense gravitational field cause a faint glow

Black hole shrinks and loses mass through Hawking radiation

X-rays emitted by superheated gas as it falls into the black hole

Black hole finally disappears, exploding with a blast of gamma rays

Gas forms a whirling vortex around the hole— the accretion disk

Disk is dark and cold around edges and heated and glowing near the center

MINI BLACK HOLES
Tiny black holes may have been created by the immense forces of the Big Bang. These black holes are the size of atoms but have masses up to billions of tons. Stephen Hawking showed that the intense gravity around a mini black hole can cause it to slowly release "Hawking radiation," which drains away its energy and mass. The mini black hole eventually disappears.

171

INSIDE A BLACK HOLE

BLACK HOLES ARE PRISONS of light, with gravity so strong that they distort space and time and allow nothing to escape. Mathematicians explore black holes using Einstein's Theory of General Relativity. This shows the strange effects of a black hole where its matter has collapsed into a singularity—a tiny point of infinite density.

Sun makes a shallow gravitational well

Steeper gravitational well

A white dwarf, being denser, dents space more noticeably

A neutron star—denser still than a white dwarf—creates a gravitational well with very steep sides

Very steep well

ANATOMY OF A BLACK HOLE
Einstein's Theory of General Relativity sees gravity as a distortion of space. He thought of space as being like a thin rubber sheet that dents, or forms a gravitational well, if heavy objects are placed on it. Black holes have this same basic structure. The singularity at the center is also surrounded by an invisible boundary called the event horizon—nothing can escape from inside here.

A black hole makes such a steep dent that objects enter at the speed of light

Objects approaching a black hole are deflected by steeply curved space

Objects may go into orbit around the black hole

Objects that come too close to the black hole are inevitably drawn in

Once inside the event horizon, the object spirals down the steep sides of the gravitational well

Objects can escape the black hole if they give it a wide berth

Event horizon—once inside it, light cannot escape from the hole

A gravitational well is bottomless, trapping matter and light in the black hole forever

1 As the fall into the black hole begins, the astronaut looks normal and undistorted, with a watch keeping normal time

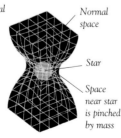

2 Closer to the black hole, the astronaut's body begins to stretch, turning redder as light struggles upward against gravity. The watch slows down

3 Long after the astronaut has been fatally spaghettified and fallen in, a frozen, reddened mirage remains on the event horizon. The watch has stopped

SPAGHETTIFICATION

Objects that fall into a black hole are "spaghettified." A hypothetical astronaut, falling in feet first, feels a stronger pull on their feet than their head as they are stretched apart. Closer to the hole, the astronaut is pulled into a tube. The effect is worse for smaller black holes, because they make steeper gravitational wells. As gravity distorts light and time around the black hole, the astronaut's colleagues see a variety of strange effects as they watch them fall in.

DISTORTING SPACE AND TIME

These diagrams offer a convenient simplification of space as two-dimensional, like a sheet. In reality, space has three dimensions. According to Einstein's Theory of General Relativity, a massive object like a star distorts space. Time—an extra, fourth dimension, not shown here—is also theoretically affected by strong gravitational fields. As something falls into a black hole, time slows down relative to the object's speed. Eventually, the object reaches the speed of light at the event horizon, and its time completely stops.

A three-dimensional view shows the star's gravity distorting space in a more complex way. Objects that would normally travel in straight lines are forced to follow the curved gridlines

Normal space

Star

Space near star is pinched by mass

Space near star is bent by mass   *Star*

A two-dimensional view of a massive body making a dent in space-time. The distortion is shown on gridlines that would lie in a flat plane if the star were absent

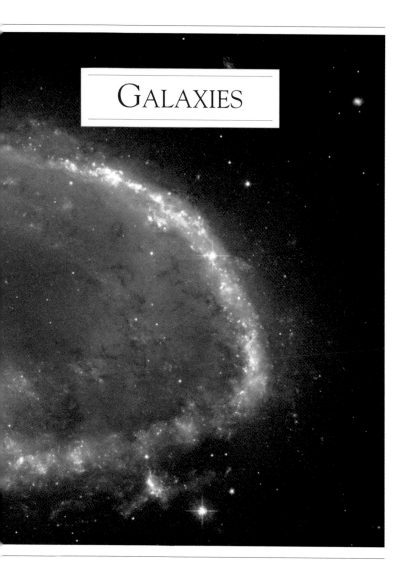

GALAXIES

WHAT IS A GALAXY?

A GALAXY IS AN enormous group of stars. A large galaxy may have billions of stars, a small galaxy only a few hundred thousand. Even the smallest galaxies are so big that it takes light thousands of years to cross them. Galaxies form from vast, spinning clouds of gas. They continue to spin, and come in a number of different shapes.

DISTANT STAR CITY
The Andromeda galaxy is so far away that its light takes 2,500,000 years to travel to Earth. We therefore see it as it was 2,500,000 years ago.

GALAXY TYPES

ELLIPTICAL
These range from ball-shaped to egg-shaped. They contain mainly old stars, and are the most common type.

SPIRAL
These are disk-shaped. Most material is in the spiral arms where new stars are formed. Old stars are in the nucleus.

BARRED-SPIRAL
These are like spiral galaxies, but the nucleus is elongated into a bar. The spiral arms extend from the ends of the bar.

BRIGHTEST LIGHTS
This is an X-ray image
of a quasistellar object—
one of the brightest and
remotest objects. The most
distant are about 14,000
million light-years away.
Known as quasars, they are
probably the cores of the
first galaxies to be formed.

BRIGHT GALAXIES: DATA		
Galaxy	Distance (in light-years)	Type
Andromeda (M31)	2,500,000	Sb
M33	2,800,000	Sc
NGC 300	4,200,000	Sc
NGC 55	5,800,000	Sc
NGC 253	8,000,000	Sc
M81	14,000,000	Sb
M82	14,000,000	peculiar
Centaurus A	16,000,000	E (peculiar)
M83	16,000,000	SBc
M101	17,000,000	Sc
M64	18,000,000	Sab
Whirlpool (M51)	27,000,000	Sbc
M104	44,000,000	Sa/b
M87	55,000,000	E0
M100	55,000,000	Sc
M77	62,000,000	Sb
NGC 1316 (Fornax A)	66,000,000	Sa (peculiar)

"TUNING-FORK" DIAGRAM OF
GALAXY CLASSIFICATION
DEVISED BY E. HUBBLE

Sc
Sb
Sa
E0 E3 E5 E7
SBa
SBb
SBc

SHAPE CLASSIFICATION
Elliptical galaxies are classified from
E0 (spherical) to E7 (very flattened). Spirals
(S) and barred spirals (SB) are graded from a to c,
according to the compactness of the central nucleus
and the tightness of the arms. Irregular galaxies (Irr)
are not shown here, but can be divided into types I
(completely irregular) and II (regular galaxies
distorted by collisions or violent activity).

IRREGULAR
Some of these have a
hint of spiral structure,
while others do not fit
any known pattern.
They are the rarest type.

COLLIDING GALAXIES

GALAXIES SOMETIMES CRASH TOGETHER in a spectacular pile-up, spawning thousands of hot new stars. One sign of a past collision is a starburst—a sudden spurt of star formation in an ordinary-looking galaxy. Colliding galaxies often merge. Eventually, most galaxies will merge with their neighbors, and the universe will consist of a smaller number of much bigger galaxies.

CARTWHEEL GALAXY

A spectacular example of a direct hit between two galaxies, the Cartwheel Galaxy was once a normal spiral, like the Milky Way. About 300 million years ago, a smaller galaxy sped through its center. The impact triggered a burst of star formation, producing the ring of young blue stars.

Turmoil in the central regions as giant gas clouds collide

Dust and gas from spiral arms have fallen into the cores of both galaxies, making the stars here appear redder

Ring could easily contain the entire Milky Way

Central region, choked with dust, hides giant clusters of young stars

Gas and dust ripple out from a direct hit on the core, creating a starburst

INTERACTING GALAXIES

When galaxies collide, the interaction is complex. Each galaxy is held together only by gravity, and the collision causes a tug of war as each galaxy pulls at the other. In the center, gas clouds crash together, while at the edge, stars are flung out into space. In galaxies NGC 4038 and 4039, the collision formed a pair of long, curved streamers of stars.

300 MILLION YEARS AGO	200 MILLION YEARS AGO	100 MILLION YEARS AGO	TODAY

GLANCING BLOW

About 300 million years ago, the Whirlpool Galaxy had a near miss with a smaller galaxy. The massive Whirlpool escaped relatively unhurt, but the collision wreaked havoc on the smaller galaxy as the Whirlpool's gravity tore out stars to form a temporary bridge between the two.

False-color image combines optical and radio observations

Blue regions are gas

WHIRLPOOL GALAXY

The Whirlpool appears to have a smaller galaxy dangling from one spiral arm. This is the galaxy that struck the Whirlpool hundreds of millions of years ago, and now lies some distance beyond it. The gravity of the passing galaxy has stirred up the gas and stars in the Whirlpool.

Green regions are stars

Red reveals strong magnetism

Blue regions are star formation clusters triggered by the collision

The collision has created more than a thousand new star clusters

HUBBLE VIEW OF ANTENNAE

Hot stars, less than 10 million years old, show that the collision is recent

In 5 billion years, our galaxy will smash into the Andromeda Galaxy, perhaps forming a system like the Antennae

STARBURST GALAXY

A starburst galaxy is usually the aftermath of a galactic collision in which the galaxy's gas clouds are squeezed together, triggering a sudden burst of star formation. Spotted in 1983 by the Infrared Astronomical Satellite, starburst galaxies are filled with hot young stars—seen as red spots in this infrared view of M82 (a galaxy in Ursa Major).

179

181

ACTIVE GALAXIES

A SMALL NUMBER of galaxies are different from all the rest, pouring out huge amounts of energy from a tiny region, about the size of the solar system, at their centers. These so-called active galaxies, which include quasars, radio galaxies, Seyfert galaxies, and blazars, have many features in common.

INSIDE AN ACTIVE GALAXY

An active radio galaxy spouts radio-emitting gas jets from either side. At its heart lies a glowing, doughnut-shaped ring of hot dust and gas. This contains a supermassive black hole, which generates enough power to outshine the Sun a trillion times.

RADIO LOBES

Jets of hot gas are blown out of the galaxy's center across hundreds of thousands of light-years. Where they encounter intergalactic gas clouds, they billow out into huge radio-emitting lobes.

Jet emits radio waves and sometimes visible light

CENTRAL DUST RING
The core of an active galaxy is an intense energy source, hidden by a ring of dust and gas. Dark on the outside, but glowing on the inner edge, the ring absorbs radiation from the core. Jets emerge from either side of its center.

Huge gas lobe emits radio waves

Core

Inner edge of gas and dust cloud is hot and rotates rapidly

Energy from the core heats the inside of the ring, making it glow

Central region

Galaxy

Outer edge of gas and dust cloud is cool and slow-moving

Jet wavers as it runs into other particles

QUASARS

Quasars are among the most powerful objects in the universe. They emit radio waves, X-rays, and infrared, as well as light, and they sometimes have visible jets. They are the brilliant cores of remote galaxies, with the dust ring tilted to reveal the radiation emitted by the accretion disk.

A faint galaxy surrounds the brilliant core of the quasar PKS 2349-01

SEYFERT GALAXIES

About one in ten big spiral galaxies has a very bright spot of light at its center. This is a Seyfert galaxy, and may be a less powerful version of a quasar, with a smaller black hole in its core. Some astronomers think that all large spiral galaxies, including the Milky Way, may become Seyferts at some time.

Seyfert galaxy NGC 1566 lies 50 million light-years away and is a dimmer version of a quasar

RADIO GALAXIES

Radio galaxies are among the largest objects in the sky. One or two jets shoot out for thousands of light-years from the center, feeding streams of gas into huge clouds on either side of the galaxy. The central dust ring is seen edge-on, so the core is hidden and the fainter jets become visible.

The blue lines show the intensity of the radio emissions from the radio galaxy 3C 368

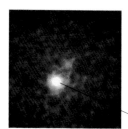

BLAZARS

Blazars are active galaxies, similar to quasars. Their brightness varies rapidly by as much as 100 times, showing daily changes. It is believed that their jets are pointed directly toward us, so that we can look into the core, seeing light and other radiation from the accretion disk around the black hole.

This gamma-ray image shows high-energy radiation from the core of the blazar 3C 279

GALAXIES

THE MILKY WAY

OUR HOME IN the universe is the Milky Way—a spiral galaxy with a nucleus of old stars surrounded by a halo of even older stars. All the young stars are located in the spiral arms. The Sun is just one of 200 billion stars that inhabit our galaxy. The Milky Way is so large that it takes light 100,000 years to travel from edge to edge. All the stars that we see at night are in the Milky Way.

SAGITTARIUS STAR CLOUD
This infrared image shows young stars in Sagittarius, looking toward the Milky Way's center. Infrared reveals millions of stars that are obscured by dust clouds when viewed in visible light.

From the side, the spiral arms look like a flattened disk

Galactic halo contains the oldest stars

MILKY WAY GALAXY:
EXTERNAL SIDE VIEW

Nucleus is the brightest region of the galaxy

SIDE-ON SPIRAL
Viewed sideways-on, from a distance of about a million light-years, the Milky Way galaxy would look like a giant lens—with flattened edges and a bright central nucleus. Around the nucleus is a roughly spherical halo that contains the oldest stars in the galaxy.

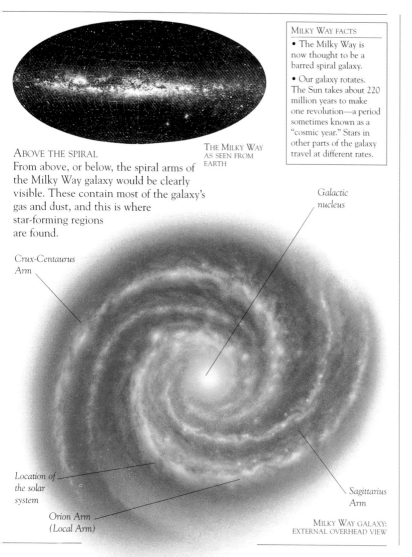

THE MILKY WAY
AS SEEN FROM
EARTH

MILKY WAY FACTS

- The Milky Way is now thought to be a barred spiral galaxy.

- Our galaxy rotates. The Sun takes about 220 million years to make one revolution—a period sometimes known as a "cosmic year." Stars in other parts of the galaxy travel at different rates.

ABOVE THE SPIRAL

From above, or below, the spiral arms of the Milky Way galaxy would be clearly visible. These contain most of the galaxy's gas and dust, and this is where star-forming regions are found.

Galactic nucleus

Crux-Centaurus Arm

Location of the solar system

Orion Arm (Local Arm)

Sagittarius Arm

MILKY WAY GALAXY:
EXTERNAL OVERHEAD VIEW

185

STRUCTURE OF THE MILKY WAY

THE MILKY WAY STARTED LIFE billions of years ago as a vast, round gas cloud that collapsed under its own gravity and was flattened by rotation. It contains 200 billion stars, and vast clouds of dust and gas—the material for future stars. In places, the clouds are pierced by glowing nebulas in which stars have just formed.

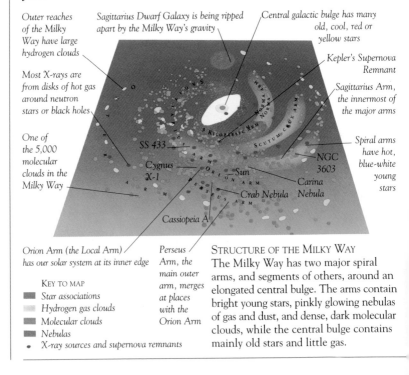

Outer reaches of the Milky Way have large hydrogen clouds

Sagittarius Dwarf Galaxy is being ripped apart by the Milky Way's gravity

Central galactic bulge has many old, cool, red or yellow stars

Most X-rays are from disks of hot gas around neutron stars or black holes

Kepler's Supernova Remnant

Sagittarius Arm, the innermost of the major arms

One of the 5,000 molecular clouds in the Milky Way

SS 433

Cygnus X-1

Sun

Spiral arms have hot, blue-white young stars

NGC 3603

Carina Nebula

Crab Nebula

Cassiopeia A

Orion Arm (the Local Arm) has our solar system at its inner edge

Perseus Arm, the main outer arm, merges at places with the Orion Arm

KEY TO MAP
- Star associations
- Hydrogen gas clouds
- Molecular clouds
- Nebulas
- X-ray sources and supernova remnants

STRUCTURE OF THE MILKY WAY
The Milky Way has two major spiral arms, and segments of others, around an elongated central bulge. The arms contain bright young stars, pinkly glowing nebulas of gas and dust, and dense, dark molecular clouds, while the central bulge contains mainly old stars and little gas.

MAPPING THE GALAXY

Astronomers map the galaxy using radio telescopes, which can penetrate the dust clouds that get in the way of optical telescopes. The key to mapping is to find the rotational speed of an object, which is done by measuring small changes in the length of the radio waves given out by the object as it moves. Astronomers know how fast the different parts of the galaxy spin, so they use the object's rotational speed to calculate its distance from the Sun.

This tiny radio telescope, only 4 ft (1.2 m) across, mapped gas clouds in our galaxy from the top of a building in the heart of New York City

OBSERVING THE MILKY WAY

The Milky Way appears especially bright from June to September, when Earth's nighttime side is turned toward the denser regions of the galactic center. Because the galaxy is relatively thin, and because we live inside it, the stars of the Milky Way appear as a band across the night sky. The dark rifts against this band are huge dust clouds that obscure the stars behind them.

MILKY WAY DATA	
Type of galaxy	Spiral (between Sb and SBc)
Luminosity	14 billion solar luminosities
Total mass (including dark matter)	1,000 billion solar masses
Mass in stars	200 billion solar masses
Mass in gas	20 billion solar masses
Mass in dust	200 million solar masses
Diameter	100,000 light-years
Thickness of disk	2,000 light-years
Thickness of central bulge	6,000 light-years
Distance of Sun from center	25,000 light-years
Time for Sun to orbit center	220 million years
Speed of Sun in orbit	149 mps (240 km/s)
Age of oldest star clusters	12 billion years
Number of globular clusters	140 known; total 200 (estimated)

INTERSTELLAR MEDIUM

SPACE IS NOT ENTIRELY empty. Tiny amounts of gas and dust between the stars add up to 10 percent of a galaxy's mass. This interstellar medium is always churning and evolving, giving birth to stars and absorbing their material when they die.

Gas 9.9%

Dust 0.1%

Stars 90%

GALACTIC COMPOSITION
Most of a galaxy's visible mass is in the form of stars. Just 10 percent is gas and dust—molecular clouds and the warm intercloud medium.

Warm intercloud medium contains hydrogen gas, which glows pink when radiation is absorbed from nearby sources

Invisible cosmic rays are high-energy protons from supernovas

Alnitak is a star in Orion's Belt

HORSEHEAD NEBULA IN ORION

BETWEEN THE STARS
The interstellar medium is not uniform. Most of it is a "warm" intercloud medium, at about 14,400°F (8,000°C). Within this are bubbles of thin gas, exceeding 1.8 million °F (1 million °C), made by supernovas or young stars. There are also cold clouds of hydrogen atoms. Finally, there are very dark, dense molecular clouds of gas and dust where stars are born.

Dust clouds look blue because dust particles scatter short wavelength light

Horsehead Nebula is 4 light-years across and part of a molecular cloud

188

EFFECTS OF DUST

Cosmic dust particles spin around and impede the passage of light through space. This has a very dramatic effect on how we see the stars. For example, the two nebulas NGC 3603 and NGC 3576 look rather like twins when viewed from Earth, but NGC 3603 is, in fact, by far the most brilliant of the two. However, it appears comparatively faint to us because its brilliant light is dimmed and reddened by dust lying in front of it.

NGC 3576 forms part of the Carina complex of star formation

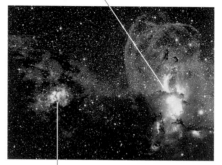

NGC 3603 is the most massive nebula in the galaxy visible to optical telescopes

Cygnus Loop is yellow-green in this infrared image

Warm intercloud medium

HOT GAS BUBBLES

The hottest but least dense parts of the interstellar medium are gas bubbles such as the Cygnus Loop, which was created by a supernova more than 20,000 years ago. It is still being heated by the shock waves from the explosion.

Magnetic fields align dust particles and make the interstellar medium behind the Horsehead appear striped

Molecular clouds are thick with dust, which blocks out light from newborn stars

MOLECULAR CLOUDS

With the naked eye, a molecular cloud can be seen in the Cygnus region of the Milky Way. It is the starless gash down the center—the Cygnus Rift—where a giant molecular cloud blocks out the light from the stars behind.

GALAXIES

189

OUR LOCAL NEIGHBORHOOD

THE PART OF THE MILKY WAY around the Sun is home to many sensational sights, such as the spectacular star-forming complex in Orion. Our neighborhood covers 5,000 light-years around the Sun. It includes the stars making up all the familiar constellations, such as Taurus, but is mostly filled with the spiral Orion Arm.

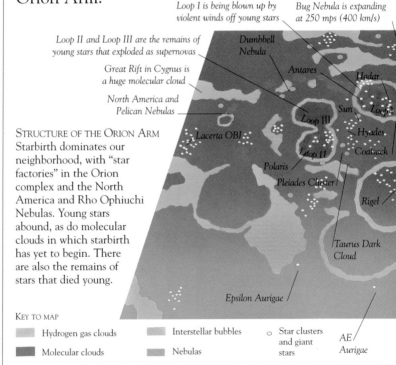

Loop I is being blown up by violent winds off young stars

Bug Nebula is expanding at 250 mps (400 km/s)

Loop II and Loop III are the remains of young stars that exploded as supernovas

Great Rift in Cygnus is a huge molecular cloud

North America and Pelican Nebulas

Dumbbell Nebula

Antares

Hadar

Sun

Loop I

Loop III

Hyades

Lacerta OB1

Loop II

Coalsack

Polaris

Pleiades Cluster

Rigel

Taurus Dark Cloud

Epsilon Aurigae

AE Aurigae

STRUCTURE OF THE ORION ARM
Starbirth dominates our neighborhood, with "star factories" in the Orion complex and the North America and Rho Ophiuchi Nebulas. Young stars abound, as do molecular clouds in which starbirth has yet to begin. There are also the remains of stars that died young.

KEY TO MAP

Hydrogen gas clouds

Molecular clouds

Interstellar bubbles

Nebulas

○ Star clusters and giant stars

HELIX NEBULA

At 450 light-years away, the Helix Nebula is the closest planetary nebula to the Sun, and covers about half the area of a full moon in the sky. Its helix shape is probably the result of a red giant puffing off its outer layers on two separate occasions.

RHO OPHIUCHI COMPLEX

This star-forming complex is the most colorful in the sky, with blue and magenta predominant. The real action, vigorous starbirth, is hidden behind a molecular cloud.

Gum Nebula

Vela Supernova Remnant

HYADES CLUSTER

The Hyades is the nearest star cluster to Earth, just 150 light-years away.

Vela Pulsar is the spinning, collapsed core of a star that exploded 11,000 years ago

Barnard's Loop is a supernova remnant 300 light-years across

Orion Nebula

Horsehead Nebula

The gas is made to glow by radiation from young stars in the molecular cloud beside it

Monoceros R2 contains a star that is 10,000 times brighter than the Sun

North America Nebula

The stars in the Hyades Cluster form a V-shape in the sky

Aldebaran forms the point of the V-shape

The "Gulf of Mexico" is a molecular cloud

Pelican Nebula is shaped like a pelican's head

NORTH AMERICA NEBULA

The shape of the North America Nebula amazingly mirrors that of the continent. This and the Pelican Nebula are the visible parts of a vast, glowing nebula 100 light-years across—six times bigger than the Orion Nebula.

THE PERSEUS ARM

IN 1951, WILLIAM MORGAN provided proof that the Milky Way is indeed a spiral galaxy. From the brightness of the stars in the Cassiopeia, Perseus, and Cepheus constellations, he realized that they must all be at about the same distance. He showed that they lie in a band 5,000–8,000 light-years away. This is the Perseus Arm, the outermost main spiral arm.

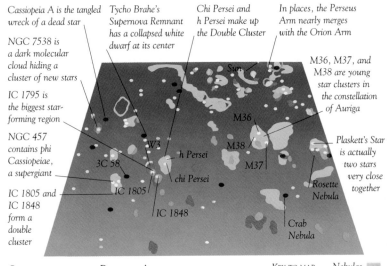

Cassiopeia A is the tangled wreck of a dead star

NGC 7538 is a dark molecular cloud hiding a cluster of new stars

IC 1795 is the biggest star-forming region

NGC 457 contains phi Cassiopeiae, a supergiant

IC 1805 and IC 1848 form a double cluster

Tycho Brahe's Supernova Remnant has a collapsed white dwarf at its center

Chi Persei and h Persei make up the Double Cluster

In places, the Perseus Arm nearly merges with the Orion Arm

M36, M37, and M38 are young star clusters in the constellation of Auriga

Plaskett's Star is actually two stars very close together

Sun

M36

W3

3C 58

h Persei

M38

M37

chi Persei

IC 1805

IC 1848

Rosette Nebula

Crab Nebula

STRUCTURE OF THE PERSEUS ARM
The Perseus Arm is one of the galaxy's main arms, but instead of wrapping itself around the galaxy, it is made up of unconnected patches of young stars and nebulas. It also contains numerous supernova remnants.

KEY TO MAP
Nebulas
Molecular clouds
Star associations
Hydrogen gas clouds
Clusters and giant stars ○
Pulsars and supernova remnants ●

The gases are spreading outward at a speed of 930 mps (1,500 km/s)

The curving filaments of the nebula look like a crab's pincers

CRAB NEBULA

While most supernova remnants are spherical, the Crab Nebula consists of countless long filaments that stretch out across 15 light-years of space. The ghostly blue glow inside the mass of filaments is synchrotron radiation produced by very fast-moving electrons. These electrons are generated by a central, rapidly spinning pulsar. The Crab Nebula Pulsar is only 16 miles (25 km) across, and yet its mass is greater than that of the Sun.

CASSIOPEIA A

The brightest radio source that can be observed from Earth is Cassiopeia A—the remains of a star that exploded 300 years ago. A radio telescope view reveals it to be a shell of gases speeding outward at 3,730 mps (6,000 km/s). The bright, color-coded parts are the dense, hot edges of the shell.

The radio waves come from electrons moving in strong magnetic fields

The yellow and red areas show where the radio waves are most intense

Young stars have already blown a hole as large as the famous Orion Nebula

The Rosette Nebula is found in the constellation of Monoceros

The stars at the center form the open cluster NGC 2244

ROSETTE NEBULA

Appearing bigger than a full moon in the sky, the huge Rosette Nebula lies 5,500 light-years away. It is gradually growing larger and fainter as the radiation and strong winds, from young stars born at its center, blow away the gas that helped create them.

THE SAGITTARIUS ARM

LYING BETWEEN THE ORION ARM and the galactic center, the Sagittarius Arm is one of the Milky Way's two major spiral arms. Although radio waves and infrared radiation can pass through the dust that blocks our view of it, astronomers find that objects are often obscured because they lie along the same line of sight as other, closer objects.

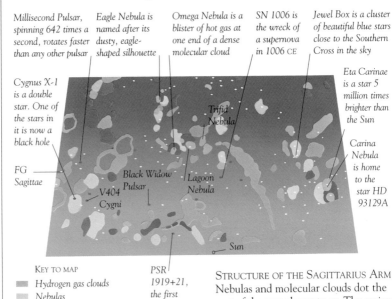

Millisecond Pulsar, spinning 642 times a second, rotates faster than any other pulsar

Eagle Nebula is named after its dusty, eagle-shaped silhouette

Omega Nebula is a blister of hot gas at one end of a dense molecular cloud

SN 1006 is the wreck of a supernova in 1006 CE

Jewel Box is a cluster of beautiful blue stars close to the Southern Cross in the sky

Cygnus X-1 is a double star. One of the stars in it is now a black hole

Eta Carinae is a star 5 million times brighter than the Sun

Trifid Nebula

FG Sagittae

Black Widow Pulsar

V404 Cygni

Lagoon Nebula

Carina Nebula is home to the star HD 93129A

Sun

KEY TO MAP

- Hydrogen gas clouds
- Nebulas
- Molecular clouds
- Star associations
- Pulsars and supernova remnants
- Star clusters

PSR 1919+21, the first pulsar discovered

STRUCTURE OF THE SAGITTARIUS ARM
Nebulas and molecular clouds dot the part of the arm closest to us. The region also has its share of star corpses, pulsars, and black holes. Closer to the galactic center, molecular clouds dominate.

BLACK HOLES IN CYGNUS

The Sagittarius Arm has its share of black holes, which astronomers can "weigh" if they are situated in double-star systems. The masses of the two bodies involved dictate how they orbit one another. In V404 Cygni, the black hole is heavier than the star, so the balance point lies almost in the hole and the star swings around the hole. In Cygnus X-1, the star is heavier than the hole, so the balance point lies inside the star and the hole orbits the star.

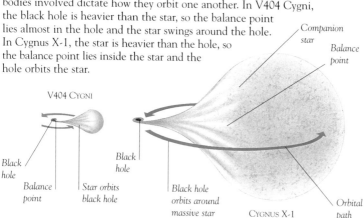

Companion
star

Balance
point

V404 CYGNI

Black
hole

Black
hole

Balance
point

Star orbits
black hole

Black hole
orbits around
massive star

CYGNUS X-1

Orbital
path

TRIFID AND LAGOON NEBULAS
These two nebulas, more than 5,000 light-years away, are among the most striking in the sky. The Trifid Nebula (top) gets its name, which means "divided into three parts," because dark dust lanes split the nebula three ways. The nebula surrounds a compact cluster of stars whose radiation heats the hydrogen inside it until it glows pink. The Lagoon Nebula (bottom) envelops a cluster of stars about 2 million years old, many of which are so massive and bright that they can be seen with the naked eye.

195

HEART OF THE MILKY WAY

THE CENTER OF THE MILKY WAY is a bar-shaped bulge of old red and yellow stars, with comparatively little gas. Radio and infrared telescopes have shown jets of gas moving at considerable speed, and areas of strong magnetism. The temperature increases toward the core. This activity is due to recent star formations, and energy from gas falling into a black hole.

Sagittarius B2, the densest and most massive molecular cloud, is a region of intensive starbirth

Molecular Ring is 1,000 light-years across

Arc is made up of narrow filaments of gas

Radio Lobe is a vast region of magnetized gas

Sagittarius A complex is a hot gas cloud consisting of two parts—Sagittarius A West and Sagittarius A East

Molecular Ring—a series of huge molecular clouds. It is expanding at 93 mps (150 km/s), set in motion by an explosion one million years ago

Sagittarius A* marks the exact galactic center

Galactic center contains millions of densely packed stars

STRUCTURE OF THE GALACTIC CENTER
The galaxy's biggest and heaviest objects congregate at the center. At its core is a star cluster, containing many red supergiants, and an intense radio source—Sagittarius A*—which is a massive black hole.

KEY TO MAP
Nebulas
Molecular clouds
Hydrogen gas clouds

MAGNETIC STRUCTURES

The innermost 100 light-years are dominated by the strongest magnetic fields. This is part of the Radio Lobe—a vast region of magnetized gas in the shape of a chimney. Within this region are many unique objects, such as the Mouse.

The Mouse
is a fast-moving pulsar that
gets its names from its shape

The Tail is a cloud
of radio-wave-
emitting particles
55 light-years long

The Arc, which curves like a colossal
solar prominence, consists of
filaments of gas 150 light-years long
but only half a light-year wide

CENTRAL SPIRAL

The central 10 light-years consist of three areas: Sagittarius A West, Sagittarius A*, and the central star cluster. The smaller spiral arms of Sagittarius A West are streams of gas falling inward, while its two main arms are parts of a tilted, spinning disk of hot gas.

Sagittarius A*

Sagittarius A*

CENTRAL STAR CLUSTER

Within Sagittarius A West is the central star cluster, which contains 2.5 million stars. This infrared image shows stars in the innermost 2 light-years. Right at the center is Sagittarius A*, a possible black hole with a mass of 2.5 million Suns. It is not active at present, but it was once. If enough gas exists to "feed" it, it may become active again in the future.

MAGELLANIC CLOUDS

JUST AS EARTH'S GRAVITY holds the Moon in orbit, so the Milky Way Galaxy holds two satellite galaxies—the Large and Small Magellanic Clouds—in orbit around it. These galaxies orbit together on an elliptical path, taking over a billion years to travel once around it.

Tarantula Nebula is the biggest and brightest gas cloud in the LMC

Site of Supernova 1987A

LARGE MAGELLANIC CLOUD
The Milky Way's "little cousin," the Large Magellanic Cloud (LMC) is only one-twentieth the size of our galaxy, but contains the same mix of stars and gas. It is too small to grow spectacular spiral arms, but is more ordered than many smaller galaxies. Lying 160,000 light-years away, the LMC is the closest major galaxy to us.

NGC 419 is a globular cluster of almost a million stars

NGC 2100 is a giant open star cluster only 20 million years old

NGC 346 is a giant nebula surrounding a cluster of massive young stars

SMALL MAGELLANIC CLOUD
Only a quarter the size of the LMC, the Small Magellanic Cloud (SMC) lies 190,000 light-years away. Because of its small size, it is being ripped apart by the gravity of the Milky Way. The galaxy contains 2,000 star clusters.

S Doradus is one of the LMC's brightest stars

Central bar of stars is 10,000 light-years long

TARANTULA NEBULA

The Tarantula is one of the biggest and brightest of all nebulas. Some 800 light-years across, it is 50 times the size of the famous Orion Nebula in our Milky Way. This gas cloud is lit up by hot young stars. The cluster at its center contains more than a hundred stars, each heavier than 50 Suns.

Faint spiral shape extends from this end of the central straight bar

LMC contains 6,500 star clusters

Dark dust clouds are less common in the LMC than in the Milky Way

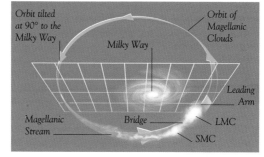

Orbit tilted at 90° to the Milky Way

Orbit of Magellanic Clouds

Milky Way

Leading Arm

Magellanic Stream

Bridge

LMC

SMC

MAGELLANIC STREAM

Pulled by the Milky Way's mighty gravity, gas from the Magellanic Clouds has spilled out into space. A pool of gas—the Bridge—envelops both Clouds, while a long gas trail—the Magellanic Stream—has been left along the galaxies' elliptical orbits. Some gas—the Leading Arm—has even splashed ahead of the two galaxies.

SPOTTING THE MAGELLANIC CLOUDS

The Clouds are easily seen from the Southern Hemisphere, and are highest in the sky during the spring. Look south on a moonless night, and they appear as two large hazy patches, like detached pieces of the Milky Way. Binoculars will show the Tarantula Nebula and the brightest clusters.

SMC   LMC

ALAXIES

LOCAL GROUP

*Elliptical
NGC 205*

GALAXIES IN THE UNIVERSE are in clusters, and our Milky Way is in a cluster known as the Local Group. This consists of about 30 galaxies spread over about 5 million light-years. The Local Group is dominated by three elliptical galaxies, these being the Milky Way, Andromeda (M31), and Triangulum (M33).

ELLIPTICAL GALAXIES
About half the Local Group galaxies are ellipticals, including NGC 205—one of Andromeda's satellites. Ellipticals are uniform balls of old red stars, with no gas to fuel further starbirth.

M32   *NGC 205*

ANDROMEDA GALAXY
At 2.5 million light-years away, this galaxy is the most distant object visible to the naked eye. It is the largest in the Local Group and, with 400 billion stars, is one of the biggest spirals known. Our galaxy would look much like it from afar.

GALACTIC NEIGHBORHOOD
The Local Group's galaxies cluster around the massive Andromeda and Milky Way. Their strong gravities allow them to gather smaller satellite galaxies around them. Other, more distant galaxies are also held into the group by gravity. Most of the members of the Local Group are dwarf elliptical and dwarf irregular galaxies.

IC 1613
WLM

Dwarf galaxies are so faint they would be undetectable in a more distant galaxy cluster

Gas-rich spiral arms

NGC 604

TRIANGULUM GALAXY
Triangulum is a spiral, half the size of the Milky Way, and with one-tenth the stars of Andromeda. It is the third-largest member of the Local Group, with many huge, bright nebulas. One of them, NGC 604, is among the biggest regions of starbirth known.

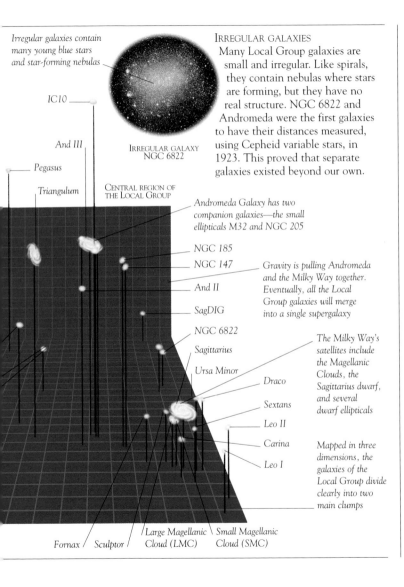

Irregular galaxies contain many young blue stars and star-forming nebulas

IC10

And III

Pegasus

Triangulum

IRREGULAR GALAXY NGC 6822

CENTRAL REGION OF THE LOCAL GROUP

IRREGULAR GALAXIES

Many Local Group galaxies are small and irregular. Like spirals, they contain nebulas where stars are forming, but they have no real structure. NGC 6822 and Andromeda were the first galaxies to have their distances measured, using Cepheid variable stars, in 1923. This proved that separate galaxies existed beyond our own.

Andromeda Galaxy has two companion galaxies—the small ellipticals M32 and NGC 205

NGC 185

NGC 147

And II

SagDIG

NGC 6822

Sagittarius

Ursa Minor

Gravity is pulling Andromeda and the Milky Way together. Eventually, all the Local Group galaxies will merge into a single supergalaxy

The Milky Way's satellites include the Magellanic Clouds, the Sagittarius dwarf, and several dwarf ellipticals

Draco

Sextans

Leo II

Carina

Leo I

Mapped in three dimensions, the galaxies of the Local Group divide clearly into two main clumps

Fornax / Sculptor / Large Magellanic Cloud (LMC) \ Small Magellanic Cloud (SMC)

CLUSTERS AND SUPERCLUSTERS

GALAXIES GATHER TOGETHER in pairs, or in clusters containing thousands of galaxies. Clusters grow by merging, and irregularly shaped clusters may have merged more recently than regularly shaped ones. Clusters are grouped into superclusters— the largest structures in space.

NGC 4473
Type E4

VIRGO CLUSTER

The Milky Way is a member of a cluster of about 30 mostly small and faint galaxies known as the Local Group. The nearest large cluster is the Virgo Cluster, which lies 50 million light-years away. It is an irregular cluster of more than 2,000 galaxies that has been known for two centuries. Though it is dominated by three giant elliptical galaxies, most of its brighter members are spirals.

NGC 4461
Type Sa

Arp 120
Type Sa

Virgo Cluster is dominated by spiral galaxies—some other clusters contain mainly ellipticals

NGC 4425
Type Sb

CLUSTER EVOLUTION

Clusters form when smaller groups of galaxies merge. This X-ray picture of gas in Abell 2256 shows a bright spot to the right of the center, caused as another group of galaxies is absorbed into the cluster. In clusters that are no longer swallowing groups, the gas is more evenly spread throughout the cluster.

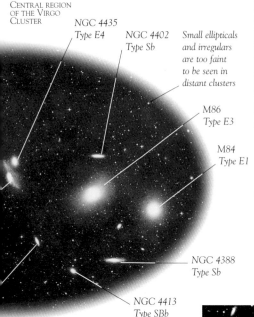

CENTRAL REGION OF THE VIRGO CLUSTER

NGC 4435
Type E4

NGC 4402
Type Sb

Small ellipticals and irregulars are too faint to be seen in distant clusters

M86
Type E3

M84
Type E1

NGC 4388
Type Sb

NGC 4413
Type SBb

GIANT ELLIPTICAL GALAXIES
Many clusters have a huge galaxy, perhaps 500,000 light-years across, at their center. These giant galaxies grow by swallowing other galaxies in the cluster. Often, they are strong sources of radio waves and X-rays. They have a halo of faint stars and globular clusters around them, and often have more than one central nucleus.

LOCAL SUPERCLUSTER
A supercluster may contain dozens of clusters and be over 100 million light-years across. Our Local Group is part of the Local Supercluster, centered on the Virgo Cluster. The Local Group is falling toward the center of the Supercluster at 155 mps (250 km/s).

Virgo Cluster   Leo Cluster   Canes Venatici Cluster   Local Group

Crater Cluster

NGC 4889
Type E4

NGC 4874
Type E0

COMA CLUSTER
The nearest dense, regular cluster to the Milky Way—the Coma Cluster—lies about 300 million light-years away. It contains over 3,000 galaxies, mostly elliptical and lenticular. It has two clumps, each centered on a giant elliptical galaxy.

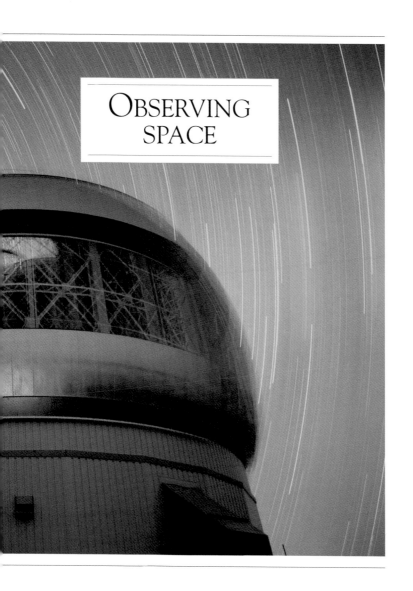

OBSERVING
SPACE

ABOVE OUR HEADS

AS OUR PLANET SPINS on its axis, it is hurtling around the Sun at 66,700 mph (107,000 km/h), providing ever-changing views of the universe. By day, the sky is dominated by the Sun. At night, the blackness of space is studded with countless stars and galaxies that are an unchanging backdrop.

CIRCULAR STAR TRAILS
Earth's daily rotation causes the stars to appear to circle around the sky. This effect can be captured by a long-exposure photograph.

Stars appear as patterns against the sphere

CELESTIAL SPHERE
From Earth, the stars appear to be set against a giant celestial sphere. As Earth travels on its yearly orbit around the Sun, different sections of the sphere are exposed to our view. At any particular time, about half the sphere is hidden by the Sun's glare. The motion of other objects, such as the planets, can also be tracked across the sphere.

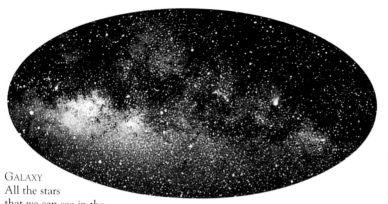

GALAXY

All the stars that we can see in the sky, including the Sun, are in the Milky Way Galaxy. This panoramic view of the Milky Way (looking toward the center of the Galaxy), was photographed from Christchurch, New Zealand.

GOOD VIEWING CONDITIONS

Some nights are good for looking at stars, while others are better for planets. Brilliantly clear evenings often have turbulent air. This spoils views of the Moon and planets, but is good for finding faint nebulas. Windless conditions are more suited for studying the Moon and planets, despite the mist that may form. It is important to get one's bearings before observing. The position of the Sun and Moon can be noted in relation to nearby objects, such as trees, that can be identified at night.

STARGAZING

ASTRONOMY CAN BE FUN by day and by night. Most celestial objects can only be seen at night, but others, like the Sun, are bright enough to be seen even when the sky is not dark. Plan carefully what to observe ahead of time—it is frustrating to miss seeing a particular favorite object while diverted by other activities in the sky. Learn how the stars and planets move.

Put red cellophane on a flashlight or use a red bicycle light

RED-COVERED FLASHLIGHT

ESSENTIAL EQUIPMENT

Keep a record of what you see. Write down the time, date, location, weather, and instruments used. To look at star maps or to take notes, use a flashlight covered with red cellophane. The reddish light will not affect night vision.

Organize your notes into categories of objects to be recorded

A notebook with plain sheets is better for drawing

CHECKLIST
- Warm clothing, including waterproof shoes
- Notebook and pen or pencil
- Accurate watch
- Red-covered light
- Binoculars
- Something to sit on
- Books and star maps
- A small table (useful to put everything on)

Posterboard mask stops Sun from shining directly onto the screen

Cut a hole in the center of the mask the same size as one of the binocular lenses. Tape the mask to the binoculars so that one lens lets light through

Prop up a second piece of posterboard to act as a screen

DAYTIME ASTRONOMY

To observe the Sun for sunspots, or during an eclipse, project its image onto posterboard, using binoculars or a telescope of less than 4 in (100 mm) and a magnification of less than 30. Aim the instrument at the Sun, turning, tilting, and focusing it until a sharp-edged disk of light appears on the screen.

STARGAZING TIPS

At night, it can take up to 30 minutes for the eyes to become properly accustomed to the dark and to get full night vision. Some types of light are particularly bad for night vision, such as fluorescent lights, and TV and computer screens, so try to avoid them before going outside to observe.

• Once outside, use only red light and try to persuade other family members not to switch on any distracting house lights.

• If outside lights are a problem, rig up a temporary light shield, such as a blanket draped over a stepladder.

FINDING OBJECTS

The brighter stars and planets can be seen in daylight with binoculars, but finding them can be difficult. The planets can always be found close to the ecliptic—the Sun's path through the sky. If a bright star is not on a star map, it is probably a planet.

Over the months, the position of Jupiter in the sky changes

EAST Orion Orion Orion WEST
at 9 p.m. at midnight at 3 a.m.

LIGHT POLLUTION

City lights cause light pollution that often drowns out the fainter stars. Town dwellers should choose a spot far from lights, and make sure that no lights shine into their eyes. If the Moon is full, even country dwellers will find it difficult to see faint objects.

All the stars and planets rise and set in the night sky

WEST Jupiter Jupiter Jupiter EAST
at 3 a.m. at midnight at 9 p.m.

ORION IN NORTHERN SKIES

Earth's rotation makes stars and planets appear to move across the sky at night. The constellation Orion is visible from November to March. It rises in the east where it appears tilted, and sets in the west. It is highest when due south.

ORION IN SOUTHERN SKIES

In the Southern Hemisphere, Orion is also visible from November to March. It reaches its highest point when due north. It seems to move right to left—the opposite of the motion seen in the Northern Hemisphere.

211

SPECIAL EFFECTS

FROM EARTH, it is possible to see several "special effects" in the sky. Some of these effects are due to some peculiarities of Earth's magnetic field and atmosphere. Other effects depend on the position of the objects in the solar system, mainly the Sun, the Moon, and Earth. Meteor showers are an effect produced by space dust burning up in the atmosphere.

AURORA BOREALIS
Charged particles from the Sun, carried by the solar wind, cause dramatic light shows when they enter Earth's atmosphere.

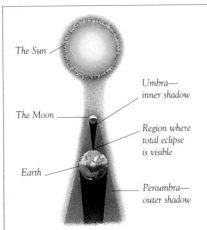

The Sun

Umbra—inner shadow

The Moon

Region where total eclipse is visible

Earth

Penumbra—outer shadow

ECLIPSE OF THE SUN
Occasionally, the Moon comes into perfect alignment between the Sun and Earth. When this happens, the Moon blocks out the Sun's light, causing what is called a solar eclipse. From some parts of Earth's surface, the disk of the Moon appears to completely cover the Sun's face, and there is a brief period of darkness. Although the Moon is a great deal smaller than the Sun, it is able to block the light totally because it is so much closer to Earth.

HALO AROUND THE MOON

On some winter nights, a halo appears around the Moon, but this has nothing to do with the Moon itself. Sunlight, reflected toward Earth by the Moon, is refracted (bent) by ice crystals high in Earth's atmosphere. This refraction of light creates a circular halo.

METEOR RADIANT

Dust particles from space are seen as meteors when they burn up in the atmosphere. In a meteor shower, which is caused by dust from a comet, all the meteors appear to come from a single point in the sky. This point is known as the radiant of the meteor shower.

OBSERVING SPACE

213

OPTICAL TELESCOPES

THE OPTICAL TELESCOPE is one of the main tools of astronomy. Today, little time is spent looking through a telescope eyepiece—modern instruments collect and store visual information electronically. The optical telescope remains an important tool because it gathers basic information.

PALOMAR DOME
The protective dome of the Hale Telescope at the Mount Palomar Observatory, California, shields the telescope from the effects of weather.

Secondary mirror

Eyepiece

Main light-gathering mirror

Main light-gathering lens

Eyepiece lens

REFLECTOR TELESCOPES
Telescopes use lenses and mirrors to gather light and produce an image. Reflector telescopes, which make use of curved mirrors, are the most useful type for astronomy.

REFRACTOR TELESCOPES
Refractor telescopes use only lenses. They cannot be made in such large sizes as reflector telescopes, but they remain very popular with amateur astronomers.

Typical diameter
of main lens is
4–6 in (10–15 cm)

The swivel mounting
allows the object to
be tracked as
Earth rotates

Different eyepieces
give a range of
magnification

AMATEUR VIEWER
This is a basic refractor telescope
as used by thousands of amateur
astronomers around the world. The
diameter of the main lens determines
the amount of light that is admitted.
The eyepiece lens provides the
magnification. A steady mounting
is essential for good viewing.

Sunlight is gathered
and directed down
an angled shaft

STUDYING THE SUN
At Kitt Peak National Observatory,
astronomers use a special telescope to study
the Sun. Called a spectrohelioscope, the device
collects sunlight and directs it via mirrors to an
underground observation room.

Important! Never look at
the Sun directly or through
a telescope or binoculars

In the underground
chamber, sunlight is
optically split into its
spectrum so that the
astronomers can make a
detailed study of the light

The Kitt Peak telescope can produce an
image of the Sun 2.5 ft (76 cm) across

RADIO TELESCOPES

WE HAVE BEEN LISTENING in on the radio energy of the universe for more than 50 years. Radio telescopes can obtain additional information about familiar objects, as well as seek out new ones. Two major discoveries—quasars and pulsars—were made by radio astronomers.

VERY LARGE ARRAY
A radio telescope consists of a large metal dish. In order to gather more information, radio astronomers sometimes use a number of large dishes linked together. The Very Large Array (VLA) in New Mexico uses up to 27 linked dishes, each one 82 ft (25 m) across to collect radio signals from space

Radio waves

The VLA dish are arranged a Y-sha

RADIO VISION
Radio telescopes, like ordinary radio sets, can be tuned to a particular wavelength, and the intensity of the radio energy can be measured. Computers are then used to produce "radio maps" of the sky, such as this image of the bar-shaped radio source known as 1952+28.

LARGEST DISH

The world's largest radio telescope, the 1,000-ft (305-m) Arecibo dish, is built into a natural hollow in the hills of Puerto Rico. The dish is "steered" using Earth's own rotation. Arecibo has also been used to send a radio message out into space.

Simple processing of the Arecibo message produces this visual image, which contains a representation of a human being

RADIO GALAXIES

Many galaxies that are quite faint visually are very "bright" at radio wavelengths. These are often called radio galaxies, or active galaxies. This optical image of radio galaxy 3C 33 has been color-coded according to the intensity of light in the visible part of the spectrum, ranging from white (most intense) to blue (the least).

OBSERVATORIES

OPTICAL TELESCOPES are usually installed in mountaintop observatories, where they suffer least interference from Earth's atmosphere. Radio telescopes can be situated almost anywhere, and are usually located near universities. The high cost of telescopes using the latest technology means that observatories are often shared between countries.

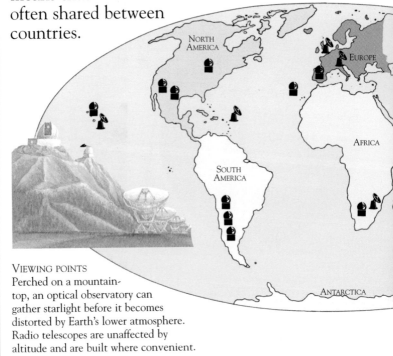

NORTH AMERICA

EUROPE

AFRICA

SOUTH AMERICA

ANTARCTICA

VIEWING POINTS
Perched on a mountain-top, an optical observatory can gather starlight before it becomes distorted by Earth's lower atmosphere. Radio telescopes are unaffected by altitude and are built where convenient.

HIGH AND DRY

The European Southern Observatory is sited
on Cerro Paranal, a 8,645-ft- (2,635-m-) high
mountain in Chile's Atacama desert.
A dry climate with cloud-free nights
and a steady atmosphere makes
this remote location ideal
for clear viewing of the
farthest galaxies, all
through the year.

OBSERVATORY FACTS

• The oldest existing
observatory was built in
South Korea in 632 CE.

• SOFIA, the flying
observatory, will begin
operation in late 2006.
It is a modified 747
jumbo jet carrying a
98-in (2.5-m) telescope.

• The 36 elements of
the Keck reflector make
a larger mirror 33 ft
(10 m) across.

• The twin Keck
Telescopes are the
world's highest, and are
situated on Mauna Kea
in Hawaii, about
13,796 ft (4,200 m)
above sea level.

AUSTRALIA

LEAST DISTURBANCE

The Keck Telescopes are situated at
the summit of Mauna Kea in Hawaii,
an ideal location for an optical
telescope. The air is clear and the sky is
dark and far removed from city lights.

MAP KEY

OPTICAL
TELESCOPE

RADIO
TELESCOPE

219

OBSERVATORY TELESCOPES

LIGHT GATHERED FROM THE SKY is still astronomers' main source of information about the universe. Apart from the Sun, most celestial bodies are far away and appear relatively dim. A telescope captures as much light as possible—the more light it collects, the more information it provides. There are two types of telescopes—reflectors, which capture light using a mirror, and refractors, which use a lens.

USES OF OPTICAL TELESCOPES
Reflectors, such as the twin Gemini telescopes, capture light with a huge curved mirror, and can reflect the image toward any part of the telescope by secondary mirrors. Collecting light with a mirror ensures there is no color fringing, and since the mirror can be supported at the back, they can now be made 32 ft (10 m) across. Refractors capture light with a lens, which focuses the image onto a photographic plate or electronic light detector.

GEMINI REFLECTOR
The twin Gemini telescopes, in Hawaii and Chile, are run by astronomers from seven countries

Main mirror is 26 ft (8 m) in diameter, and captures light from objects 500 million times fainter than can be seen by the naked eye

Axle for tilting telescope up and down

Data-recording equipment is placed behind the main mirror or on the observing platform

Observing platform   *Mirror cell*

MIRRORS
Telescope mirrors are made of low-expansion glass ceramic and are coated with a film of aluminum. It takes over a year to polish them, keeping them smooth to avoid blurring. The Gemini Telescope mirror is accurate to 1/20th of the wavelength it is reflecting.

The telescope can be pointed to any part of the sky, and can then track the chosen object as it moves across the sky. Long exposures produce the best data for analysis

Secondary mirror

Open frame lessens weight

Incoming light from objects in space is collected by the main mirror

Convex secondary mirror

Concave main mirror

Light is reflected from the main mirror toward the secondary mirror

Light is focused onto a battery of instruments waiting to record the data

Light reflected from secondary mirror passes through hole in the main mirror

With an equatorial mount, the telescope swivels around the polar axis to follow the stars as they circle the pole. The axis of the mount points to the celestial pole (north or south, depending on the hemisphere)

North-south position is fixed for viewing a particular star

Telescope swings around polar axis at a steady rate

Whole telescope mounting swings around horizontally

Polar axis points at the pole

Telescope tilts up and down

MOUNTINGS

A telescope's mounting is important because it supports its weight, and swings it around as Earth spins on its axis in order to keep objects being observed in view. The two main types of mounting are equatorial and altazimuth. The altazimuth is the mainstay of today's professional telescopes. Continuous computer control allows giant telescopes such as Gemini to follow the paths of objects as they move across the sky.

Telescope swings around horizontally

With an altazimuth mount, the telescope has to be driven up and down (in "altitude") and be swung around (in "azimuth") to follow a star

221

NEW DESIGNS

THE BIGGER THE MIRROR in a telescope, the more light it can collect and the more detail can be seen. But mirrors more than 26 ft (8 m) in diameter have limitations. One is the atmosphere—even a huge mirror will have its vision blurred by moving pockets of air. The other is size—bigger mirrors are more difficult to transport and handle. The latest ground-based telescopes use ingenious solutions to get around these limitations.

Keck mirror has a total light-collecting area 17 times greater than the Hubble Space Telescope and can see farther, though not as clearly, as Hubble

ACTIVE OPTICS

The first segmented mirror was built in 1992 on the Keck 1 Telescope. It uses active optics systems to counteract distortions caused by the weight of the mirrors or the wind. A computer adjusts each mirror segment twice every second to an accuracy that is a thousand times finer than a human hair. As a result, the 36 segments behave as a single unchanging sheet of glass.

KECK TELESCOPES

These two telescopes are situated on the 13,796-ft (4,200-m) summit of Mauna Kea in Hawaii, high above the clouds and water vapor of the lower atmosphere. Their mirrors measure 33 ft (10 m) across. A single mirror this size would bend under its own weight, so every mirror is made of 36 six-sided segments, which weigh 882 lb (400 kg) each.

VERY LARGE TELESCOPE

The European Southern Observatory's Very Large Telescope (VLT) in Chile is the biggest in the world. It consists of four 27-ft (8.2-m) telescopes linked together—each a billion times more powerful than the naked eye. The telescopes can scoop up as much light as a single mirror 54 ft (16.4 m) across.

Swiveling mirror gathers light

Small mirror reflects light into aluminum tubes

Domes protect the Keck Telescope, which weighs 328 tons (298 metric tons) and stands eight stories tall

Fixed telescope mirror focuses light

OPTICAL SYNTHESIS

The Cambridge Optical Aperture Synthesis Telescope (COAST) is made up of five small telescopes, each with a mirror. Radio astronomy techniques are used to combine light from the telescopes, giving improved resolution.

ADAPTIVE OPTICS

In adaptive optics, a powerful laser creates an artificial star high in the atmosphere, in the same direction as the star under observation. A computer works out the distortion of its light as it travels through the atmosphere. It then shapes a constantly moving flexible mirror to focus the light back into a point, sharpening the images the telescope is seeing.

UNUSUAL TELESCOPES

OUR KNOWLEDGE OF THE distant universe comes from studying radiation—light, radio waves, infrared, ultraviolet, X-rays, and gamma rays. Cosmic rays and neutrinos are more exotic messengers. Some messengers, such as dark matter and gravitational waves, have been predicted but are still undiscovered.

VIOLENT BEGINNINGS

Mighty explosions erupt in space due to stars dying as supernovas, neutron stars colliding, and superhot gas being sucked into black holes. These explosions generate radiation—light, radio waves, gamma rays, plus other more exotic particles and waves, which carry unique information about these events.

Incoming cosmic ray

Collision with atom in air

Airborne detectors

Low-energy particles include electrons and neutrinos

Detectors on ground pick up most low-energy particles

Underground detectors record more penetrating particles

COSMIC RAYS

Cosmic rays are not radiation. They are fragments of atoms, smashed in explosions, that whiz through space at almost the speed of light. The most energetic cosmic rays come from the centers of quasars.

COSMIC AIR SHOWER

Several low-energy particles are created when a cosmic ray collides with atoms in Earth's upper atmosphere. These particles rain down on Earth over a wide area.

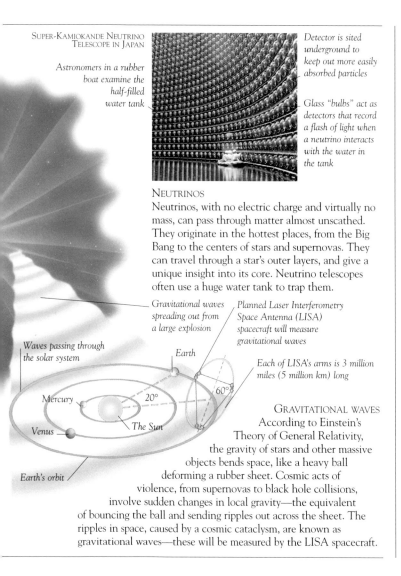

SUPER-KAMIOKANDE NEUTRINO
TELESCOPE IN JAPAN

Astronomers in a rubber
boat examine the
half-filled
water tank

*Detector is sited
underground to
keep out more easily
absorbed particles*

*Glass "bulbs" act as
detectors that record
a flash of light when
a neutrino interacts
with the water in
the tank*

NEUTRINOS

Neutrinos, with no electric charge and virtually no
mass, can pass through matter almost unscathed.
They originate in the hottest places, from the Big
Bang to the centers of stars and supernovas. They
can travel through a star's outer layers, and give a
unique insight into its core. Neutrino telescopes
often use a huge water tank to trap them.

*Gravitational waves
spreading out from
a large explosion*

*Planned Laser Interferometry
Space Antenna (LISA)
spacecraft will measure
gravitational waves*

*Waves passing through
the solar system*

Earth

*Each of LISA's arms is 3 million
miles (5 million km) long*

Mercury

Venus

The Sun

Earth's orbit

$20°$

$60°$

GRAVITATIONAL WAVES

According to Einstein's
Theory of General Relativity,
the gravity of stars and other massive
objects bends space, like a heavy ball
deforming a rubber sheet. Cosmic acts of
violence, from supernovas to black hole collisions,
involve sudden changes in local gravity—the equivalent
of bouncing the ball and sending ripples out across the sheet. The
ripples in space, caused by a cosmic cataclysm, are known as
gravitational waves—these will be measured by the LISA spacecraft.

ANALYZING LIGHT

PROFESSIONAL ASTRONOMERS rarely
look directly through telescopes.
Instead, sensitive electronic cameras
build up an image over minutes
or even hours if the object is very
faint. Spectrographs split up the
light, and computers analyze the
results. Photographic plates are
now rarely used.

LIGHT-SENSITIVE CHIPS
Pictures of galaxies are built from a grid of squares,
or pixels (picture elements). They are taken with
electronic cameras built around a light-sensitive
computer chip called a charge-coupled device (CCD).
CCDs are more sensitive than photographic plates.

Spider mount

*CCD from a big
telescope, containing
524,288 pixels on a
surface the size of a
postage stamp*

CHARGE-COUPLED DEVICE (CCD)
A CCD is a light-sensitive silicon
chip, with a surface divided into
thousands or millions of pixels.
Light falling on a pixel builds up
an electric charge, which is read
by circuits built into the chip and
fed into a computer, where it is
stored as part of a digital image.

SEEING IN COLOR
A CCD sees in black and
white. To obtain full-color images,
the same view is taken several times
with different filters and the images
are combined. All astronomers use the same
color filters—green, blue, and red—making
comparison of images taken by different
telescopes easier.

*Rotating disk
of filters*

*Light from
telescope*

*The CCD is
exposed three
times, once
through each filter*

CCD IMAGE OF SPIRAL
GALAXY NGC 5457

SPECTROSCOPY

Light is a mixture of different wavelengths, each corresponding to a different color. The shortest are violet and the longest red. In spectroscopy, astronomers use a prism or a diffraction grating (a glass plate etched with thousands of closely spaced lines) to split light into a spectrum. The spectrum is crossed by bright or dark lines at different wavelengths. These lines are analyzed to reveal the elements that are present in the object and how hot it is.

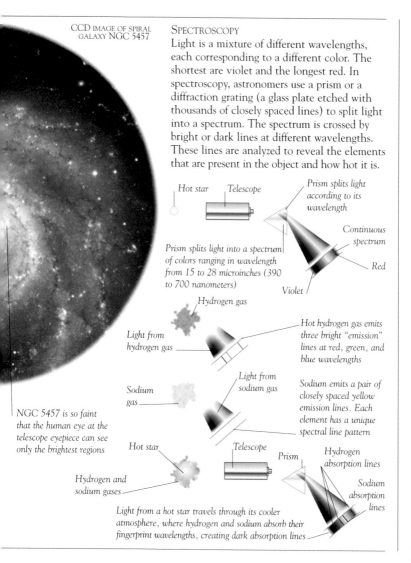

Hot star   Telescope

Prism splits light according to its wavelength

Continuous spectrum

Red

Prism splits light into a spectrum of colors ranging in wavelength from 15 to 28 microinches (390 to 700 nanometers)

Violet

Hydrogen gas

Light from hydrogen gas

Hot hydrogen gas emits three bright "emission" lines at red, green, and blue wavelengths

Light from sodium gas

Sodium gas

Sodium emits a pair of closely spaced yellow emission lines. Each element has a unique spectral line pattern

NGC 5457 is so faint that the human eye at the telescope eyepiece can see only the brightest regions

Hot star   Telescope   Prism

Hydrogen absorption lines

Sodium absorption lines

Hydrogen and sodium gases

Light from a hot star travels through its cooler atmosphere, where hydrogen and sodium absorb their fingerprint wavelengths, creating dark absorption lines

227

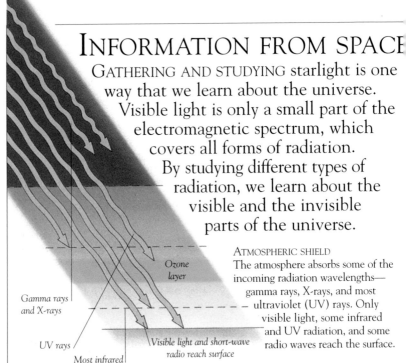

INFORMATION FROM SPACE

GATHERING AND STUDYING starlight is one
way that we learn about the universe.
Visible light is only a small part of the
electromagnetic spectrum, which
covers all forms of radiation.
By studying different types of
radiation, we learn about the
visible and the invisible
parts of the universe.

ATMOSPHERIC SHIELD
The atmosphere absorbs some of the
incoming radiation wavelengths—
gamma rays, X-rays, and most
ultraviolet (UV) rays. Only
visible light, some infrared
and UV radiation, and some
radio waves reach the surface.

Ozone layer

Gamma rays and X-rays

UV rays

Most infrared stopped here

Visible light and short-wave radio reach surface

INFORMATION SPECTRUM
Electromagnetic radiation travels
through space as waves of varying
length (the distance between
wave crests). Gamma rays have
the shortest wavelength, then
X-rays, and so on through the
spectrum to the longest radio
waves. Visible light, which is all
that we can see naturally, occupies
a very narrow portion (less than
0.00001 percent) of the spectrum.

10^{-13} M
0.0000000000001 METERS

X-RAYS

GAMMA RAYS

CRAB NEBULA IN INFRARED LIGHT

The Crab Nebula—the remnant of a supernova explosion seen in 1054 CE—emits a wide range of radiation wavelengths. When viewed in infrared light, the nebula looks like a huge cloud. The red areas represent the cooler parts of the nebula.

CRAB NEBULA IN VISIBLE LIGHT

In visible light, vast filaments of hot gas can be seen spreading out into space after the explosion. The blue glow comes from fast-moving particles accelerated by the strong magnetic field of the inner nebula.

CRAB NEBULA UNDER X-RAY

An X-ray image reveals the source of the magnetism—a rapidly spinning pulsar at the heart of the nebula. The pulsar is surrounded by high-energy particles that spiral around the pulsar's magnetic field lines.

10^{-7} M
0.0000001 METERS

10^{5} M
100,000 METERS

VISIBLE LIGHT

MICROWAVES

ULTRAVIOLET LIGHT

INFRARED LIGHT

RADIO WAVES

IMAGES OF SPACE

MUCH OF THE information that astronomers obtain through their instruments is presented as visual images. Conventional and electronic cameras are used to record these images. The information is usually stored on computers that can process images to improve the picture and bring out details.

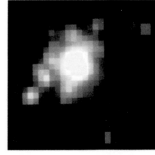

PIXELATED VIEW
Electronic cameras make images with a grid of tiny square picture-elements (pixels). This view of a dim and distant star cluster was obtained with a ground-based telescope. The individual pixels are clearly visible, although it takes a trained eye to identify the image as a star cluster.

MARTIAN CHEMICAL PHOTOMAP
This image of the Martian surface was produced from data collected by a device called a neutron spectrometer aboard the Mars Odyssey probe. It is color-coded to show concentrations of hydrogen in the soil. Deep blue areas contain the most hydrogen, and red areas the least. In the deep blue regions near the poles, the hydrogen is mostly combined with oxygen in the form of water ice.

Soil near the poles may be up to 50 percent water ice

ADDING FALSE COLOR

Astronomers have several techniques for analyzing the information contained in images. One of the most important is adding false color to the image. Saturn has a fairly muted appearance in ordinary photographs. This image has been color-coded to emphasize the banding of the planet's upper atmosphere.

COLORING THE SUN

This false-color ultraviolet image from the TRACE spacecraft shows plasma exploding off the Sun's surface and traveling through the solar atmosphere along loops of the Sun's magnetic field. The colors represent different temperatures. The red regions are the hottest, at 27 million °F (15 million °C).

COMBINING SERIES OF IMAGES

Images of space are often obtained through a series of colored filters. The object is photographed through each filter in turn, and the resulting images are then combined to give a much fuller picture than with any single ordinary photograph.

This series was taken with the Hubble Space Telescope, and shows Pluto and its moon, Charon.

SUPERNOVA REMNANT
Infrared, visible, and X-ray radiation combine to highlight the supernova remnant Cassiopeia A.

INFRARED ASTRONOMY

IF OUR EYES WERE SENSITIVE to infrared radiation, the night sky would be filled with glowing cosmic clouds and scattered galaxies ablaze with newborn stars. Everything in the universe cooler than about 5,400°F (3,000°C) emits most of its energy in the infrared, which can travel through interstellar dust.

By using infrared telescopes, we can reveal information invisible to the optical telescope.

INFRARED WAVELENGTHS
As its name suggests, infrared lies just beyond the red end of the visible spectrum. It covers a much wider part of the electromagnetic spectrum than visible light: from 28 µin (700 nm) to 0.04 in (1 mm), where radio waves begin. Astronomers divide infrared into four bands: near, mid-, and far infrared, and submillimeter waves. Observing infrared radiation is always a struggle within Earth's atmosphere, where carbon dioxide and water vapor absorb infrared. Some of the shorter and longer wavelengths, however, do reach mountaintops.

Young stars, often emitting jets of hot gas, are best observed at near infrared wavelengths

Distant starburst galaxies emit much more heat (infrared) radiation than light

"The higher the location, the better" is the rule for infrared telescopes. Satellites are best, but the most expensive

Far infrared can only be observed from planes or satellites

Near and mid-infrared wavelengths reach mountain tops

SOFIA

NEAR INFRARED	MID-INFRARED
0.000039 in (0.001 mm)	0.00039 in (0.01 mm)

µin = microinch, nm = nanometer

ELECTROMAGNETIC SPECTRUM LOCATER

Visible light

Infrared wavelengths

Radio waves

EARTH-BASED TELESCOPES

Infrared telescopes resemble optical telescopes. In fact, the latest big reflectors are designed to observe both infrared and visible light. An infrared camera, however, must have a cooling system so that any heat it gives off does not overwhelm the faint infrared from space.

Liquid helium in an infrared camera cools it to –454°F (–270°C)

The constellation of Orion is dominated at optical wavelengths by seven stars making the Hunter's outline

Immense, cool dust clouds dominate the same region in this image captured by the Infrared Astronomical Satellite (IRAS)

Cool dust clouds shine in the far infrared

Cool glow from the Big Bang emits submillimeter wavelengths

Infrared Astronomical Satellite (IRAS)

Cosmic Background Explorer (COBE)

Infrared Space Observatory (ISO)

62 miles (100 km)

Some submillimeter waves reach mountaintops

Height at which all radiation is absorbed

6.2 miles (10 km)

Sea level

FAR INFRARED 0.0039 in (0.1 mm)	SUBMILLIMETER 0.039 in (1 mm)	RADIO

Submillimeter telescopes are like small, high-precision radio telescopes

INTERSTELLAR CLOUDS IN ORION

Infrared telescopes are sensitive to hot and cool material, including vast clouds of dust and gas stretching hundreds of light-years across the constellation of Orion. Generally, they have temperatures of about –328°F (–200°C)—red in the IRAS image. In the denser regions, the heat from newborn stars warms the dust and gas to around 1,830°F (1,000°C)—these are the white areas in the IRAS image. To optical telescopes, they are visible only as dark silhouettes.

ULTRAVIOLET ASTRONOMY

A STAR HOTTER than 18,000°F (10,000°C) shines brightest at ultraviolet wavelengths, and can be tracked with ultraviolet radiation. Ultraviolet can also reveal what is in the hot gas clouds between the stars. Earth's ozone layer protects us from the Sun's ultraviolet radiation, and this makes observation difficult. Hydrogen in space absorbs extreme ultraviolet wavelengths and acts as a fog, hiding most of the distant universe.

Hot gas streams around massive black holes produce extreme ultraviolet radiation

Rosat satellite carried an extreme ultraviolet telescope to seek out very hot stars and gas

The Sun's chromosphere is hotter than the surface and shines at ultraviolet wavelengths

Solar and Heliospheric Observatory (SOHO) observes fine details in the Sun's atmosphere

Height where all ultraviolet is absorbed

Ozone layer

EXTREME ULTRAVIOLET		ULTRAVIOLE
1.9 μin (50 nm)	3.9 μin (100 nm)	5.9 μin (150

μin = microinch, nm = nanometer

Visible light

X-rays — Ultraviolet wavelengths

ELECTROMAGNETIC SPECTRUM LOCATER

ULTRAVIOLET WAVELENGTHS
Ultraviolet radiation has shorter wavelengths than visible light and stretches from the violet end of the visible spectrum (15 μin or 390 nm) down to the start of the X-ray region (0.4 μin or 10 nm). Wavelengths between 0.4 and 3.6 μin (10 and 91 nm) are called extreme ultraviolet. Oxygen and nitrogen atoms at high altitudes block the shorter ultraviolet wavelengths, and the ozone layer blocks the remainder, so telescopes must fly above Earth's atmosphere.

GLOWING GASES IN SOLAR ATMOSPHERE
A color-coded extreme ultraviolet image of the Sun reveals a thin, patchy shell of glowing gas around a black globe. The Sun's visible surface appears dark, while the chromosphere shines brightly. The temperature and density of gas varies with changes in the Sun's magnetic field.

Red is the gas producing the faintest radiation in ultraviolet, and white is the brightest

The hottest stars shine most brilliantly in the ultraviolet

Distant galaxies glitter with hot, young, ultraviolet-bright stars

The Astro ultraviolet observatory is carried in the Space Shuttle

Rocket-borne telescopes provided the first brief ultraviolet views

	124 miles (200 km)
	62 miles (100 km)
	Sea level

ULTRAVIOLET		
n (200 nm)	9.8 μin (250 nm)	11.8 μin (300 nm)

Hot gas in central core

Individual massive stars

HOT STARS IN GALAXIES
Spiral galaxies appear most spectacular in the ultraviolet, which reveals the hottest stars. This is a view of galaxy M81, which lies 12 million light-years away in Ursa Major. The bright spots are clusters of massive stars that will quickly burn out.

STARBURST GALAXY
An ultraviolet image of M94 shows a different structure than an optical image. Instead of the central bulge of cool old stars, there is a giant ring of hot young stars formed within the past 10 million years.

ULTRAVIOLET IMAGE OF M94

Hot young stars

OPTICAL IMAGE OF M94

Old cool stars

237

X-RAY ASTRONOMY

AT X-RAY WAVELENGTHS, the sky is filled with large glowing clouds of gas and strange fluctuating X-ray stars. X-rays are very-short-wavelength, high-energy radiation, given out by objects that are hotter than 1.8 million °F (1 million °C). Supernova remnants and the gas around pulsars and black holes, where the temperatures may reach 180 million °F (100 million °C) or more, are powerful X-ray sources.

X-RAY SPECTRUM

X-rays are high-energy electromagnetic radiation with wavelengths between 3.9 x 10⁻³ and 3.9 x 10⁻¹ microinches (0.01 and 10 nanometers), much shorter than visible light. The shortest X-rays carry the most energy. X-rays may be extremely penetrating on Earth—doctors use them to show the body's interior—but the upper atmosphere absorbs all the X-rays from space. So X-ray detectors must be carried beyond the atmosphere on rockets or satellites.

Clusters of galaxies lie in a pool of gas at temperatures of up to 180 million °F (100 million °C)

Distant quasar emits X-rays from its tiny energetic core

Electrons in quasar jets emit weaker X-rays

X-rays are emitted by hot gas pulled into a black hole from a nearby star

Supernova remnant

Gas in the Sun's corona is just hot enough to emit X-rays

Mir

Rosat

Einstein Observatory

Rocket-borne Geiger counters

X-rays are absorbed 62 miles (100 km) above Earth's surface

124 miles (200 km)

62 miles (100 km)

Sea level

0.0004 μin (0.01 nm) 0.004 μin (0.1 nm) 0.04 μin (1 nm) 0.4 μin (10 nm)

μin = microinch, nm = nanometer

Gamma rays   Ultraviolet

X-rays   Visible light

ELECTROMAGNETIC SPECTRUM LOCATER

X-RAY TELESCOPES

X-rays are very difficult to focus because they are absorbed by traditional curved mirrors. They can be reflected only if they hit a metal surface at a very shallow angle, grazing it like a bullet ricocheting off a wall. X-ray telescopes use highly polished tapering metal cylinders, called grazing incidence mirrors, to focus radiation.

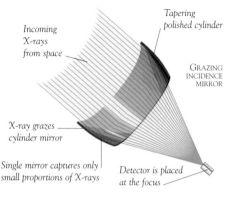

Incoming X-rays from space

Tapering polished cylinder

GRAZING INCIDENCE MIRROR

X-ray grazes cylinder mirror

Single mirror captures only small proportions of X-rays

Detector is placed at the focus

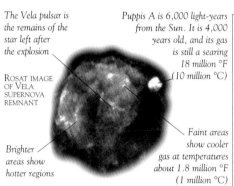

The Vela pulsar is the remains of the star left after the explosion

ROSAT IMAGE OF VELA SUPERNOVA REMNANT

Brighter areas show hotter regions

Puppis A is 6,000 light-years from the Sun. It is 4,000 years old, and its gas is still a searing 18 million °F (10 million °C)

Faint areas show cooler gas at temperatures about 1.8 million °F (1 million °C)

SUPERNOVA REMNANTS

About 11,000 years ago a supernova exploded in the constellation Vela, 1,500 light-years from Earth. It may have been very bright once, but all that remains is a hot bubble of gas, 140 light-years across. Optical telescopes can barely detect it, but Rosat's sensitive X-ray telescope revealed the gas, which is still 14 million °F (8 million °C) in places. It also detected a smaller, more distant supernova remnant, Puppis A.

ROSAT VIEWS THE MOON

In this view, the right side of the Moon is illuminated by the Sun's X-rays. The dark side is silhouetted against the scattered dots of an X-ray background that comes from distant galaxies. Each dot is an individual X-ray hit. (The bright dots on the dark side are electronic noise in the X-ray detector.)

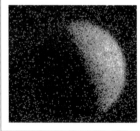

GAMMA-RAY ASTRONOMY

GAMMA RAYS REVEAL the most violent corners of the universe, including pulsars, quasars, and black holes. They are radiation with the shortest wavelengths and highest energies of all. Gamma rays are created by radioactive atoms in space, by particles colliding at almost the speed of light, and by matter and antimatter annihilating each other.

CERENKOV DETECTOR
Gamma rays never reach Earth, but a Cerenkov detector can detect them. It looks for flashes of light in Earth's atmosphere, caused by gamma rays colliding with gas atoms.

GAMMA-RAY SPECTRUM
Even the longest gamma rays, bordering on X-rays, have wavelengths that are smaller than an atom. There is no lower limit to gamma-ray wavelengths—the shortest ever detected is a million billion times shorter than ordinary light. Such short-wavelength gamma rays are uncommon, because objects with the energy to create them are extremely rare in the universe. All gamma rays from space are absorbed by Earth's atmosphere.

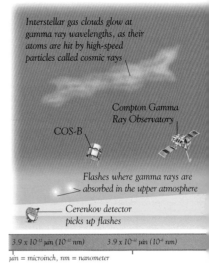

Interstellar gas clouds glow at gamma ray wavelengths, as their atoms are hit by high-speed particles called cosmic rays

Compton Gamma Ray Observatory

COS-B

Flashes where gamma rays are absorbed in the upper atmosphere

Cerenkov detector picks up flashes

3.9×10^{-12} μin (10^{-10} nm) 3.9×10^{-6} μin (10^{-4} nm)

μin = microinch, nm = nanometer

Gamma rays   X-rays

Visible light

ELECTROMAGNETIC SPECTRUM LOCATER

Clouds of gas in the Milky Way, bombarded by high-speed electrons

Cygnus X-1—gas swirling around a black hole

The whole-sky map from the Compton satellite. Red shows the strongest gamma-ray sources, while yellow and green show less intense regions

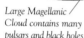

Large Magellanic Cloud contains many pulsars and black holes

Crab Pulsar flashes 30 times a second

Quasar 3C 279—a distant galaxy with a massive central black hole

Center of the Milky Way Galaxy

Vela Pulsar flashes 13 times a second

SKY IN GAMMA RAYS

The sky looks very different when viewed at gamma-ray wavelengths. We see none of the usual stars and constellations. Instead, huge glowing clouds of gas stretch across the view. Among them are bright points, flashing on and off. Some are pulsars, with a regular period to their flashing. Others, called gamma-ray bursters, flare brilliantly for just a few seconds, outshining everything else in the gamma-ray sky.

High-speed electrons from a spinning neutron star generate pulses of gamma rays

A gamma-ray burster may be a neutron star collision or a hypernova—a spinning black hole within an exploding star

Gamma rays can smash through the matter in space, traveling for billions of light-years

Altitude at which gamma rays are absorbed by the atmosphere

Balloon gamma-ray telescope

62 miles (100 km)

Sea level

10^{-8} μin (10^{-6} nm)   3.9 x 10^{-6} μin (10^{-4} nm)   3.9 x 10^{-4} μin (10^{-2} nm)

CODED MASK GAMMA-RAY DETECTOR

Gamma rays from space

Cross-shaped mask absorbs gamma rays

Shadow cast by mask

No sparks in shadow

Gamma rays trigger sparks

CODED MASKS

When exposed to a gamma-ray source, a coded mask detector casts a shadow where no gamma rays are detected. The position of this shadow can pinpoint the position of the gamma-ray source.

241

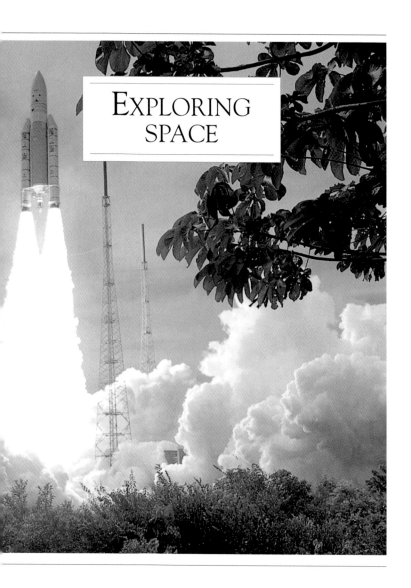

EXPLORING
SPACE

TELESCOPES IN SPACE

BY PLACING THEIR TELESCOPES in orbit above Earth's atmosphere, astronomers get a much better view. They can see farther and can collect information from wavelengths that are absorbed by the atmosphere. Information and images gathered in orbit are transmitted back to Earth for study and analysis.

ORBITING TELESCOPE
Two astronauts from the Space Shuttle *Columbia* make repairs to the Hubble Space Telescope in 2002.

Protective hinged cover

Antenna transmits information to Earth

Cameras and instruments located inside

HUBBLE SPACE TELESCOPE IN ORBIT

Large solar panels power the equipment aboard the HST

EYE ABOVE THE EARTH
The orbiting Hubble Space Telescope (HST) uses a large mirror to gather light. The light is then directed by a secondary mirror into one of the onboard scientific instrument packages or high-resolution cameras.

CHANDRA X-RAY TELESCOPE

Sunshield door

High-resolution
mirror assembly

HOT-SPOT
DETECTOR
X-rays are
given out by
objects hotter than a
million degrees. Orbiting
X-ray telescopes, such as
Chandra (above), enable
scientists to examine the
universe's hot spots. Special
mirrors, called grazing
incidence mirrors, have
to be used, because X-rays
are not reflected by
conventional mirrors.

Star
trackers

Thrusters

Solar panels

DIRECTION FINDER
Gamma rays cannot be
focused to form images,
but they can be used to
plot the direction and
intensity of gamma-ray
sources. The gamma-ray
observatory Integral,
launched in 2002, will
study features such as
black holes, pulsars,
and quasars.

Gamma-ray
spectrometer

INTEGRAL
GAMMA-RAY
OBSERVATORY

HERSCHEL SPACE
OBSERVATORY

INFRARED
INITIATIVE
The Herschel
Space Observatory,
an orbiting infrared
telescope to be launched
in 2007, will study the
universe at infrared
wavelengths not covered
before. One of its tasks
will be to investigate how
stars and galaxies form.

ROCKETS

SATELLITES, SPACE PROBES, and
astronauts are lifted into space
by rockets. There are two main
types: the conventional tall, thin
rocket made from several stages
stacked on top of each other,
and the newer Space Shuttle
design, which lifts off with the
aid of massive booster rockets.
When it returns from space, the
Shuttle lands like an aircraft.

LIFTOFF
A Soyuz-Fregat rocket blasts
off from its launch pad. Its
engines burn thousands of
gallons of fuel per second.

*Nozzle shapes the
stream of hot
exhaust gases*

*Liquid fuel and oxygen
are combined in the
combustion chamber*

FUEL TANK

OXYGEN TANK

ROCKET ENGINE

*Pumps control the flow
of fuel and oxygen to the
combustion chamber*

*Fuel and oxygen stored in
reinforced pressurized tanks*

ROCKET POWER
A rocket is propelled upward by hot exhaust
gases streaming from nozzles at the tail. These
gases are the result of burning a mixture of liquid
oxygen and fuel (such as liquid hydrogen) inside
a combustion chamber. Carrying its own oxygen
supply enables a rocket engine to function in
the airless vacuum of space.

ESCAPE VELOCITY

A rocket, or any other object, is held on Earth's surface by the force of gravity. To escape the effects of Earth's gravity and enter space, a rocket needs to achieve a speed of 25,000 mph (40,000 km/h)—this is the "escape velocity" of Earth. On the Moon, where the force of gravity is only one-sixth as powerful as on Earth, the escape velocity is lower—only about 5,300 mph (8,600 km/h).

Payload—satellite or space probe

Third stage rocket engines

ARIANE: A TYPICAL THREE-STAGE LAUNCH VEHICLE

Second stage rocket engines

First stage rocket engines

External booster rockets assist first stage engines at liftoff

REUSABLE SPACECRAFT

A streaming exhaust trail marks the beginning of another Space Shuttle mission. Unlike conventional rockets, which can be used only once, the Shuttle is reusable. The massive booster rockets are jettisoned two minutes after launch and recovered. The Shuttle's own engines carry it on into orbit, and small thruster rockets steer it as it travels around Earth.

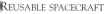

ROCKET FUELS

COMPARED TO WHEN the space age began, rockets are now far more reliable as rocket scientists have learned the best way to make, combine, and supply the propellant, or fuel. The fuels carried by rockets need oxidants to burn and release energy. Fuel and oxidants can be solid or liquid.

SPACE SHUTTLE FUEL
At liftoff, nearly 90 percent of the Space Shuttle's weight is propellant, both solid and liquid. Liquid hydrogen and liquid oxygen are carried, separately, in the external tank. About 1,036 lb (470 kg) of fuel is delivered to each of the three main engines every second. The 91-ton (83-metric-ton) boosters carry 555 tons (504 metric tons) of fuel each.

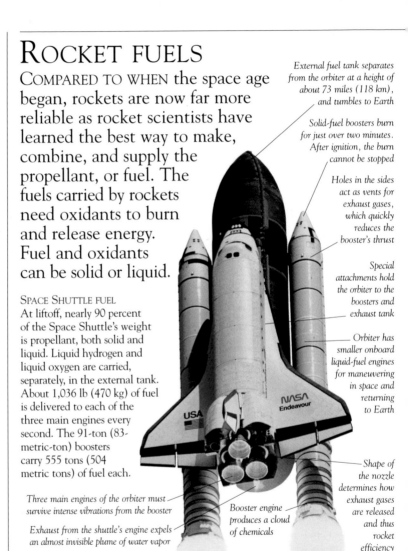

External fuel tank separates from the orbiter at a height of about 73 miles (118 km), and tumbles to Earth

Solid-fuel boosters burn for just over two minutes. After ignition, the burn cannot be stopped

Holes in the sides act as vents for exhaust gases, which quickly reduces the booster's thrust

Special attachments hold the orbiter to the boosters and exhaust tank

Orbiter has smaller onboard liquid-fuel engines for maneuvering in space and returning to Earth

Shape of the nozzle determines how exhaust gases are released and thus rocket efficiency

Three main engines of the orbiter must survive intense vibrations from the booster

Booster engine produces a cloud of chemicals

Exhaust from the shuttle's engine expels an almost invisible plume of water vapor

SOLID ROCKET FUEL

The propellant in solid-fuel rockets is shaped into pellets, which contain an oxidant, a fuel, and substances to prevent them decomposing in storage. The way the propellant is packed into the casing determines whether the surface will burn at a constant rate (neutral burn), providing an even thrust; whether it will increase gradually, causing thrust to increase (progressive burn); or whether it will decrease, causing thrust to decrease gradually (regressive burn).

NEUTRAL BURN   Casing   Burning surface   Propellant

Propellant   Nozzle

The propellant is packed in the casing like a firework. The burn rate and thrust remain constant

PROGRESSIVE BURN   Casing   Burning surface   Propellant

Propellant   Nozzle

The propellant is packed so that the middle is hollow. Burning occurs along the length of the hollow area, increasing, as does thrust

REGRESSIVE BURN   Casing   Burning surface   Propellant

Propellant   Nozzle

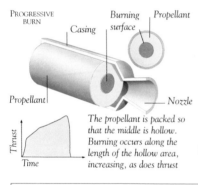

The propellant is loosely packed in a rodlike casing. Burning occurs along its length. Thrust decreases as the rod shrinks

LIQUID ROCKET FUEL

Liquid propellants produce more thrust per second than solid propellants. Liquid oxygen boils at −297°F (−183°C), cold enough to crack metal or shatter rubber, while liquid hydrogen boils at −423°F (−253°C). Though difficult to handle, these make an efficient propellant.

Liquid oxygen and liquid hydrogen mix and burn in the combustion chamber, propelling the rocket

SPACE LAUNCHERS

RELIABILITY, COST, AND TECHNICAL capability are the important factors in determining which air-launch rocket should place a spacecraft in orbit. Heavy-lift launchers send space probes on interplanetary journeys or put satellites into high geostationary orbit. Smaller air launch rockets are used to place small payloads in low Earth orbit.

Proton launches large satellites, such as the Asiasat HSG-1, which beams television and telephone signals to Asia and the Pacific

HEAVY-LIFT ROCKETS
The Russian Proton rocket and Europe's Ariane 5 can be thought of as rockets with muscle. They can place 22 tons (20 metric tons)—the equivalent of 20 cars—into low Earth orbit. For such launches, Proton has three stages. There is also a four-stage version for launching spacecraft on interplanetary journeys.

AIR-LAUNCH ROCKETS
L1011 Stargazer aircraft carry the Pegasus rocket to an altitude of 7.5 miles (12.2 km), releasing it above the open ocean. Thereafter, three rocket stages place a payload of up to 1,100 lb (500 kg) in orbit.

WORKHORSE OF ROCKETRY

The Delta family has launched satellites since 1960 and Delta II since 1989. Delta II can launch 2 tons (1.8 metric tons) into a transfer orbit for geostationary orbit. Delta II's reliability led to the Delta family being called the "workhorse" of rocketry. Delta III, the latest addition, can place 8.8 tons (8 metric tons) in low-Earth orbit, or 4.4 tons (4 metric tons) in geostationary orbit (see p 262).

Delta rockets ferry large satellites, such as the Thor III communications satellite, to orbit

Long March rockets have carried small satellites, like the Asia-Pacific Mobile Telecommunications system, to orbit

ROCKET CHALLENGERS

Spacecraft are complicated. A tiny mistake can destroy a multimillion-dollar mission. Nearly all orders for launchers go to companies (usually in the United States, Russia, Europe, or Japan) with the most experience of manufacturing space technology. Other countries launch their own rockets, but find it hard to sell them to others. China is now trying to sell its rockets overseas.

LAUNCH CENTERS

LAUNCH CENTERS ARE the gateways to space. They can be small sites, or vast, expensive complexes sprawling over many acres. Larger spaceports have many launch pads. Before the launch, engineers assemble the launch vehicle in multistory buildings. Then giant platforms lumber to the pad carrying the assembled launcher. Scattered around the site are the control room from which mission specialists oversee the final countdown, huge tanks for the propellant, weather stations to check conditions on the day of launch, and tracking stations to monitor the ascent to space.

KENNEDY SPACE CENTER
The 139,862-acre (56,600-hectare) Kennedy Space Center at Cape Canaveral is NASA's launch site for the Space Shuttle. The 2.8-mile (4.5-km) runway is checked for stray animals before a landing.

The Alcantara launch center in Brazil is the newest one in the world

Vandenberg •

• Kennedy

Equator

Kourou •

Alcanta

KOUROU SPACE CENTER
Kourou is used by
Arianespace and
the European Space
Agency to launch
satellites. It is close
to the equator and
therefore favorable
for placing satellites
into geostationary
orbit directly above
the equator.

BAIKONUR COSMODROME
Baikonur, in Kazakhstan, is the
world's largest space center and
one of the oldest. The very first
satellite, Sputnik, was launched
from Baikonur in 1957.

LAUNCH LOCATIONS
Several factors influence the choice of a launch
site. It has to be away from populated areas,
yet it must be accessible because of the
heavy equipment needed for a launch.
The United States and Europe have
sites located in coastal areas, launching
over oceans. Geography is also
important—launches to the east
are preferred because they benefit
from Earth's eastward rotation, as
are those near the equator,
where rotation is greatest.

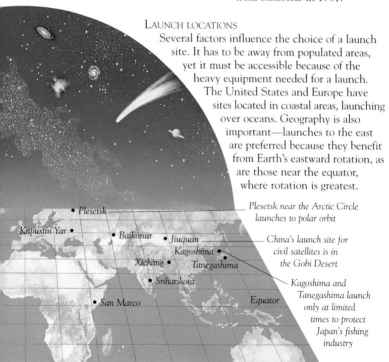

Plesetsk near the Arctic Circle
launches to polar orbit

China's launch site for
civil satellites is in
the Gobi Desert

Kagoshima and
Tanegashima launch
only at limited
times to protect
Japan's fishing
industry

• Plesetsk
Kapustin Yar •
• Baikonur
• Jiuquan
Kagoshima •
Xichang •
Tanegashima
• Sriharikota
• San Marco
Equator

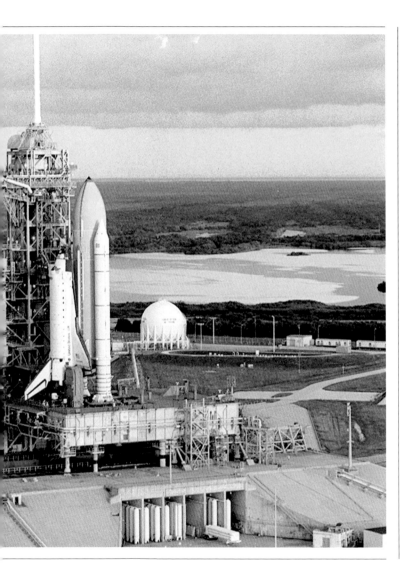

BLASTOFF
The US Space Shuttle awaits launch at Cape Canaveral, Florida

COUNTDOWN

Communications satellite being prepared for Ariane 5

THE FINAL PART of every launch campaign begins when all the separate components arrive at the launch center to be assembled into the launch vehicle. During this final countdown, engineers make the site ready for launch, and personnel are evacuated from the area in preparation for liftoff.

MISSION CONTROL

The Jupiter control room in Kourou, French Guiana, directs the Ariane 5 liftoff. Three teams monitor the status of the launcher, the payload, and the tracking stations that will follow its ascent, while weather and safety teams work elsewhere.

PAYLOAD INTEGRATION

Satellites are mounted on the launcher in the final assembly building eight days before liftoff. The satellite is linked via Ariane 5 to the Jupiter control room so that the payload can be monitored.

The leader of the tracking team monitors the launcher's path with radar

Mission controllers monitor launch support equipment

Four computers are reserved for senior personnel from the French and European Space Agencies, the satellite owner, and Arianespace

Director of operations (DDO) authorizes the final countdown

Leader of the launch team filters information about launcher status to DDO

Screen displays the trajectory of launch

Telecoms link with stations that track the launcher's ascent

Payload team ensures that the tracking stations receive signals once the satellite is in orbit

Deputy leader of the launch team acts as backup to DDO

TO THE LAUNCH PAD
A 960-ton (870-metric-ton) launch table supports the launcher during assembly. The day before liftoff, a truck tows the launcher and table along rail tracks to the launch pad. Propellant is piped into the launcher at the pad.

ON THE LAUNCH PAD
There are three trenches at the launch area through which flames from the boosters and main engine escape during liftoff. A tower supplies water to reduce noise and to cool the trenches and launch table, in order to avoid damage to the launcher and its payload.

LIFTOFF
Six hours before liftoff, the launch area is prepared. The flight program is loaded into the two onboard computers, and then initiated to check radio links between launcher and ground. Five hours before launch, the main stage tanks are filled with propellant. Six minutes before liftoff, the synchronized sequence leading to liftoff begins.

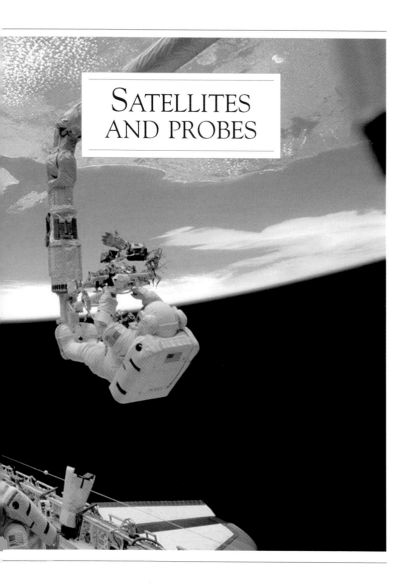

SATELLITES
AND PROBES

HUBBLE SPACE TELESCOPE

THE ULTIMATE TELESCOPE for astronomers seeking pin-sharp views of the depths of the universe, the Hubble Space Telescope was launched in 1990 after decades of planning. It is an uncrewed observatory in orbit far above the clouds and atmospheric haze that block the view of Earth-based telescopes.

HOW HUBBLE WORKS

Hubble is a reflecting telescope much like those on Earth. In space, however, it must operate without main-supply electricity, a mounting to swivel it around, or cables linking it to control computers. Instead, it has solar panels to provide power, reaction wheels for pointing, and radio antennas for communicating with Earth.

HUBBLE DATA	
Launched	April 25, 1990
Main mirror	7.9-ft (2.4-m) diameter
Secondary mirror	1.1-ft (0.34-m) diameter
Length	43 ft (13.1 m)
Diameter	14.1 ft (4.3 m)
Solar panels	39.7 x 7.9 ft (12.1 x 2.4 m)
Mass	12.7 tons (11.6 metric tons)
Height of orbit	379 miles (610 km)
Period of orbit	95 minutes
Speed	17,213 mph (27,700 km/h)
Intended lifetime	15 years +
Cost (at launch)	$1.5 billion

Reaction wheels point Hubble at targets in space

Tape recorders

Wide Field and Planetary Camera (WF/PC)

Space Telescope Imaging Spectrograph splits light into its constituent wavelengths

COSTAR replacement optics correct Hubble's defective mirror

Position occupied by COSTAR

Faint Object Camera is very sensitive, but its view is more restricted than the WF/PC

Fine guidance sensors lock on to bright stars, keeping the telescope steady and the images sharp

Near-Infrared Camera and Multi-Object Spectrometer with three infrared detectors

Main mirror, 8 ft (2.4 m) in diameter, collects and focuses light

TDRS ground station in New Mexico relays signals to and from Hubble and the Goddard Space Flight Center

Tracking and Data Relay Satellite (TDRS)—a go-between for Hubble's radio messages. From its high orbit, it keeps both Hubble and ground control in sight

Signals to and from TDRS and Earth

High-gain antenna receives commands from Earth, and returns Hubble pictures as TV signals

Sunshade protected the telescope at launch, and helps to prevent bright sunlight spoiling images

Magnetometer senses Hubble's movement through Earth's magnetic field

Handrail for astronauts

Secondary mirror, supported within the telescope tube

Light is reflected from the main to the secondary mirror, and then to the cameras and detectors behind the main mirror

Solar arrays convert sunlight into electricity

Second high-gain antenna

Computers coordinate onboard systems

ADVANTAGES OF HUBBLE
Telescopes viewing the universe from Earth must look upward through our turbulent atmosphere, which constantly shifts and distorts the light from stars and galaxies—rather like looking through the water in a busy swimming pool. That's why stars seem to twinkle. From its perch above the atmosphere, Hubble has a clear view of objects in the universe, from planets to quasars billions of light years away.

DEFECTIVE MIRROR
The first pictures received from Hubble were out of focus, though still better than any ground-based telescope. NASA realized that the mirror was 0.00008 in (0.002 mm) too shallow at the outer edge.

HUBBLE'S IMAGE OF GALAXY M100

SATELLITES AND PROBES

SATELLITES AND ORBITS

ANYTHING IN ORBIT around another object is called a satellite. The Moon is a natural satellite of Earth. Since 1957, hundreds of artificial satellites of all shapes and sizes have been launched into orbit around Earth. They occupy different types of orbit, depending on what they are designed to do. Satellites must remain stable so that their instruments always point in the right direction.

Highly elliptical orbit   Polar orbit   Geostationary orbit

Low Earth orbit

TYPES OF ORBIT
Most satellites are launched into one of four main orbits. A nearly circular low Earth orbit is about 155 miles (250 km) above Earth. Polar orbits are often 500 miles (800 km) high. A highly elliptical orbit has a far lower altitude when it is at its closest to Earth (its perigee) than at its most distant (its apogee). A geostationary orbit is 22,320 miles (36,000 km) above the equator.

TELEMETRY, TRACKING, AND COMMAND
Telemetry allows people on the ground to receive measurements from satellites in orbit. These measurements, sent as radio signals, include information that allows operators to pinpoint the satellite's position so that they can track it, and send command signals to change its orbit.

Ground antenna sends and receives signals to and from the satellites

HS 376 SPIN-STABILIZED COMMUNICATIONS SATELLITE

Antenna for telemetry
and command

Antenna feed
radiates radio
signals that
reflect off the dish

Antenna
dish does
not spin

Equipment is
designed to fit
into the satellite's
cylindrical shape

If sensors detect
a wobble in the
satellite, thrusters
correct spin and
restore stability

Outer panels slip
down in orbit to
uncover solar
panels beneath.
This increases the
power available to
the satellite

Solar cell panels

SOLAR CELLS
Solar cells produce electrical
power when light falls on them.
On satellites, the cells are
arranged into solar panels,
sometimes called arrays. They
provide a satellite with the
electrical power to do its job
and to keep both the satellite
and its payload in orbit.

Space Shuttle astronaut
retrieves the Westar
satellite to bring it back
to Earth for repair

SPIN STABILIZATION
Things that spin are naturally stable.
A spinning top remains stable if it is
spun fast enough. In the early days of
satellites, designers decided to exploit
this principle. The result is spin-
stabilized satellites. These are often
cylindrical in shape, and make about
one revolution every second. The
antenna dish must always point to Earth,
so it does not spin. Designers must take
care that the dish does not destabilize
and unbalance the satellite.

HOUSEKEEPING
DATA
Information
about a satellite's
health is called
housekeeping data.
This data alerts ground control
when something is wrong—if the
satellite is becoming unstable, for
instance. Ground-based operators
can often send a command to
solve the problem, or even plan
a rescue mission.

COMMUNICATIONS SATELLITES

TELEPHONE CALLS, TELEVISION BROADCASTS, and the Internet can all be transmitted by communications satellites. Many are in geostationary orbit (GEO), but so great is the demand for communications that this orbit has become crowded. Now, satellites are being launched into low Earth orbit (below GEO).

GEOSTATIONARY SATELLITES
Satellites in GEO above the equator appear stationary because at this altitude, they take the same time to complete one orbit as Earth takes to spin on its axis.

Three satellites, spaced evenly in GEO, can view the entire planet, except the poles

Telephone calls are now possible between aircraft and ground

EARTH STATIONS
The antennas and other equipment needed on the ground to transmit signals to and from satellites are known as the Earth station. These can be housed in large buildings and their antennas act as a gateway through which, for example, thousands of telephone calls are transmitted. Earth stations can also be small units, designed to fit on ships or planes.

Antennas transmit and receive signals, and are the key to an Earth station's operation

SATELLITE FOOTPRINT
Radio waves from a satellite fall on Earth with a pattern—the satellite footprint. Antennas within it can transmit signals to and from the satellite.

A satellite footprint might cover a whole continent or one small country

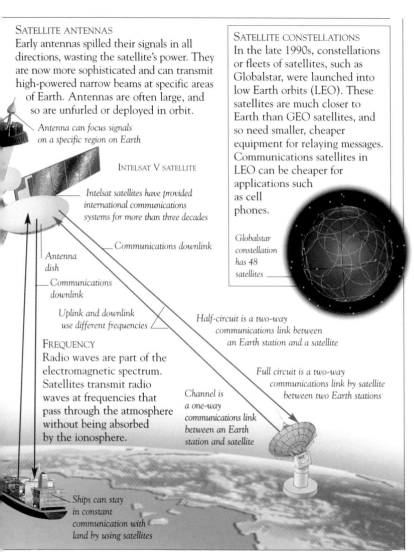

SATELLITE ANTENNAS

Early antennas spilled their signals in all directions, wasting the satellite's power. They are now more sophisticated and can transmit high-powered narrow beams at specific areas of Earth. Antennas are often large, and so are unfurled or deployed in orbit.

Antenna can focus signals on a specific region on Earth

INTELSAT V SATELLITE

Intelsat satellites have provided international communications systems for more than three decades

Communications downlink

Antenna dish

Communications downlink

Uplink and downlink use different frequencies

FREQUENCY

Radio waves are part of the electromagnetic spectrum. Satellites transmit radio waves at frequencies that pass through the atmosphere without being absorbed by the ionosphere.

Channel is a one-way communications link between an Earth station and satellite

Half-circuit is a two-way communications link between an Earth station and a satellite

Full circuit is a two-way communications link by satellite between two Earth stations

SATELLITE CONSTELLATIONS

In the late 1990s, constellations or fleets of satellites, such as Globalstar, were launched into low Earth orbits (LEO). These satellites are much closer to Earth than GEO satellites, and so need smaller, cheaper equipment for relaying messages. Communications satellites in LEO can be cheaper for applications such as cell phones.

Globalstar constellation has 48 satellites

Ships can stay in constant communication with land by using satellites

NAVIGATION SATELLITES

SATELLITES CAN BE USED in navigation
to establish an exact position on Earth.
They transmit radio waves that can be
detected even if it is cloudy. As a
result, navigation is now possible in
any weather. The Global Positioning
System (GPS) is the most reliable
and accurate navigation system ever.

HOW GPS WORKS

GPS consists of 24 satellites as well as equipment on
the ground. The satellites broadcast their positions
and the time as given by their accurate atomic clocks.
They are spaced in orbits so that a receiver anywhere on
Earth can always receive signals from at least four
satellites, and they remain at an altitude of 12,550 miles
(20,200 km). The GPS receiver knows precisely when the
signal was sent and when it arrived, and so can calculate the
distance between itself and each of the satellites. With this
information, it works out its own position, including altitude. Each
satellite is designed to last for seven-and-a-half years.

GLONASS

The Global Orbiting Navigation
Satellite System (GLONASS), owned
by Russia, allows users to work out their
positions to between 66 and 328 ft (20
and 100 m). Special techniques permit
greater precision, if needed. These satellites
give worldwide coverage. The European
Space Agency is improving coverage of
Europe by building equipment designed to
receive signals from both GLONASS and GPS.

Antennas

Thrusters keep
the satellite oriented
correctly toward Earth

There are four satellites in each GPS orbit

GPS receivers can be as small as cellular phones

GPS RECEIVERS
Early receivers displayed the user's position as latitude and longitude, which had to be plotted on a map. Modern ones display a map marking the user's position to within a few yards (meters). The receivers also calculate speed and direction of travel.

Satellites were launched into six different circular orbits to give global coverage

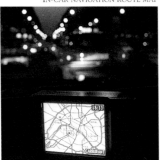

IN-CAR NAVIGATION ROUTE MAP

ATOMIC CLOCKS
Atomic clocks keep time accurately. They are used on GPS satellites to keep time to within one second every 300,000 years, allowing accurate time signals to be transmitted.

CESIUM ATOMIC CLOCK

CAR NAVIGATION
Several car manufacturers now install GPS receivers to aid route planning. Companies that own a large fleet of vehicles may also use GPS to keep track of them. Some emergency vehicles use GPS signals to quickly find the fastest route to the scene of an emergency.

METEOROLOGY SATELLITES

METEOROLOGY SATELLITES RECORD images to make weather forecasts, show cloud cover, and monitor hurricanes across oceans. They carry instruments to take readings, which are converted to temperatures, pressures, and humidities. These, together with information from sources such as weather buoys, balloons, and ships, help forecasters make predictions.

HURRICANE FRAN IN 1996

HURRICANE FORECASTING

Before weather satellites existed, hurricanes would develop unseen over oceans and strike land with very little warning, sometimes killing thousands of people. Hurricanes are extreme tropical storms, with wind speeds over 75 mph (120 km/h). In tropical storms, winds circle a calm eye of low air pressure. Now weather satellites constantly monitor the oceans for possible tropical storms.

Hurricane eye

SCANNING THE GLOBE

Geostationary satellites scan the region beneath them every 30 minutes. If a tropical storm develops, they scan in more detail every 15 minutes. The satellites also measure temperature.

HURRICANE
FLORENCE IN 1994

HOMING IN

As a tropical storm becomes a hurricane and nears land, the US Air Force sends its Weather Squadron—the Hurricane Hunters—into the storm to take further measurements.

Meteosat satellites collate weather data over Europe and Africa and relay it to computing and forecasting centers around Europe

METEOSAT SATELLITE

Meteosat's instruments record both images and temperatures in the atmosphere

SATELLITES AND COMPUTING

Computers are essential for scientists to turn satellite measurements into the temperatures, pressures, humidities, and wind speeds needed for a weather report. The computers also combine data from radar, ships, buoys, planes, and satellites to give timely and accurate forecasts.

WEATHER ORBITS

Weather satellites occupy both geostationary and polar orbits. Geostationary satellites, such as GOES, stay above the same place on the equator and record changes continually. They have a wide view, except of the northern regions. Polar orbit satellites, such as NOAA 10, do not have a constant view of the same region, but can see the poles and more detail than is possible from geostationary orbit.

NOAA 10 orbits Earth in 100 minutes. It is over the same place once every 12 hours

NOAA 10 SATELLITE

The geostationary orbit is 22,320 miles (36,000 km) above Earth

Scale exaggerated for clarity

GOES satellites are positioned in geostationary orbit to observe the US and either the Atlantic or Pacific Ocean

GOES SATELLITE

The polar orbit is typically 560 miles (900 km) above Earth, passing over the poles

HURRICANE NEARING JAPAN

PREDICTING LANDFALL

For each year during the past 20 years, satellites have contributed to improvements of between 0.5 and 1 percent in the accuracy of hurricane forecasts. The place where a hurricane will meet land—known as landfall—can now be predicted to within 100 miles (160 km).

Japan

269

EARTH RESOURCES SATELLITES

SATELLITES THAT HELP SCIENTISTS to study Earth's surface are called Earth resources satellites. Their instruments analyze light and radiation reflected and emitted from surface features. Satellites pass regularly over the globe, allowing scientists to map how an area changes over time.

THEMATIC MAPPER

Different types of radiation have different wavelengths. The thematic mapper— an instrument aboard Landsat satellites— measures the intensity of radiation in seven different wavelength bands as they cover more than two-thirds of the globe. By assigning different colors to each band, scientists can build up a map of an area.

Thematic mapper

LANDSAT 4 SATELLITE

WHAT THE MAPPER REVEALS

Each of a thematic mapper's bands reveals something different. Band five, for example, detects the range of infrared wavelengths that shows moisture content in vegetation. If the intensity is low, the crops might be on the verge of failing.

OCEAN SURVEILLANCE

To understand Earth and its climate, we need to know what happens in and above its oceans, since they cover more than two-thirds of the globe. ERS-1 was one of the first satellites for ocean surveillance.

Infrared instrument measured sea-surface and cloud temperature

MONITORING
CROPS IN
CALIFORNIA

ERS-1 carried instruments to measure infrared and microwave radiation, which are the wavelength bands that give the most information about ocean and atmospheric conditions

Radar worked with two types of antennas to give a microwave image of the ocean and coastal areas and to show the winds on the ocean's surface

MULTISPECTRAL SCANNER

Antennas monitored the choppiness of the ocean

Antennas collected data for a microwave image of the ocean and coastal areas

Radar altimeter recorded wave height and the shape of the ocean surface to help deduce wind speed

SPECTRAL RESOLUTION
The multispectral scanner (MSS) on Landsat 1 was the first satellite instrument to record radiation intensity in different wavelength bands. It uses a range of wavelengths to gather information about different aspects of Earth's surface.

DEFORESTATION
A Landsat image shows forests in the Ivory Coast in Africa. The colors identify different types of surface: red is forest and pale blue is soil, while brown indicates crops. Successive images taken over months or years showed the red areas decreasing as trees were cut down.

MINERAL DEPOSITS IN CHILE

FALSE COLORS
People cannot see infrared, so scientists give each wavelength band an identifying color. Maps that use this are called false-color images. In this image, volcanic soil is brown, vegetation is red, water is blue, and mineral deposits are white.

271

SPACE DEBRIS

ANYTHING IN ORBIT that has no use is called space debris. This includes discarded rockets and obsolete satellites, or fragments of destroyed ones, that could stay in orbit for hundreds of years. Space nations are trying to reduce "space junk," which accounts for 90 percent of all objects orbiting Earth.

HAZARDS IN SPACE

There are an estimated 8,500 items of space debris bigger than 3.9 in (10 cm) in orbit around Earth. The rubbish is created at many stages of a space operation, such as during separation, when the nose cone is discarded once a satellite is in orbit. Space junk accumulates most quickly in those orbits that are used most often. Satellites and debris could collide at speeds of up to 24,855 mph (40,000 km/h), causing serious damage.

Each yellow dot is a piece of space junk orbiting Earth

Most space debris is in low Earth orbit

TRACKING DEBRIS

The worldwide radar network of the North American Aerospace Defense Command (NORAD) monitors objects in orbit. Items as small as a tennis ball are routinely detected in low Earth orbit, while 3.2-ft (1-m) objects can be observed in geostationary orbit. Computers use this information to predict the likelihood of a collision with spacecraft.

DEBRIS ORBITING EARTH

Debris in geostationary orbit is marked as a loop around Earth

MEEP MODULE ON MIR

DAMAGE CONTROL

The best form of damage control is not to be hit in the first place, so the International Space Station (ISS) is designed to move out of the path of large chunks of debris. Experiments such as the Mir Environmental Effects Payload (MEEP) provide data on the risks that the ISS faces.

PROTECTION

One way to protect sensitive areas of a spacecraft is to wrap it in layers of lightweight ceramic fiber. Each layer disperses the energy of a particle, which disintegrates before it hits the spacecraft wall. These ceramic bumpers are used on the ISS to prevent the type of damage recorded in hypervelocity test chambers.

INTERNATIONAL SPACE STATION

APOLLO 12 AFTER SPLASHDOWN FROM ORBIT

REENTRY

Satellites return to Earth slowly. Friction with the air heats them when they reenter Earth's atmosphere. Some disintegrate, while others survive and hit the ground or sea. Today, owners have to control the end of their satellite's life so that it is removed from orbit and does not remain as debris.

FLYBYS AND ORBITERS

LIFTED INTO SPACE by rockets, space probes are computer-controlled robots packed with scientific instruments. Probes are sent to fly by a planet, or even orbit around it, sending data and images back to Earth. After they have completed their planned missions, some probes continue on into space.

VOLCANIC DISCOVERY
The probe Voyager I obtained this image of Io, which shows the first active volcano seen beyond Earth.

Three probes used Saturn's gravity to propel them along

Earth

Jupiter's orbit

Saturn's orbit

Pioneer 10 left the solar system after passing Jupiter

Uranus's orbit

Pioneer 11

Voyager 1

Voyager 2 is the only probe to visit Uranus and Neptune

SPACE PROBES: FLYBY ROUTES TO THE OUTER PLANETS

Neptune

BOOSTED BY GRAVITY
Space probes can make use of a planet's gravity as they fly by. The pull of gravity acts like a slingshot, accelerating the probe for the next stage of its journey.

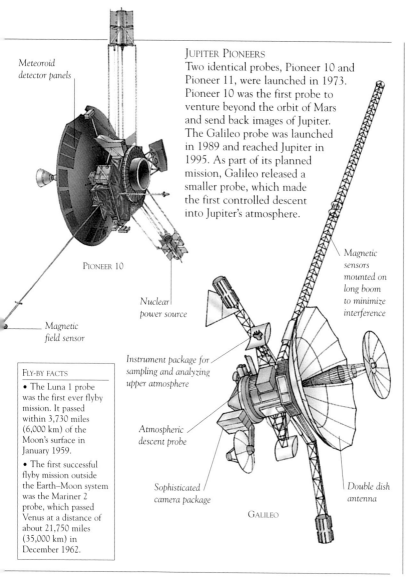

Meteoroid
detector panels

JUPITER PIONEERS

Two identical probes, Pioneer 10 and
Pioneer 11, were launched in 1973.
Pioneer 10 was the first probe to
venture beyond the orbit of Mars
and send back images of Jupiter.
The Galileo probe was launched
in 1989 and reached Jupiter in
1995. As part of its planned
mission, Galileo released a
smaller probe, which made
the first controlled descent
into Jupiter's atmosphere.

PIONEER 10

Magnetic
field sensor

Nuclear
power source

Magnetic
sensors
mounted on
long boom
to minimize
interference

Instrument package for
sampling and analyzing
upper atmosphere

Atmospheric
descent probe

Sophisticated
camera package

Double dish
antenna

GALILEO

SATELLITES AND PROBES

LANDERS

SPACE PROBES SENT to orbit a planet can release a second craft to land on the surface. The lander, a scientific robot, carries out its preprogrammed tasks and then relays the data it has obtained back to Earth. Only six piloted spacecraft have made landings, during the Apollo Moon program.

COMING IN TO LAND
This dramatic photograph of the Hadley Rille valley was taken from the piloted Apollo 15 lander during its low-altitude descent to the Moon's surface.

IS THERE LIFE ON MARS?
Two Viking orbiters released one lander each onto Mars. In total, about 3,000 photographic images were sent back to Earth. The landers also tested the Martian soil to check for any sign of life; none was found. In 2004, Spirit and Opportunity, two expedition rovers, landed on Mars and have sent back useful data and images.

VIKING LANDER CRAFT

Television cameras

Sensors for testing atmospheric conditions

Robot arm to take soil samples

SATELLITES AND PROBES

276

VENERA 9 LANDER CRAFT

The two parts separate and the lander begins its descent through the atmosphere

The protective atmospheric shield is jettisoned

Onboard braking engines begin to slow Venera 9

Parachutes further slow the descent

Venera 9 obtains and transmits several images before failing

LANDER FACTS

• The first successful lander was Luna 9, which soft-landed on the Moon in 1966.

• Venera 7 became the first lander to transmit data from the surface of Venus in 1970.

• The Viking landers analyzed Mars's soil and found that it contained the following chemical elements:

silica	14%
iron	18%
aluminum	2.7%
titanium	0.9%
potassium	0.3%

HOT LANDING

A series of Venera space probes was sent to Venus. Each consisted of two parts, one of which descended to the surface. Conditions on Venus—very high temperature and pressure—meant that the landers could function for only a few minutes.

PROBES TO THE PLANETS

ONCE THE FIRST ROCKETS had reached space, scientists and astronomers began to use space probes—car-sized robot craft launched by rockets to a predetermined target, which they investigate using their onboard instruments. Probes have given us close-ups of moons, comets, asteroids, and all but one of the planets, and have taught us much about the solar system.

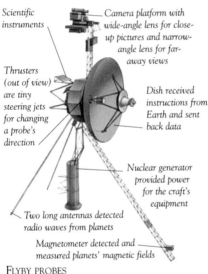

Scientific instruments

Camera platform with wide-angle lens for close-up pictures and narrow-angle lens for far-away views

Thrusters (out of view) are tiny steering jets for changing a probe's direction

Dish received instructions from Earth and sent back data

Nuclear generator provided power for the craft's equipment

Two long antennas detected radio waves from planets

Magnetometer detected and measured planets' magnetic fields

FLYBY PROBES
These probes survey the target as they fly past, often at distances of several thousand miles (kilometers). The most successful were Voyagers 1 and 2, which investigated Jupiter, Saturn, Uranus, and Neptune between 1979 and 1989.

ORBITERS AND LANDERS
Orbiters travel to the target, move into orbit around it, and then survey it. Landers, like Pathfinder, which landed on Mars in 1997, land on a target and survey it. Probes may be combinations of orbiter and lander, like the Viking probes.

Vikings 1 and 2 landed on Mars in July and September 1976

Magellan launched in 1989

Magellan orbited Venus in 1990

Orbit of Mars

Sun

Orbit of Venus

Orbit of Earth

Vikings 1 and 2 launched in August and September 1975

EQUIPMENT AND EXPERIMENTS

Antenna dish allows
probes to stay in
touch with Earth

A probe may receive instructions from Earth or may
follow a mission programmed into its onboard computers.
It may be powered by electricity generated by solar panels
or a nuclear generator. On board are control systems
that operate the probe and its scientific equipment.
The Huygens lander, part of the Cassini orbiter, landed
on Titan—Saturn's largest moon—in January 2005 to
investigate its surface and atmosphere.

Experiment platform
with equipment
to test Titan's
surface and
atmosphere

Surface science
package, with
separate
experiments

This instrument
was the first part
of Huygens to
touch Titan's
surface

Cassini
reached Saturn
in 2004 and
will orbit the
ringed planet
and its moons
for 4 years

Huygens
was released to
investigate
Titan

Heat-resistant
shield stops Huygens
from burning up in
Titan's atmosphere

Device to test
water's depth had
Huygens landed
in an ocean

Instruments to measure
the density, composition,
and temperature of
Titan's atmosphere
and surface

KEY SPACE PROBES

Probe	Type	Target	Encounter	Achievements
Pioneer 10	Flyby	Jupiter	1973	First to cross asteroid belt; took close-ups of Jupiter
Mariner 10	Flyby	Mercury	1974–75	Only probe to Mercury
Venera 9	Orbiter / lander	Venus	1975	First views of Venusian surface
Vikings 1 and 2	Orbiter / lander	Mars	1976	Photographed surface; searched for life
Giotto	Flyby	Halley's comet	1986	First view of the nucleus of a comet
Voyagers 1 and 2	Flyby	Jupiter	1979	Details of all four planetary systems;
		Saturn	1980–81	
		Uranus	1986	Voyager 2 was first probe
		Neptune	1989	to Uranus and Neptune
Galileo	Flyby / orbiter	Gaspra	1991	First flyby of an asteroid;
		Jupiter	1995	first orbit of Jupiter
Cassini	Flyby / lander	Saturn	2004	Detailed views of Saturn; launched the Huygens probe to Titan

SEARCH FOR LIFE ON MARS

SPECULATIONS THAT LIFE EXISTS on Mars have been rife since the late 18th century, fueled by various theories. Hopes of finding life on the Red Planet received a setback in July 1965, when the Mariner 4 probe sent back images of its barren surface. Even so, life may have existed or may still exist today in places not yet explored.

EVIDENCE OF A WATERY PAST

Life as known on Earth needs water. Although liquid water cannot exist on Mars in today's frozen conditions, surface features, such as the channels detected by probes, suggest that water must once have flowed on the planet. A huge block-strewn area—the chaotic region— may have formed when water locked in the ground escaped rapidly, fracturing the surface.

The Martian surface probably had water 3 billion years ago

ORIGINS OF THE WATER

Liquid water was widespread on Mars in its early days. Intense meteorite bombardment and volcanic activity kept the planet warm, even at its great distance from the Sun. Life may have started then. Today, most of the water is locked up as ice in the soil. Pure sheets of ice occur at the poles.

Mangala Vallis dried river bed photographed by the Viking Orbiter

Primitive life may have existed in channels billions of years ago

Lowell's 1905 map shows canals that do not match the channels actually observed on Mars

Channels crisscross the border between Mars's northern lowlands and southern highlands

CANALS ON MARS?
Channels were first observed by astronomers in the 19th century and were mapped in the 1890s by Percival Lowell from his observatory in Flagstaff, Arizona. Lowell argued that they were canals that carried water from the Martian poles to arid equatorial regions, and converged at oases. The channels later proved to be an optical illusion.

Channel was formed when huge volumes of groundwater were released on to the Martian surface

The Martian meteorite ALH84001 (magnified 100,000 times) contains tubes that might be fossils of bacterium-like organisms

METEORITE INVESTIGATION
The most intriguing, but inconclusive, evidence of life on Mars comes from an ancient Martian meteorite known as ALH84001, which landed in Antarctica about 13,000 years ago. It contains organic chemicals that could be evidence of life and tiny structures that could have been made by living organisms.

MISSIONS TO MARS

SINCE 1996, A STREAM of robotic spacecraft has left Earth for Mars. These space probes aim to find out how geology and climate combine to tell the story of the planet, and whether primitive life may have existed there in the past. These probes will pave the way for human exploration, or even colonization, of Mars.

Antenna relays signals back to Earth

Cameras can detect surface features just 5 ft (1.5 m) across

Solar panels supply power

EXPLORING THE SURFACE
NASA's Pathfinder spacecraft landed on Mars on July 4, 1997. It deployed a small rover (Sojourner) and made measurements of conditions on Mars. The rover explored the Martian surface and analyzed rocks and soil. Communications ended in September 1997. Since then, two much-improved landers, Spirit and Opportunity, have touched down, providing amazing results.

PATHFINDER MARTIAN PANORAMA

This panoramic image is a mosaic of many individual pictures sent back by Pathfinder

Distribution of rocks on the surface indicates that large bodies of water once flowed on Mars

PROBES TO MARS			
Name	Year of arrival	Country	Type of probe
Mariner 4	1965	US	Flyby
Mars 3	1971	Russia	Orbiter and lander
Viking 1	1976	US	Orbiter and lander
Viking 2	1976	US	Orbiter and lander
Global Surveyor	1997	US	Orbiter
Pathfinder	1997	US	Lander and rover
Mars Express	2003	Europe	Orbiter
Nozomi	2004	Japan	Orbiter
Exploration Rover	2004	US	Lander

Hazy clouds of water ice are sometimes observed

GLOBAL SURVEYOR
In September 1997, Global Surveyor reached Mars and spent 18 months slowing down into a low orbit just 217 miles (350 km) above the surface. It carried cameras and spectrometers designed to map the planet in detail and study its weather patterns and chemical composition.

HOSTILE TO LIFE
There is no liquid water on Mars, since it is too cold most of the time. The oxygen is not breathable, and the surface is scoured by violent winds carrying dust particles. There is also no ozone in the upper atmosphere to protect life from damaging ultraviolet radiation.

The depth of the Sojourner Rover's tracks showed that the soil is fine and powdery

The Rover samples a rock nicknamed "Yogi"

Pathfinder found that Martian airborne dust is magnetic

283

SPACE TRAVEL

FLYING TO SPACE

AT ONE TIME, people considered satellites and spaceflight to be science fiction. But some scientists and engineers did believe in technology that could launch satellites and people into space. In 1957, the believers in space exploration were proved right.

OCTOBER 4, 1957

SPACE AGE DAWNS

Fascination, excitement, and fear dominated people's emotions when they learned that the Soviet Union had launched the first-ever artificial satellite, named Sputnik. The satellite transmitted a tracking signal for 21 days.

APRIL 12, 1961

RECOVERY
Sputnik 5 carried two dogs—they became the first creatures to survive the weightlessness of space and the forces of reentry.

AUGUST 20, 1960

FIRST PERSON IN SPACE
Yuri Gagarin, the first person in space, flew in a spherical Vostok spaceship, seated in an ejector seat on rails. His successful flight followed two Soviet space program disasters.

US CREWED SPACE PROGRAM
The US crewed space program began with Alan Shepard reaching an altitude of 112 miles (180 km) and returning to Earth. His suborbital flight was part of the Mercury program.

MAY 5, 1961

MAY 25, 1961

LUNAR CHALLENGE
President John F. Kennedy boosted American space ambitions by launching the Apollo lunar exploration program. The Apollo program was one of the most technically complex projects of the 20th century.

SPACEWALK

Soviet cosmonaut Alexei Leonov made the first spacewalk from the Voskhod 2 spacecraft. During the spacewalk, which lasted 20 minutes, his spacesuit expanded, so he had to struggle to close the airlock's outer hatch on reentry.

APRIL 24, 1967

SOYUZ SPACECRAFT

Soviet cosmonaut Vladimir Komorov became the first person to die in space when he was killed aboard his Soyuz 1 spacecraft. Four months earlier, three American astronauts had died in a fire on the launch pad while testing Apollo 1. All four were victims of the race to be first to land on the Moon.

JULY 15–24, 1975

MARCH 18, 1965

JULY 20, 1969

MOON LANDING

Neil Armstrong, Commander of US Apollo 11, marked the arrival of people on the Moon. Armstrong and Buzz Aldrin guided Eagle, the lunar module, to the surface while Michael Collins remained in control of the command module. Armstrong and Aldrin spent 22 hours on the surface, collecting rock and dust samples.

APOLLO-SOYUZ LINK

In the midst of the Cold War, the United States and the Soviet Union achieved one cooperative space mission—the Apollo-Soyuz rendezvous. The crews maneuvered their craft together and docked. For a few days, they worked on scientific experiments in each other's spacecraft; then they completed their missions independently.

287

SPACE SHUTTLE

THE FIRST TEST FLIGHT of the Space Transportation System (STS)—the Space Shuttle—was in 1981. The Shuttle is an orbiter with three main engines, an external tank, and two solid rocket boosters. Cargo is carried in the orbiter's payload bay. After each mission, the orbiter returns to Earth. The STS launches satellites and space probes and is used for construction and repairs in space.

Payload bay

Flight deck where commander and pilot sit

SHUTTLE ORBITER

An orbiter is a space plane. It can carry seven crew members and stay in orbit for at least 10 days. The orbiters' cabins have three decks—the flight deck, a mid-deck, and a lower deck that houses life-support equipment.

SHUTTLE ORBITER

Ladder to mid-deck, which has sleeping bunks, washroom, galley, and the airlock to access space

4. *Orbiter reaches low Earth orbit*

3. *External tank released*

2. *Boosters discarded*

Fuel tank falls back to Earth

Solid rocket booster

External tank

BOOSTER

The external tank carries fuel and is discarded after each flight. Boosters support the orbiter and propel it to an altitude of 28 miles (45 km). They last for 20 flights.

Parachutes open as boosters fall back to Earth

Ships recover the rockets

1. *Space Shuttle blasts off*

FLIGHT PROFILE

Space Shuttle assembly building

The payload bay doors open when the orbiter reaches low Earth orbit, to prevent it from overheating

Remote manipulator arm helps move satellites in and out of the payload bay

Rudder divides in half and acts as a brake on approach to landing

Vertical tail

Three main engines

Orbital maneuvering engines

Thrusters for small orbital adjustments

The delta-shaped wing has no function in space but helps the orbiter glide to a landing

Lower deck houses equipment to maintain a habitable environment for the flight crew in the orbiter

5. Orbiter stays in space for 10–16 days

6. Orbiter positions itself ready to return to Earth

7. Orbiter re-enters Earth's atmosphere

8. Orbiter gets ready for high-speed glide onto runway

9. Orbiter glides in to land on runway

LAUNCH TO LANDING
The three main engines start at 0.12-second intervals, followed by the solid rocket boosters. Bolts holding down the STS are released for liftoff. The orbital maneuvering system (OMS) places the orbiter into the correct orbit once the boosters and tank are discarded. One hour before landing, the OMS and thrusters position the orbiter for reentry.

ORBITAL SPECIFICATIONS
• Orbiter length: 122 ft (37 m)
• Orbiter height: 57 ft (17 m)
• Wingspan: 98 ft (30 m)
• Payload bay: 60 x 15 ft (18 x 5 m)
• Orbit speed: 17,896 mph (28,800 km/h)
• Withstands temperatures up to 2,732°F (1,500°C)
• Altitude in orbit between 115 and 620 miles (185–1,000 km)
• Mission duration between 10 and 16 days

289

WORKING IN SPACE

ASTRONAUTS NOW WORK in space on a regular basis. Many experiments take place aboard orbiting laboratories, while satellites can be launched, retrieved, and repaired while circling Earth.

WORKING ON THE MOON
In this picture, Buzz Aldrin (the second person to walk on the Moon) is seen setting up one of the scientific experiment packages that the Apollo 11 crew left behind on the lunar surface.

Antenna

Television camera

Steering control

Equipment storage rack

LUNAR ROVING VEHICLE (LRV)

Wire-mesh wheels

MOON BUGGY
Crew members of the Apollo 15, 16, and 17 missions made effective use of the LRV. This "moon buggy" enabled them to travel significant distances across the lunar surface, collecting samples over a wide area.

SPACE SCIENCE
Orbiting laboratories allow scientists to carry out experiments in conditions where gravity's influence is negligible. This scientist is testing how fuel burns in a weightless environment.

SPACE STATION

Assembled in space by astronauts aided by tools, cranes, and a robotic arm, the International Space Station (ISS) is a collaboration between 16 countries. Pressurized living modules for up to seven astronauts are linked to laboratories and work stations. Astronauts live and work on the ISS for up to six months at a time.

Some 43,000 sq ft (4,000 sq m) of solar panels provide power to the ISS

RUNNING REPAIRS

Attached securely to the Space Shuttle's robotic arm—the Remote Manipulator System—astronauts can carry out repairs to satellites, telescopes, and the International Space Station in safety.

The Space Shuttle's robotic arm (at foot of picture) maneuvers the astronaut into the correct position to carry out a particular task

LIVING IN SPACE

ENGINEERS DESIGN SPACE STATIONS so that astronauts can live in the hostile environment of space, where there is no oxygen, no soil in which to grow food, no water, and no air pressure. Life support systems on board provide oxygen and filter the carbon dioxide people breathe out. The air on board is pressurized to levels close to those on Earth, and the temperature is maintained at comfortable levels. Crews must also be supplied with food and water.

BUOYANCY TANK TRAINING
Astronauts train in weightless environments on Earth, simulated in enormous "neutral buoyancy" water tanks. A full-scale mockup of an orbiter's payload bay and airlock can be placed in the deep water tanks, allowing trainees wearing pressurized spacesuits to practice spacewalks for extended periods. Such tanks are also used to design, test, and develop spacecraft and crew equipment.

PERSONAL HYGIENE
On the Space Shuttle, astronauts take sponge baths, and male astronauts shave with foam or not at all, since whiskers tend to escape and get into the eyes if an electric razor is used.

Astronaut shaving on board the Space Shuttle

SPACE FOOD

Food on the Shuttle must be lightweight since it is ferried from Earth. Bits of food may float away, so chunks are sometimes covered in edible gelatin to prevent crumbs. Usually, however, food is dried and water added to it when needed. The Space Shuttle produces some of its own water.

SPACE MENU

Breakfast	Fruit or cereal, beef pasty or scrambled eggs, cocoa, fruit drink
Lunch	Turkey pasta or hot dogs, bread, bananas or almond crunch bar, fruit drink
Dinner	Soup or fruit cocktail, rice pilaff or steak, broccoli au gratin, pudding, fruit drink

SPACE TOILET

On the Space Shuttle, restraints hold astronauts in place and a vacuum ensures a good seal between body and toilet seat. Solid waste is dried, treated for bacteria, and stored, while urine and waste water are stored and periodically dumped.

Handhold

Seat

Operating handle

Control panel

Control to shut off vacuum

Foot restraint

Waist strap

SLEEP TIGHT

Waist straps stop crew from floating around when asleep. The Sun rises and sets every hour and a half in near-Earth orbit, so eyeshades are used. Earmuffs may also be used if crew members are working nearby.

Special straps attach the astronaut to the walkway

STAYING IN SHAPE

The body does not have to work as hard in space, because there is so little gravity, so muscles tend to waste away. To prevent this, space crews follow exercise plans, and space stations carry equipment such as exercise bikes.

Using a moving walkway is one way an astronaut can work out

293

SPACEWALK
An astronaut's spacesuit keeps the body at atmospheric pressure and shields it from harmful radiation.

SCIENCE IN SPACE

THE FORCE OF GRAVITY cannot be changed on Earth, so scientists go into orbit to carry out gravity experiments. In orbit, they experience weightlessness, or microgravity, which helps them to study the effects of gravity on biological and physical processes.

SPACELAB

The European Space Agency designed the Spacelab space station to be carried in the payload bay of the Space Shuttle. It was made up of two pressurized laboratories for microgravity experiments, and three unpressurized laboratories, or external pallets, for experiments that needed exposure to space. Launched first in 1983, the last Spacelab mission flew in 1997.

Skylab was used by three teams of astronauts between May 1973 and February 1974

SKYLAB

Skylab, the first US space station, was launched in 1973. It studied how people behave if they live in space for long periods of time, and also investigated solar flares.

INSIDE SPACELAB

The crew slept in the Shuttle orbiter and floated through the access tunnel to work in Spacelab's pressurized modules. Experiments were contained in specially designed units, called racks.

In orbit, the payload bay housing Spacelab remained open

Shuttle orbiter

Access tunnel between Spacelab and orbiter

SPACELAB

BIORACK AND ANTHRORACK

The Spacelab carried a Biorack, which had incubators for samples of cells and microorganisms in order to study how microgravity affected their behavior. Anthrorack carried equipment to examine the effect of microgravity on the human body.

EXTERNAL PALLET

Some instruments for observing Earth or radiation in space need to be exposed to space. These were fitted to external pallets. Control equipment was normally housed in the pressurized module. If Spacelab was in a pallet-only mode, then this was put in a cylindrical container at the front of the first pallet.

Single external pallet

MICROGRAVITY EXPERIMENTS

• Russian scientists studied how the heart and lungs behave during long stays in space.

• Mir crews grew wheat seeds to find out how the seeds mature in microgravity.

• Studying combustion in microgravity has yielded information that will help in the design of jet engines.

• Crystal growth experiments on Mir and Spacelab allowed testing of better ways to produce semiconductors for computers.

Pressurized modules were 14 ft (4 m) wide

Spacelab was designed to look as though it had a roof, a floor, and walls

Footholds helped to keep the astronauts upright while they worked

SPACE STATIONS

Name	Nationality	Launch year
Salyut 1	Soviet Union	1971
Skylab	US	1973
Spacelab	Europe	1983
Mir	Russia	1986
International Space Station	International	1998

INTERNATIONAL MICROGRAVITY LAB

Spacelab flew two international microgravity laboratory missions. Projects included studying the effect of microgravity on the nervous system, and on the development of shrimp eggs, lentil seedlings, and bacteria.

BIOLOGY IN MICROGRAVITY

In 1996, Shannon Lucid, a NASA astronaut, put eggs into Mir's incubator, and each day removed one to stop development. These were compared with eggs on Earth to find out what influences the way fertilized eggs develop.

INTERNATIONAL SPACE STATION

THE UNITED STATES AND RUSSIA launched the first parts of the International Space Station (ISS) in 1998. Brazil, Canada, the European Space Agency, and Japan have also contributed elements. It carries a permanent crew, and completion is scheduled for 2006. Astronauts carry out a wide-ranging program of research while on board.

STATION ELEMENTS
The International Space Station is made up of more than 100 elements contributed by various countries, including connecting nodes, solar panels, habitation and unpressurized modules, laboratories, a core module, and robotic arms.

The ISS is the size of a football field

Thermal panels to control temperature

Interior of the European laboratory

LABORATORIES
The ISS has a research complex with laboratories supplied by the US, Russia, Europe, and Japan. Here, scientists investigate materials and fluids in microgravity, as well as life sciences and technology development. Japan provided an external platform for experiments that require prolonged exposure to space.

There are 43,056 sq ft (4,000 sq m) of solar panels on the ISS

Solar panels convert the Sun's energy into electricity for powering the station

INTERNATIONAL SPACE STATION

SPACE STATION ASSEMBLY
Over 45 spaceflights were made during the ISS assembly, which took over five years. Robotic equipment connected the elements, and astronauts made the final adjustments by hand. Crew members performed 850 hours of space walks during the years of assembly.

US general research laboratory

Living and work space is the same size as the passenger space on two 747 aircraft

Astronauts use a water tank on Earth to simulate weightlessness

ISS is one of the brightest objects in the night sky— second only to Venus

ISS has 60 times more electrical power for research than Mir

Truss acts as framework

Japanese external experiment platform exposed to space

European laboratory

Resupply ship docks with the ISS

SPACESUIT
Suits used by Space Shuttle crews are normally refurbished between flights and altered to fit the next astronaut. The ISS suit, however, is adjusted for size on the station. It is used for 25 space walks before being sent back to Earth.

SPACE STATION NODES
There are three nodes on the ISS linking other ISS elements and pressurized modules, and containing ports for spacecraft. Node 1 is for storage, Node 2 contains equipment for converting electrical power, and Node 3 houses life support equipment.

SPACE MISSIONS I

THE SPACE AGE began in 1957 with the launch of the first satellite. Four years later, Yuri Gagarin became the world's first astronaut. The next 20 years saw a surge of interest in space exploration.

FIRST SPACE VEHICLE
A model of Vostok I, the craft in which Yuri Gagarin made his historic first orbit of Earth on April 12, 1961.

CONTROLLED LANDING
The probe Luna 9 was the first to make a successful soft landing on the Moon in February 1966. Luna 9 sent back the first panoramic images taken from the surface of the Moon.

Lower part was left behind on the Moon's surface

LUNA 9

PASSENGER SHIP
The Apollo 11 Lunar Module (LM) carried two astronauts—Neil Armstrong and Buzz Aldrin—down to the Moon's surface on July 20, 1969. Slightly more than 24 hours later, the upper part of the LM returned them to lunar orbit.

LUNAR MODULE

ROBOT MOON ROVER

Two Lunokhod robot vehicles were sent to the Moon in the early 1970s. Equipped with television cameras that enabled them to be driven from a control room on Earth, the two vehicles traveled a total of 29.5 miles (47.5 km) across the Moon.

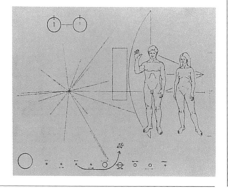

Television camera

LUNOKHOD I

SCIENTIFIC PLATFORM

Launched in 1973, the Skylab orbiting laboratory and observatory gave astronauts the opportunity to work in space for weeks at a time. Skylab also enabled scientists to study the workings of Earth's atmosphere and climate systems from the viewpoint of space.

Apollo Telescope Mount

SKYLAB

MESSAGE TO THE STARS

The two Pioneer probes each carry a gold-covered plaque that shows a visual representation of human beings, as well as simple directions for locating the solar system and planet Earth.

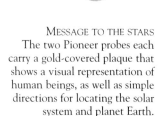

301

SPACE MISSIONS II

WORKING IN ORBIT became much easier with the introduction of the Space Shuttle in 1981. Probes have now visited all but one of the outer planets, and further exploration is under way.

The Shuttle has a mechanical arm that can be used to launch or retrieve satellites

The external fuel tank breaks away at a height of 68 miles (110 km)

The booster rockets operate for about two minutes and are jettisoned at a height of 28 miles (45 km)

The Shuttle can lift off with eight crew and up to 32 tons of cargo

INCREASING COMMUNICATIONS
The communications satellite Intelsat was launched by astronauts on the 49th Space Shuttle mission in May 1992. Improved communications is just one of the benefits of space technology now enjoyed by the general public.

ENDURANCE RECORD

Russian astronauts (cosmonauts) have spent increasingly long periods of time in space. The present record of 438 consecutive days was achieved aboard the space station Mir during 1994–95. The picture shows a cosmonaut on the rigorous exercise program devised to keep the crew fit during long periods of weightlessness. Mir burned up when it reentered Earth's atmosphere in 2001, after 15 years in orbit.

ROSETTA PROBE

COMET-CHASER

The Rosetta orbiter/lander (right) will attempt to rendezvous with a comet. The lander will detach from the orbiter and descend to the comet's nucleus. Having anchored itself to the surface, it will transmit data to the orbiter, for relaying back to Earth. Scientists hope that Rosetta will shed light on how comets form.

CASSINI-HUYGENS PROBE

Launched in 1997, Cassini reached Saturn in 2004 and will now spend four years studying the planet and its moons. On arrival, it released the mini-probe Huygens, which touched down on Titan, the largest of Saturn's many moons.

303

SPACEPLANES

GETTING INTO SPACE IS expensive. It typically costs more than $17,000 for every 2.2 lb (1 kg) of payload carried. Huge sums of money are wasted when a multistage rocket is used to reach orbit, since much of the spacecraft is simply lost. Using vehicles that reach orbit in one stage—single-stage-to-orbit (SSTO) spacecraft—might be a way around the problem in the future.

CLIPPER GRAHAM (DC-XA)
A test vehicle for future spaceplane technologies, Clipper Graham was a subsonic aircraft. However, it crashed in 1996 after four flights.

DC-XA was made from advanced, lightweight composite materials

CLIPPER GRAHAM (DC-XA)

VENTURESTAR (X-33)
NASA's VentureStar, or X-33, has a distinctive wedge shape—a "lifting body" design—which helps it to fly. It takes off vertically but glides to a landing. It was a prototype for an SSTO spaceplane. These may take over the role of the Space Shuttle in the future, but NASA is currently looking at simply improving the "old generation" shuttle designs.

Short wings

Rugged thermal protection system

The aerospike engines are designed for all altitudes

Advanced, lightweight composite materials make the X-33 easier to lift into orbit

United States

NASA

LOCKHEED MARTIN

X-33

VentureStar

A wedge-shaped body gives aerodynamic lift

X-34 is designed for wheeled landing

X-34 technology is a bridge between DC-XA and VentureStar (X-33)

TEST FLIGHT OF X-34

X-34 PROTOTYPE

The X-34 tested the lightweight materials, thermal protection, and landing systems needed for SSTO. It was designed to be launched from the air, beneath an airplane. X-33 and X-34 were disaster-prone and ultimately abandoned. A new type of rocket is needed, but progress is slow.

ROTON

A radical but ultimately unsuccessful idea, developed to make rockets light enough for SSTO launches, was to design them without the heavy equipment that pumps propellant. In the Roton rocket, a motor on the launch pad would spin its engine to throw propellant into the combustion chambers. For stability during reentry, and a soft landing, rotor blades similar to a helicopter's would be deployed.

AEROSPIKE ENGINE

Peak performance is possible all the way to orbit with an aerospike engine. The conventional bell-shaped nozzle is turned inside out to give an inner solid surface. The "outer" surface is simply air pressure and, as air pressure decreases with altitude, the nozzle shape changes as the rocket ascends.

SPACE TOURISM

Access to space may become cheaper and easier with SSTO spacecraft, and many people's dreams of traveling to space may then be realized. One space tourism idea is a hotel in a 750-mile (1,200-km) orbit. A tether 620 miles (1,000 km) long would connect the hotel to a space dock 155 miles (250 km) above Earth. People would travel to the dock in reusable suborbital planes, and take an elevator to the hotel.

INTERPLANETARY TRAVEL

SPACE SCIENTISTS ARE experimenting with new technologies for interplanetary travel, for growing crops in space, and for living long periods with limited resources. This will help interplanetary travelers be self-sufficient.

DEEP SPACE 1

The first of a new series of small NASA spacecraft, known as deep space probes, Deep Space 1 was launched in 1998. It tested risky technologies, such as more efficient solar cells and ion drives.

INTERPLANETARY SPACE PROBES

These probes are initially put into orbit around Earth. Rocket boosters are then fired to put them into a new solar orbit, which is carefully plotted to cross the orbit of the target planet.

ION DRIVE
Spacecraft with ion drives can reach 10 times the speed of conventional spacecraft. Ion-loaded gas is pulled toward a charged grid and expelled at high speed, pushing the spacecraft in the opposite direction.

Jupiter

Saturn

Uranus

Sun   Venus   Mars

Mercury   Earth

To reach Mercury and Venus, a probe accelerates away from Earth, opposite from Earth's motion.

SOLAR SYSTEM

SELF-SUFFICIENCY AND PSYCHOLOGY IN SPACE

Future space colonies need to be self-sufficient, growing their own food and recycling the atmosphere as well as plant, animal, and human waste. Such total recycling is very difficult to achieve. If space colonies are to succeed, psychologists need to understand more about how people in small groups interact when completely isolated.

BIOSPHERE II, ARIZONA

In 1991–93, eight people tried to live in a self-contained artificial environment as part of the Biosphere II project in Arizona

Mung beans were successfully grown in space by cosmonauts on Mir

SPACE AGRICULTURE

Scientists on the Mir space station made a modest attempt to grow plants. Successful space colonies will have to cultivate plants for food and to produce oxygen to breathe.

Neptune

Once a probe approaches a planet, planetary gravity attracts it. Boosters can then be fired to maneuver the probe into orbit.

Pluto

To reach Mars and the planets beyond, a probe accelerates away from Earth in the same direction as Earth's orbit around the Sun.

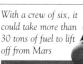

With a crew of six, it could take more than 30 tons of fuel to lift off from Mars

CREATING FUEL ON MARS

One idea to help Mars colonists make fuel is to export a fuel plant from Earth; the plant would use carbon dioxide from Mars's atmosphere and hydrogen shipped from Earth to manufacture water and methane.

SPACE TRAVEL

307

FUTURISTIC STARSHIPS

THE SOLAR SYSTEM'S NEAREST NEIGHBOR, the Alpha Centauri star system, is about 25 trillion miles (40 trillion km) away from Earth. Using the fastest current technology, it would take spacecraft 10,000 years to get there. Light would take four years. For interstellar exploration such as that aboard *Star Trek's* USS Enterprise, a spaceship would need to travel faster than light. No one yet knows whether this would be possible.

LASER DRIVES
Beaming lasers from spaceships in orbit to sails attached to a stellar probe could eliminate the need for fuel. Pressure from the laser light would drive the probe to 20% of the speed of light.

American scientist Robert Forward's proposed laser-driven stellar probe

LIMITS OF CONVENTIONAL ROCKETS
The Voyager spacecraft, traveling at 37,300 mph (60,000 km/h), would take around 80,000 years to reach Alpha Centauri. Traveling there and back again is therefore impossible due to the limitations of current technology.

Solar system and Alpha Centauri are 4.3 light-years apart in the Orion Arm, 25,000 light-years from the center of the Milky Way

MILKY WAY

Forward's arrangement of nested solar sails

ANTIMATTER ENGINES

Antimatter exists and releases huge amounts of energy when it collides with matter. Indeed, matter-antimatter engines may one day power spaceships— but not at speeds faster than light.

Andromeda galaxy is 2.5 million light-years away from Earth

The TV series Star Trek *made antimatter engines famous. In Star Trek, they power the warp drive that propels the Enterprise faster than light*

WARP DRIVE

In 1915, Einstein published his Theory of General Relativity, which deals with how space and time are distorted or "warped" near massive objects. *Star Trek* writers first coined the phrase "warp drive" for traveling faster than light, though antimatter engines could not have done so. Nevertheless, *Star Trek* inspired Mexican physicist Miguel Alcubierre to investigate whether it might be possible to build a warp drive.

NEGATIVE MASS

A warp drive would need negative mass to expand space behind a starship, and equal amounts of positive mass to contract space in front of it. Quantum physics suggests that negative mass might exist, but no one knows.

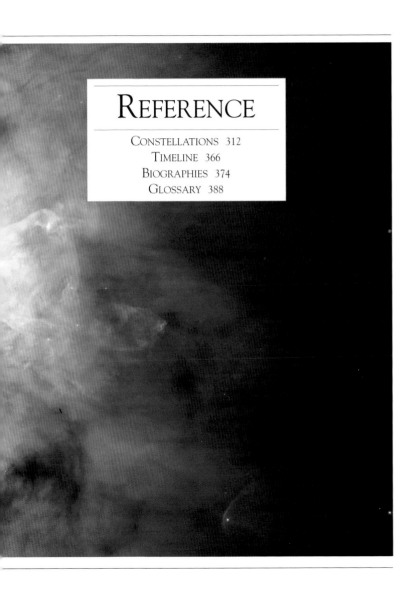

REFERENCE

CONSTELLATIONS 312
TIMELINE 366
BIOGRAPHIES 374
GLOSSARY 388

THE NORTHERN SKY

THE MAP ON THE RIGHT shows the main stars that lie north of the celestial equator. The stars seen on a particular night by people living in the Northern Hemisphere depend on the observer's latitude, the time of year, and the time of night. The stars near the center of the sky map are called circumpolar and can be seen throughout the year. Polaris (the North Star) appears to remain directly over the North Pole.

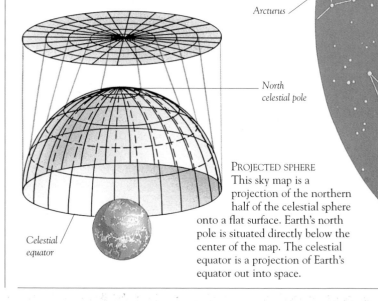

Arcturus

North celestial pole

Celestial equator

PROJECTED SPHERE
This sky map is a projection of the northern half of the celestial sphere onto a flat surface. Earth's north pole is situated directly below the center of the map. The celestial equator is a projection of Earth's equator out into space.

The edge of the map marks the celestial equator—stars here can also be seen by Southern Hemisphere observers

Polaris

The Big Dipper

The stars around the edge come into view month by month during the year

Betelgeuse

313

THE SOUTHERN SKY

THE MAP ON THE RIGHT shows the main stars that lie south of the celestial equator. The stars seen on a particular night by people living in the Southern Hemisphere depend on the observer's latitude, the time of year, and the time of night. The stars near the center of the sky map are called circumpolar and can be seen year-round. Alpha Centauri, one of the closest stars to the Sun, is a Southern Hemisphere star.

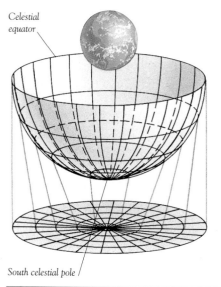

Celestial equator

South celestial pole

Alpha Centauri

Antares

PROJECTED SPHERE
This sky map is a projection of the southern half of the celestial sphere onto a flat surface. Earth's south pole is situated directly below the center of the map. The celestial equator is a projection of Earth's equator out into space.

The edge of the map marks the celestial equator—stars here can also be seen by Northern Hemisphere observers

Sirius

Canopus

The stars near the edge become visible month by month through the year

315

CONSTELLATIONS GUIDE

There are 88 internationally agreed constellations and all have Latin names, listed here alphabetically. They provide a useful map of the night sky and help astronomers describe the positions of planets, stars, and other objects in the cosmos. You can only see a fraction of the constellations each night. The constellations you will see depend on the time of night, the time of year, and your location. The maps under each constellation will help you figure out which constellations are visible where you live.

KEY TO CONSTELLATION VISIBILITY CHARTS

— Area from which constellation is not visible
— Area from which only part of the constellation can be seen

— Area from which entire constellation is visible

Andromeda

Aquila

Boötes

Canes Venatici

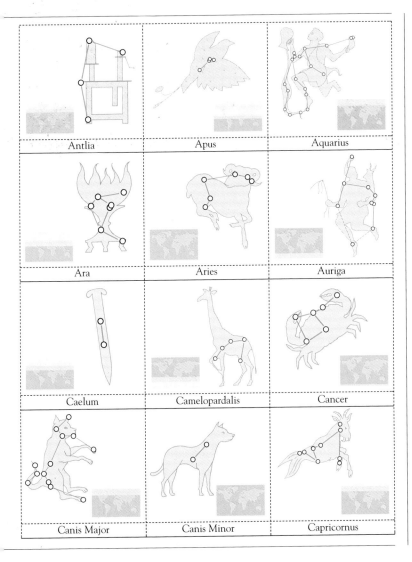

Antlia	Apus	Aquarius
Ara	Aries	Auriga
Caelum	Camelopardalis	Cancer
Canis Major	Canis Minor	Capricornus

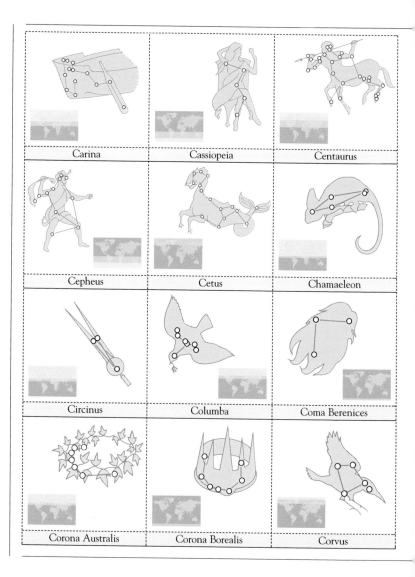

Carina

Cassiopeia

Centaurus

Cepheus

Cetus

Chamaeleon

Circinus

Columba

Coma Berenices

Corona Australis

Corona Borealis

Corvus

Crater	Crux	Cygnus
Delphinus	Dorado	Draco
Equuleus	Eridanus	Fornax
Gemini	Grus	Hercules

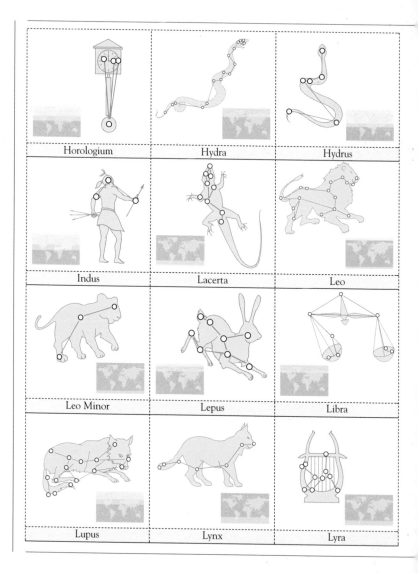

Horologium

Hydra

Hydrus

Indus

Lacerta

Leo

Leo Minor

Lepus

Libra

Lupus

Lynx

Lyra

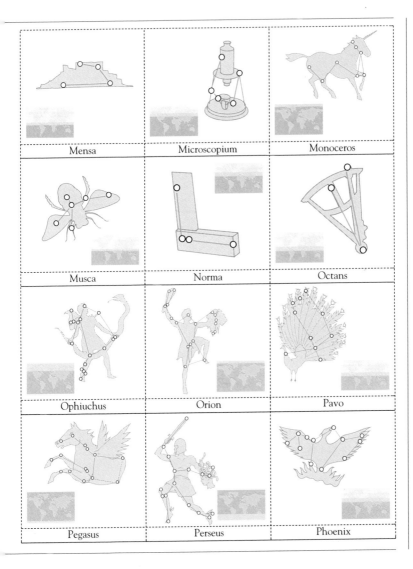

Mensa

Microscopium

Monoceros

Musca

Norma

Octans

Ophiuchus

Orion

Pavo

Pegasus

Perseus

Phoenix

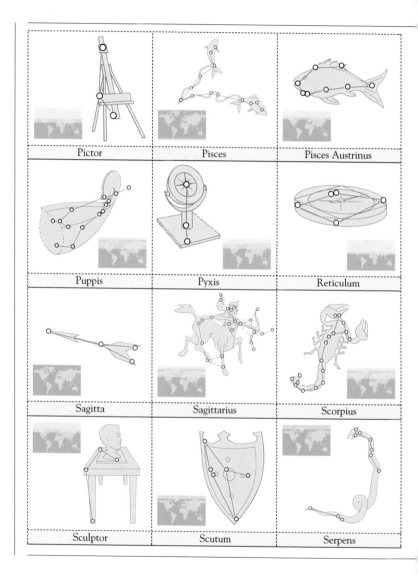

Pictor	Pisces	Pisces Austrinus
Puppis	Pyxis	Reticulum
Sagitta	Sagittarius	Scorpius
Sculptor	Scutum	Serpens

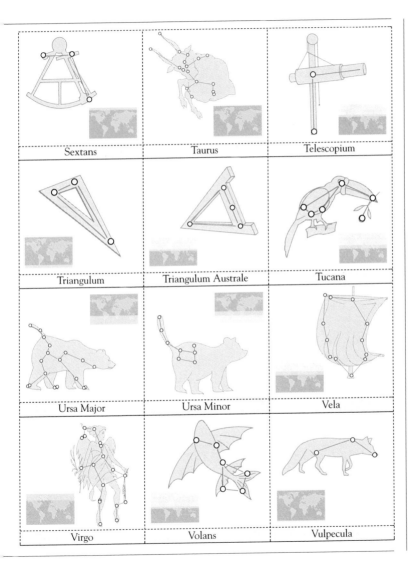

Sextans	Taurus	Telescopium
Triangulum	Triangulum Australe	Tucana
Ursa Major	Ursa Minor	Vela
Virgo	Volans	Vulpecula

ANDROMEDA

DEPICTING A GREEK PRINCESS who
was rescued by Perseus, Andromeda
contains the nearest major galaxy
to us, M31—the Andromeda
Galaxy—which is the most distant
object visible to the naked eye.

ANDROMEDA GALAXY

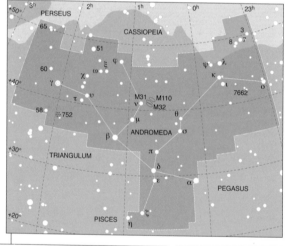

M31 (THE ANDROMEDA GALAXY) 👁️🔭 A spiral galaxy, similar to the Milky Way but larger. On a clear night, it can be seen by the naked eye as an elongated smudge. A large telescope is needed to see its spiral arms.

NGC 752 An open cluster, visible through binoculars, consisting of faint stars spread over an area of sky wider than a full moon. It lies about 1,300 light-years away.

NGC 7662 A planetary nebula, about 4,000 light-years away. It looks small but prominent through a telescope, like a blue-green star of 9th magnitude.

GAMMA (γ) ANDROMEDAE A double star that appears as a single star to the naked eye. A small telescope will reveal an orange-colored primary giant star, with a blue companion of 5th magnitude.

KEY ON PAGE 324

AQUARIUS

THIS CONSTELLATION REPRESENTS a youth pouring
water from a jar. The "Water Jar" is
represented by a Y-shaped group of
four stars, Gamma (γ), Zeta (ζ), Eta
(η), and Pi (π) Aquarii. The stream
of water flows into the mouth of a
large fish, represented by the Piscis
Austrinus constellation to the south.

THE HELIX NEBULA

NGC 7293 (THE HELIX NEBULA) ♁ ⊁
Possibly the closest planetary nebula to Earth
(only about 300 light-years away), and over a
third the diameter of a full moon. Its light is
spread over a wide area, making it difficult to
spot. It can be seen through binoculars or a
wide-field telescope as a pale gray patch.

M2 ♁ ⊁ A globular cluster, resembling a fuzzy
star, too faint to be seen with the naked eye but
easy to see with binoculars or a small telescope.

NGC 7009 (The Saturn Nebula) ⊁ A
planetary nebula. When seen through a
telescope with an aperture of 8 in (200 mm)
or more, it appears to have appendages that
resemble the rings of Saturn, hence its
popular name.

ZETA (ζ) AQUARII ⊁ A close binary of white,
4th-magnitude stars that orbit each other every
760 years or so. They can be separated using a
high magnification 3-in (75-mm) telescope.

325

CARINA

THIS LARGE CONSTELLATION contains Canopus, the second-brightest star. In Greek times, it was part of Argo Navis, a larger constellation, representing the Argonauts' ship, but was made separate in the 18th century. It represents the ship's keel, with Canopus as the rudder. The other parts of the ship—Vela (the sails) and Puppis (the stern)—lie to the north.

KEY ON PAGE 324

STAR CLUSTERS AND NEBULAS IN CARINA

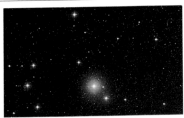

IC 2602 (The Southern Pleiades)

ETA (η) CARINAE A remarkable variable star. Currently it is of 5th magnitude, but it has been much brighter in the past, most noticeably in the 19th century, when it flared up to nearly –1. Eta Carinae is thought to be either a supergiant with a mass of 100 Suns—one of the most massive stars known—or possibly a massive binary. Through a telescope, it appears as a hazy orange ellipse, because of matter thrown off in its last outburst. Its distance is estimated at over 8,000 light-years, and it lies within the extensive nebula NGC 3372.

NGC 3372 (The Eta Carinae Nebula) A large, bright, diffuse nebula, four times the apparent width of a full moon, surrounding the star Eta (η) Carinae. The nebula is visible to the naked eye against the Milky Way and is best seen with binoculars. A V-shaped lane of dark dust runs through it. Near Eta Carinae itself, telescopes show a dark and bulbous cloud of dust called the Keyhole Nebula.

IC 2602 (The Southern Pleiades) A large and prominent open cluster, containing eight stars brighter than magnitude 6. The brightest member is Theta (θ) Carinae, a blue-white star of magnitude 2.7. The cluster appears twice the size of a full moon and lies about 500 light-years away.

NGC 3532 A bright and dense open cluster, elliptical in shape. It is visible to the naked eye and is a glorious sight through

binoculars, being nearly twice the apparent diameter of a full moon at its widest. It is 1,300 light-years away.

NGC 2516 An open cluster, visible to the naked eye. Using binoculars, it is possible to pick out its individual stars, the brightest being a 5th-magnitude red giant, scattered over an area of sky the size of a full moon. It is about 1,300 light-years away.

NGC 3114 An open cluster, visible to the naked eye and appearing about the same size as the disk of a full moon. Its individual stars can be seen through binoculars. It lies nearly 3,000 light-years away.

ALPHA (α) CARINAE (CANOPUS) The second brightest star in the sky, at magnitude –0.6. It is a white supergiant, 14,000 times more luminous than the Sun, lying 310 light-years away.

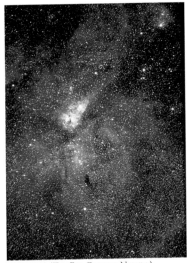

NGC 3372 (The Eta Carinae Nebula)

CENTAURUS

A LARGE CONSTELLATION in the southern Milky
Way, Centaurus depicts a centaur, the mythical
beast with the legs of a horse and the upper body
of a man. Its brightest star, Alpha (α) Centauri,
is the third-brightest in the sky.

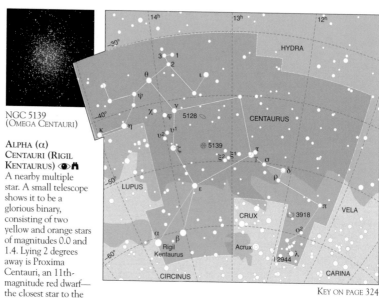

NGC 5139
(OMEGA CENTAURI)

**ALPHA (α)
CENTAURI (RIGIL
KENTAURUS)** ◉🄼🄰
A nearby multiple
star. A small telescope
shows it to be a
glorious binary,
consisting of two
yellow and orange stars
of magnitudes 0.0 and
1.4. Lying 2 degrees
away is Proxima
Centauri, an 11th-
magnitude red dwarf—
the closest star to the
Sun, being 4.2 light-years away, but 0.2 light-
years closer to us than the two brighter
members of the Alpha Centauri system.

NGC 5139 (OMEGA (Ω) CENTAURI) ◉🄼🄰
The largest, brightest globular cluster in the sky,
NGC5139 is about 17,000 light-years away.
Seen with the naked eye or binoculars, it appears

KEY ON PAGE 324

as a hazy 4th-magnitude patch larger than a
full moon. A small telescope shows its main stars.

NGC 5128 (CENTAURUS A) 🄰 An unusual
galaxy. With a small telescope, it looks like an
elliptical galaxy, but larger apertures show that it is
bisected by a dark dust lane due to a merger with
another galaxy. It is a strong radio source.

CRUX

THE SMALLEST CONSTELLATION, Crux forms one of the most famous star patterns. For the Greeks, it formed part of the hind legs of Centaurus, the centaur. It lies in a brilliant region of the Milky Way, and its longer axis points to the south celestial pole.

USING CRUX TO LOCATE
THE SOUTH CELESTIAL POLE

KEY ON PAGE 324

SOUTH CELESTIAL POLE
◉ ♄ ☆ The pole lies at the intersection of two imaginary lines—one between Alpha (α) and Gamma (γ) Crucis (top of picture), the other is at right angles to a line joining Alpha (α) and Beta (β) Centauri (bottom of picture).

NGC 4755 (THE JEWEL BOX, THE KAPPA (κ) CRUCIS CLUSTER) ◉ ♄ ☆ An open cluster visible to the naked eye as a bright knot between Beta (β) Crucis and the Coalsack. It is, in fact, far more distant than either of them, lying 7,600 light-years away. Most of its stars are blue-white supergiants, such as Kappa (κ) Crucis, although near its center there is a prominent red supergiant of 8th magnitude.

THE COALSACK ◉ ♄ A prominent, dark, wedge-shaped nebula 600 light-years away that blots out the light from the stars in the Milky Way behind it. It has no NGC reference number.

329

CYGNUS

THIS CONSTELLATION DEPICTS the swan into which, according to Greek myth, the god Zeus transformed himself. The swan's beak is marked by Beta (β) Cygni and its tail by Alpha (α) Cygni, named Deneb (from the Arabic for "tail"). Deneb forms one corner of the Summer Triangle, with Vega (in Lyra) and Altair (in Aquila) marking the other two. Identifiable by its cross shape, Cygnus is sometimes called the Northern Cross.

CYGNUS (INSET: ALBIREO)

KEY ON PAGE 324

NGC 6992 (THE VEIL NEBULA)

Part of a large, complex nebula called the Cygnus Loop, which is the remains of a star that exploded as a supernova perhaps 50,000 years ago. In clear skies, the Veil Nebula section can be seen with binoculars or a small telescope, but the whole nebula is best seen on photographs.

NGC 7000 (THE NORTH AMERICA NEBULA)

A large nebula, visible under dark skies with binoculars or a wide-field telescope, extending for up to four full moon diameters. It is best seen on long-exposure photographs, where it takes the shape of the continent of North America.

BETA (β) CYGNI (ALBIREO)

A beautiful double star. The two stars, magnitudes 3.1 and 5.1, can be divided with powerful binoculars. They are easy to separate with a telescope, which shows a contrast of orange and blue-green. Both stars lie 380 light-years away, but it is not known if they form a true binary.

M39

An open cluster, just visible to the naked eye under good conditions. Binoculars or a small telescope show its brightest stars. It lies nearly 900 light-years away.

61 CYGNI

An attractive double star. The two components, of magnitudes 5.2 and 6.1,

NGC 6992 (THE VEIL NEBULA)

NGC 7000 (THE NORTH AMERICA NEBULA)

can be seen separately through a small telescope or even powerful binoculars. Both are orange dwarfs, smaller and fainter than the Sun, and are easily visible because they are only 11.4 light-years away.

OMICRON-1 (o¹) CYGNI (31 CYGNI)

An orange-colored giant, magnitude 3.8, which has a wide 5th-magnitude, bluish companion (30 Cygni), ideal for binocular observation. A closer bluish star of 7th magnitude is also visible with binoculars or a small telescope.

NGC 6826 (THE BLINKING PLANETARY)

A planetary nebula visible with a small telescope as a bluish disk similar in size to the disk of Jupiter. Looking alternately at it and to one side gives the impression that it is blinking on and off.

CHI (χ) CYGNI

A pulsating red giant, one of the Mira class of variable stars, that ranges in brightness between 3rd and 14th magnitudes every 13 months or so.

ALPHA (α) CYGNI (DENEB)

The brightest star in Cygnus, at magnitude 1.3. It is a luminous blue-white supergiant lying more than 3,000 light-years away, which makes it the most distant star of all first-magnitude stars.

CYGNUS A

A peculiar galaxy, thought to be two distant galaxies in collision. A large telescope is needed to see it, since it is of 15th magnitude. It is also a strong radio source.

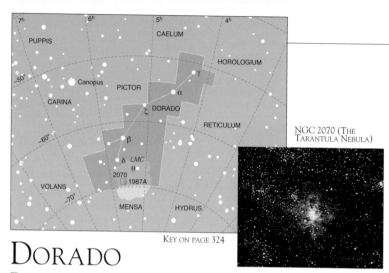

7h 6h 5h 4h

CAELUM

PUPPIS

HOROLOGIUM

-50°

Canopus   PICTOR

γ

CARINA   α

ζ   DORADO

RETICULUM

-60°   β

δ   LMC

θ

2070

1987A

VOLANS

-70°

MENSA   HYDRUS

KEY ON PAGE 324

NGC 2070 (THE TARANTULA NEBULA)

DORADO

DORADO, A SOUTHERN CONSTELLATION, was introduced in the 16th century by two Dutch navigators. It represents the goldfish of tropical seas, or a swordfish. It is significant for astronomers because it contains the bulk of the Large Magellanic Cloud—our nearest neighboring galaxy. Its brightest star is Alpha (α) Doradus of magnitude 3.3.

THE LARGE MAGELLANIC CLOUD (LMC)
A small galaxy, a satellite of our own, lying 170,000 light-years away. It is somewhat elongated in shape. It has about one-tenth the mass of our galaxy and a true diameter of 20,000 light-years. It is usually classified as an irregular galaxy, but there are traces of a barred spiral structure. Scanning it with binoculars or a small telescope brings many star clusters and glowing nebulas into view.

NGC 2070 (THE TARANTULA NEBULA)
A bright nebula in the LMC, visible to the naked eye. It appears about the same

size as a full moon, but its true diameter is about 800 light-years. The nebula is a star-forming region, and binoculars or a small telescope reveal a star cluster—30 Doradus—at its center.

BETA (β) DORADUS A bright Cepheid variable, ranging between magnitudes 3.5 and 4.1 every 9.8 days. It is a yellow-white super-giant and lies about 1,000 light-years away.

SUPERNOVA 1987A The brightest super-nova visible from Earth since 1604. In 1987, it reached magnitude 2.8 in the LMC.

DRACO

THIS EXTENSIVE CONSTELLATION represents a dragon that was slain by Hercules. In the northern sky, Hercules is represented with one foot on the dragon's head. Draco's brightest star is Gamma (γ) Draconis, a red giant about 150 light-years away. With the stars Beta (β), Nu (ν), and Xi (ξ) Draconis, it forms the head of the dragon.

MU (μ) DRACONIS
A double star, each star of 6th magnitude. The stars are 88 light-years away and orbit each other every 670 years.

NU (ν) DRACONIS
A wide, double star with twin white 5th-magnitude components that are almost identical in color and brightness. Both stars lie 100 light-years away.

PSI (ψ) DRACONIS
A double star. The two components, of magnitudes 4.6 and 5.8, may be divided with powerful binoculars.

KEY ON PAGE 324

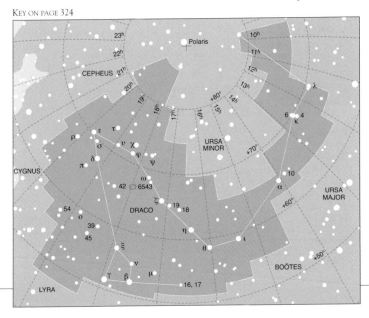

333

ORION

ORION IS THE MOST magnificent constellation. It represents a hunter with his dogs (marked by Canis Major and Canis Minor) at his heels. In Greek mythology, Orion was killed by a scorpion sting, and his position in the sky is such that he sets as the scorpion (the constellation Scorpius) rises. Orion's most celebrated feature is the M42 nebula.

ORION

KEY ON PAGE 324

M42 (THE ORION NEBULA) ⬤🔭☌
One of the most spectacular objects in the sky, the M42 nebula is a cloud of glowing gas with an apparent diameter over twice that of a full moon. Visible to the naked eye, it becomes larger and more complex when viewed with binoculars and telescopes of increasing aperture. It is 1,500 light-years away and is lit up by the stars of the Trapezium that lie within it.

NGC 1981 🔭 A large, scattered open cluster visible with binoculars, its brightest stars being of 6th magnitude. The cluster appears to the north of the Orion Nebula and lies at about the same distance as it does from Earth—approximately 1,400 light-years.

M42 (ORION NEBULA) WITH THE TRAPEZIUM INSET

THETA-1 (θ¹) ORIONIS (THE TRAPEZIUM) ✭
A multiple star, located at the heart of the
Orion Nebula. A small telescope shows it
to be a quadruple star, with components of
magnitudes 5.1, 6.7, 6.7, and 8.0 arranged
in a trapezoid shape.

ALPHA (α) ORIONIS (BETELGEUSE) 👁
A red supergiant star of variable brightness,
ranging from about magnitude 0 to 1.3 every
6 years or so. It lies 430 light-years away.
The name Betelgeuse is derived from an
Arabic term that incorporates a reference
to an armpit, although the star actually lies on
the hunter's shoulder.

BETA (β) ORIONIS (RIGEL) 👁 A blue supergiant of magnitude 0.2, the brightest star in the
constellation, and the seventh brightest in the
sky. It is 770 light years away. The name Rigel
means "left leg," which is the part of the
hunter's body that the star represents.

THETA-2 (θ²) ORIONIS ♙ A double star. The
two stars, magnitudes 5.0 and 6.4, are divisible
through binoculars. Theta-2 also forms a wide,
bright double with Theta-1 Orionis when
viewed through binoculars.

IOTA (ι) ORIONIS ♙✭ A double star. The two
components, of magnitudes 2.8 and 7.0, can be
split with a small telescope. Binoculars show
another nearby double—Struve 747—which
consists of stars of magnitudes 4.8 and 5.7.

SIGMA (σ) ORIONIS ✭ A remarkable multiple
star. The main star, of magnitude 3.8, has two
7th-magnitude companions to one side, and a
9th-magnitude companion on the other. A
faint triple star, called Struve 761, should
be visible in the same telescopic field of view.

THE HORSEHEAD NEBULA ♟ A dark nebula,
shaped like a chess knight, seen silhouetted
against a strip of brighter nebulosity that
extends south from Zeta (ζ) Orionis.
However, it is too faint to be viewed without
a large telescope, and its shape is most easily
seen on a long-exposure photograph.

THE HORSEHEAD NEBULA

335

SAGITTARIUS

THIS CONSTELLATION OF THE ZODIAC lies between Scorpius and Capricornus. It depicts Crotus, the inventor of archery, aiming his bow at a scorpion, represented by Scorpius. The Sun passes through Sagittarius from December 18 to January 19.

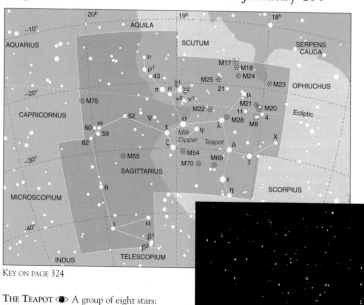

KEY ON PAGE 324

THE MAIN STARS IN SAGITTARIUS

THE TEAPOT ◉ A group of eight stars: Gamma (γ), Epsilon (η), Delta (δ), Lambda (λ), Phi (φ), Zeta (ζ), Sigma (σ), and Tau (τ) Sagittarii. Together, they form the outline of a teapot, with a pointed lid and a large spout. The stars Lambda (λ), Phi (φ), Zeta (ζ), Sigma (σ), and Tau (τ) Sagittarii also form a shape known as the Milk Dipper, so named because it lies in a rich area of the Milky Way.

M8 (THE LAGOON NEBULA) ◉▶♠ A bright nebula, visible to the naked eye and a good target for binoculars. Elongated in shape, it is

M8 (THE LAGOON NEBULA)

almost three times the apparent width of a full moon. A dark lane of dust bisects it—one half contains the cluster NGC 6530, with stars of 7th magnitude and fainter, while the most prominent object in the other half is the 6th-magnitude star 9 Sagittarii. The nebula, and the stars within it, are 5,200 light-years away.

M17 (THE OMEGA NEBULA) 🔭 A cloud of glowing gas of similar apparent size to a full moon. It can be seen through binoculars, although a telescope is needed to see its true shape. A small telescope shows a star cluster, NGC 6618, within the cloud. The nebula and cluster both lie about 4,900 light-years away.

M22 🔭 The third brightest globular cluster in the sky, 10,000 light-years away. It is visible to the naked eye under favorable conditions and easy to find with binoculars, which show it as a rounded patch about two-thirds the apparent size of a full moon.

M17 (THE OMEGA NEBULA)

M23 🔭 A rich open cluster, which is elongated in shape and is almost the same apparent width as a full moon. It can be seen with binoculars, while a small telescope will resolve its stars. The cluster lies 2,100 light-years away.

M24 🔭 A large and bright field of stars lying in the Milky Way. It is visible to the naked eye and is an excellent sight through binoculars. Viewing it with a small telescope reveals a small open cluster—NGC 6603—within it.

M20 (THE TRIFID NEBULA)

M25 🔭 An open cluster, just visible to the naked eye, and a good object for observation with binoculars or a small telescope. Its stars, of 7th magnitude and fainter, are scattered over an area of sky the same apparent size as a full moon. It lies 1,900 light-years away.

M20 (THE TRIFID NEBULA) 🔭 A nebula with a faint double star at its center, both of which are visible with a small telescope. Larger apertures show dust lanes trisecting the nebula.

BETA (β) SAGITTARII 🔭 A multiple star, although all the components lie at different distances and are unrelated. The naked eye sees it as a wide double with components of magnitudes 4.0 and 4.3. The brighter star, Beta-1 (β¹), has a 7th-magnitude companion that can be seen though a small telescope.

KEY ON PAGE 324

SCORPIUS

A CONSTELLATION OF THE ZODIAC, Scorpius lies between Libra and

THE MAIN STARS IN SCORPIUS

Sagittarius. It depicts the scorpion that, in Greek mythology, killed Orion with its sting—fittingly, Orion sets as Scorpius rises. The constellation lies in a rich region of the Milky Way, in the same direction as the center of our galaxy. The Sun passes through it briefly, from November 23 to 29.

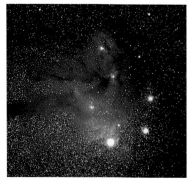

those with good eyesight. Zeta-1 (ζ^1) is a blue-white supergiant of magnitude 4.7, the brightest star in the cluster NGC 6231. Zeta-2 (ζ^2), a red giant of magnitude 3.6, is much closer at 150 light-years away.

ALPHA (α) SCORPII (ANTARES) A red supergiant star of variable brightness, ranging between magnitudes 0.9 and 1.2. It has a blue-white companion of 5th magnitude that can be seen with a telescope of moderate aperture.

BETA (β) SCORPII A double star, which has components of magnitudes 2.6 and 4.9 that are easy to separate with a small telescope. The two stars are unrelated, lying at distances of 530 and 1,100 light-years.

M6 An open cluster, 2,000 light-years away. It is visible to the naked eye, and its individual stars can be seen with binoculars. Its brightest star is BM Scorpii, an orange giant that varies between 5th and 7th magnitudes.

NU (ν) SCORPII A multiple star. A small telescope, or even good binoculars, will reveal an optical double, with components of magnitudes 4.0 and 6.3. The fainter star of the pair has an 8th-magnitude companion that can be seen through a telescope with an aperture of 3 in (75 mm). Larger apertures show that the brighter star has an even closer companion of 5th magnitude—hence it appears to be a quadruple.

M7 A large, glorious open cluster, visible with the naked eye and binoculars, and more than twice the apparent width of a full moon. Its brightest stars, of 6th magnitude, are seen against a bright Milky Way background. The cluster is 780 light-years away.

OMEGA (ω) SCORPII A naked-eye double star, with components of magnitudes 3.9 and 4.3, 420 and 260 light-years away.

M4 One of the closest globular clusters, under 7,000 light-years away. It can be seen with binoculars or a small telescope. A dark sky is needed—its stars are spread over a large area.

MU (μ) SCORPII A double star that can be divided with the naked eye. The brighter component is an eclipsing binary that varies between magnitudes 2.9 and 3.2 every 34 hours. Its companion is of magnitude 3.6.

NGC 6231 A prominent open cluster 5,900 light-years away. Its individual stars are easy to see with binoculars or a small telescope. Zeta-1 (ζ^1) Scorpii is its brightest member.

ZETA (ζ) SCORPII A wide pair of unrelated stars, divisible with the naked eye by

M4

Key on page 324

Taurus

THIS IMPOSING ZODIAC CONSTELLATION, between Aries and Gemini, represents the bull into which the Greek god Zeus transformed himself. It contains two major star clusters—the Pleiades and Hyades. The Hyades cluster marks the bull's face, while the red giant star Aldebaran forms its bloodshot eye. The bull's horn-tips are marked by Beta (β) and Zeta (ζ).

M1 (THE CRAB NEBULA)

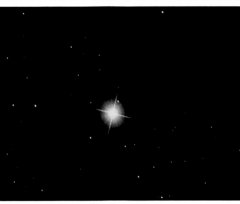

ALDEBARAN (ALPHA TAURI)

M45 (THE PLEIADES) ◉♠⚹ A large, bright, open star cluster, easy to see with the naked eye and a superb sight through binoculars, appearing almost four times wider than a full moon. Its brightest star is Eta (η) Tauri (Alcyone), a blue-white giant of magnitude 2.9. The naked eye can see about six stars, but dozens are visible with binoculars or a small telescope. The cluster is about 380 light-years away. Long-exposure photographs show nebulosity around the stars, but a large telescope is needed to see this directly.

THE HYADES ◉♠⚹ A large, loose, V-shaped star cluster, easily visible to the naked eye. It is best viewed with binoculars due to its considerable size, being scattered across the apparent width of 10 full moons. The cluster lies about 150 light-years away.

M1 (THE CRAB NEBULA) ♠⚹ The remains of a supernova that was seen from Earth in 1054 CE. Under good conditions it can be found with binoculars or a small telescope, but a moderate aperture is needed to see it well. It is elliptical in shape, appearing midway in size between the disk of a planet and a full moon. It lies about 6,500 light-years away.

THETA (θ) TAURI ◉♠ A wide double star in the Hyades cluster. Observers with good eyesight can divide the two stars with the naked eye. Theta-1 (θ¹) is a yellow giant, magnitude 3.8; Theta-2 (θ²) is a white giant of magnitude 3.4—the brightest member of the Hyades.

ALPHA (α) TAURI (ALDEBARAN) ◉ A red giant star, which varies irregularly in brightness between magnitudes 0.75 and 0.95. Although it appears to be a member of the Hyades cluster, it is actually much closer to us, being 65 light-years away.

LAMBDA (λ) TAURI ◉ An eclipsing binary star, which is of the same type as Algol. The magnitudes of this star range from 3.4 and 3.9 in a cycle lasting just under 4 days.

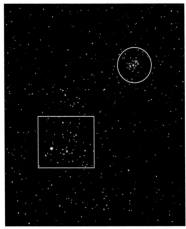

THE HYADES AND PLEIADES

URSA MAJOR

THE THIRD LARGEST CONSTELLATION, Ursa Major represents Callisto, who, in Greek myth, was a hunting partner of Artemis. She was seduced by Zeus and then turned into a bear by the angry Artemis. Its brightest stars are Alpha (α) and Epsilon (ε), both with magnitude 1.8.

KEY ON PAGE 324

CONSTELLATIONS

344

URSA MAJOR

THE BIG DIPPER ◉ One of the best-known patterns in the sky, consisting of the naked-eye stars Alpha (α), Beta (β), Gamma (γ), Delta (δ), Epsilon (ε), Zeta (ζ), and Eta (η) Ursae Majoris. The outline that they form is visualized in various cultures as that of a ladle, a plow, a saucepan, and even a wagon. All the stars in the Big Dipper, with the exception of the outermost two (Alpha and Eta), are traveling in the same direction through space and form what is known as a moving cluster.

M81 AND M82 ♈⚹ Two contrasting galaxies, about 10 million light-years away. M81 is a beautiful spiral, visible with binoculars or a small telescope. One moon diameter to the north is the smaller and fainter M82, a galaxy of peculiar appearance, which is now thought to be a spiral, seen edge-on, that is passing through a dust cloud.

ZETA (ζ) URSAE MAJORIS (MIZAR) ◉♈⚹ A multiple star. Observers with good eyesight or using binoculars will see that this star, of magnitude 2.2, has a partner of magnitude 4.0, known as Alcor or 80 Ursae Majoris. Mizar and Alcor are 78 and 81 light years away, so they are not a true binary pair. However, a small telescope reveals that Mizar has a closer 4th-magnitude companion. This pair forms a true binary with a very long orbital period.

M101 ♈⚹ A spiral galaxy, which appears face-on to us. It covers almost as much sky as a full moon but it is quite faint, and good conditions are required if it is to be seen with binoculars or a small telescope.

XI (ξ) URSAE MAJORIS ⚹ A binary star, with close components of magnitudes 4.3 and 4.8 that can be separated through a telescope of 3 in (75 mm) aperture. The yellowish stars, similar to the Sun, are 26 light-years away and have an orbital period of 60 years.

M81

M101

POLAR STAR MAPS

THESE MAPS SHOW stars, clusters, and galaxies visible all year in both hemispheres. To see what is visible, face north in the Northern Hemisphere and south in the Southern, turning the map so that the observing month is at the top. This will show the sky at 10 p.m. (11 p.m. during daylight saving time). If it is earlier, for each hour before 10 p.m., turn the map 1 hour clockwise in the Northern Hemisphere and counterclockwise in the Southern.

KEY TO THE STAR MAPS

Magnitudes								Open cluster
	-1	0	1	2	3	4	5 6	Globular cluster
Double stars								Bright nebula
Variable stars				M i l k y W a y				Planetary nebula
								Supernova remnant
Constellation outline			Constellation boundary					Galaxy

CONSTELLATIONS

Originally, a constellation was a distinct pattern of stars, given a Latin name. In 1930, astronomers agreed to divide the sky into 88 areas, like countries on an Earth map, each containing a different constellation. The constellation name can now refer to this area of sky as well as the star pattern it contains.

NORTH POLAR HIGHLIGHTS
The seven main stars of Ursa Major make an easily recognized pattern, called the Big Dipper. The stars Merak and Dubhe point toward Polaris, the Pole Star, which is in almost exactly the same position every night. Opposite the Big Dipper from Polaris is the W-shape of Cassiopeia.

BIG DIPPER

CIRCUMPOLAR STARS
Stars that never rise and set are called circumpolar. Though they are always visible, their position is constantly changing. The circumpolar area of sky varies by distance from the equator. At the Poles, all stars are circumpolar; at the equator, they all rise and set.

URSA MINOR

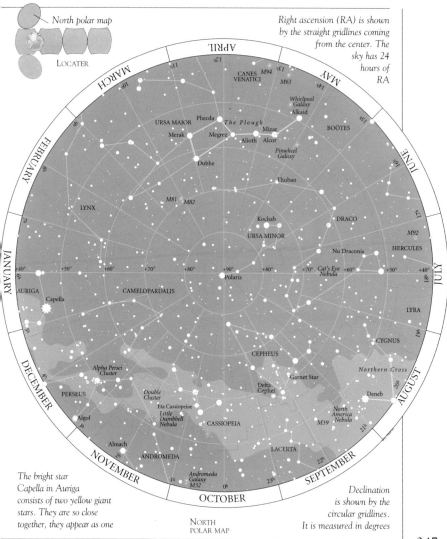

North polar map

LOCATER

Right ascension (RA) is shown by the straight gridlines coming from the center. The sky has 24 hours of RA

APRIL
MARCH
MAY

CANES VENATICI
M94
13ʰ
Whirlpool Galaxy
M63
14ʰ

URSA MAJOR
Phecda
The Plough
Mizar
Alkaid
BOÖTES

Merak
Megrez
Alioth
Alcor

FEBRUARY
10ʰ
9ʰ

Dubhe
Pinwheel Galaxy
15ʰ

Thuban
JUNE
16ʰ

M81
M82
Kochab
DRACO
17ʰ

LYNX
URSA MINOR
M92
HERCULES

JANUARY
8ʰ
+40° +50° +60° +70° +80° +90° +80° +70° +60° +50° +40°
Nu Draconis
18ʰ
JULY

AURIGA
Polaris
Cat's Eye Nebula

Capella
CAMELOPARDALIS
LYRA

CYGNUS

CEPHEUS

DECEMBER
Alpha Persei Cluster
Garnet Star
Northern Cross
AUGUST

PERSEUS
Double Cluster
Delta Cephei
Deneb
20ʰ

Algol
Eta Cassiopeiae
Little Dumbbell Nebula
North America Nebula
M39

Almach
CASSIOPEIA
LACERTA
21ʰ

ANDROMEDA
22ʰ

NOVEMBER
Andromeda Galaxy
M32
23ʰ
SEPTEMBER

The bright star Capella in Auriga consists of two yellow giant stars. They are so close together, they appear as one

1ʰ
0ʰ
OCTOBER

NORTH POLAR MAP

Declination is shown by the circular gridlines. It is measured in degrees

347

Crux is the smallest constellation in the sky but is one of the best known. Its main stars are on the flags of Australia and New Zealand

LOCATER

South polar map

APRIL

MARCH

MAY

FEBRUARY

JUNE

JULY

AUGUST

SEPTEMBER

OCTOBER

NOVEMBER

DECEMBER

CENTAURUS

Centaurus A

Omega Centauri

Eight-Burst Nebula

Southern Cross

VELA

Gacrux

Blue Planetary Nebula

LUPUS

Mimosa

NGC3532

CRUX

Acrux

Eta Carinae

Gamma Velorum

Jewel Box

Hadar

Coalsack

Carina Nebula

IC2391

Southern Pleiades

NGC2547

Alpha Centauri

NORMA

CIRCINUS

MUSCA

NGC2516

PUPPIS

NGC6231

TRIANGULUM AUSTRALE

CHAMAELEON

CARINA

SCORPIUS

ARA

APUS

VOLANS

Canopus

OCTANS

Sigma Octantis

MENSA

PICTOR

COLUMBA

TELESCOPIUM

Tarantula Nebula

Large Magellanic Cloud

DORADO

CORONA AUSTRALIS

PAVO

Small Magellanic Cloud

HYDRUS

RETICULUM

CAELUM

SAGITTARIUS

Peacock

47 Tucanae

HOROLOGIUM

MICROSCOPIUM

INDUS

TUCANA

Achernar

ERIDANUS

GRUS

Alnair

PHOENIX

Delta Gruis

Alpha Centauri is the closest bright star to the Sun, 4.4 light-years away. It is actually a double star

SOUTH POLAR MAP

The Large and Small Magellanic Clouds are galaxies in orbit around the Milky Way. Both are visible to the naked eye

348

SOUTH POLAR HIGHLIGHTS

The best-known feature of the southern sky is the Southern Cross, which is made up of the five brightest stars of Crux. Follow a line from Gacrux through Acrux to locate the south celestial pole, which is at the center of the map. Two bright stars, Alpha Centauri and Hadar, point toward the Southern Cross.

SOUTHERN CROSS

PHOENIX

SOUTHERN PLEIADES

This open star cluster, also known as IC 2602, is easily seen with the naked eye. It is called the Southern Pleiades because of its similarity to the Pleiades in Taurus. It contains about 30 stars, eight of which are brighter than magnitude 6.

USING A PLANISPHERE

A planisphere is a circular star map with a mask that rotates to show the area of sky visible over a specific latitude at any given date or time. Held upside down, it shows the stars visible at that point. Know your latitude before buying one.

PHOENIX

Phoenix lies near the southern end of Eridanus, close to the bright star Achernar. It is the largest of the 12 constellations invented at the end of the 16th century, and represents the mythical bird that was supposedly reborn from the dead body of its predecessor.

SCALE IN THE SKY

Hands can be used to measure distances in the sky. A full circle, with you at the center, is 360°. A finger at arm's length covers about 1°—twice the size of the Moon. A closed hand is about 10°, the width of the Big Dipper's bowl, while an open hand is 16° to 20°, the width of the Square of Pegasus.

Full Moon   *Big Dipper*   *Square of Pegasus*

ONE FINGER   CLOSED HAND   OPEN HAND

CONSTELLATIONS

NORTHERN HEMISPHERE STAR MAPS, JUNE TO NOVEMBER

The Northern Hemisphere maps show the stars with the observer facing south. Choose the map with the month in which you are observing. This will show the night sky as it appears at 10 p.m. (11 p.m. during daylight saving time), with stars to the west visible earlier and those to the east visible later. The stars near the bottom of the map will be visible on the southern horizon, and those at the top will be almost overhead.

LOCATER

Nov., Oct., Sept.

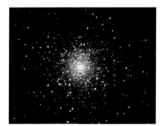

M15 GLOBULAR CLUSTER
This cluster can be seen about 20° to the right of the bottom of the Square of Pegasus. With binoculars, M15 looks hazy, but a telescope shows it to be ball-shaped.

KEY ON PAGE 346

SEPTEMBER TO NOVEMBER HIGHLIGHTS
The Square of Pegasus is the key pattern to look for. Its four stars, although not very bright, are easy to find because there are few other stars around. Use the edges to point to Andromeda, which shares one star—Alpheratz—with the Square. Alpheratz is actually in Andromeda.

MAP DATA

•The maps are designed to overlap. Stars at the sides are repeated on the next map. Stars at the top also appear on the outer edge of the north polar map, and those along the bottom on the south polar map. If joined together, they would form one continuous map.

• Right Ascension, the equivalent of longitude on Earth, is labeled in hours along the top and bottom. Declination, the equivalent to latitude, is labeled in degrees on both edges.

• Andromeda Galaxy is the most distant object visible to the naked eye. Find it by moving northeast from Alpheratz.

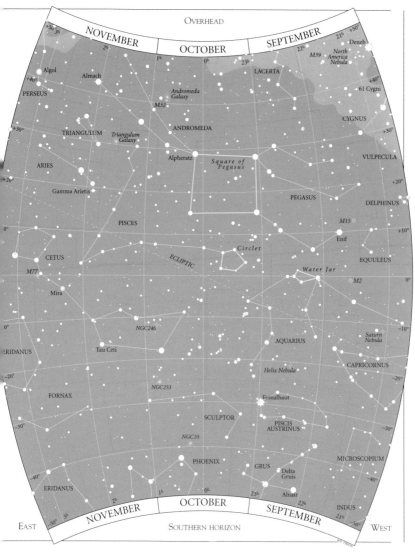

OVERHEAD

NOVEMBER
OCTOBER
SEPTEMBER

+50° 3ʰ
2ʰ
1ʰ
0ʰ
23ʰ
22ʰ
21ʰ Deneb
+50°

Algol
Almach
M39
North
America
Nebula

LACERTA

+40°
PERSEUS
Andromeda
Galaxy
61 Cygni
+40°

M32
CYGNUS

+30°
TRIANGULUM
Triangulum
Galaxy
ANDROMEDA
VULPECULA
+30°

ARIES
Alpheratz
Square of
Pegasus
DELPHINUS

+20°
Gamma Arietis
PEGASUS
+20°

PISCES
M15
EQUULEUS
+10°

0°
Enif
Circlet

CETUS
ECLIPTIC
Water Jar
M2
0°

M77
Mira

Saturn
Nebula

0°
NGC246
AQUARIUS
-10°

ERIDANUS
Tau Ceti
CAPRICORNUS

-20°
Helix Nebula
-20°

NGC253
Fomalhaut

FORNAX
PISCIS
AUSTRINUS

-30°
SCULPTOR
-30°

NGC55
MICROSCOPIUM

PHOENIX
GRUS
Delta
Gruis

-40°
Alnair
-40°

ERIDANUS
INDUS

-50° 3ʰ
2ʰ
1ʰ
0ʰ
23ʰ
22ʰ
21ʰ
-50°

EAST
NOVEMBER
OCTOBER
SEPTEMBER
WEST

SOUTHERN HORIZON

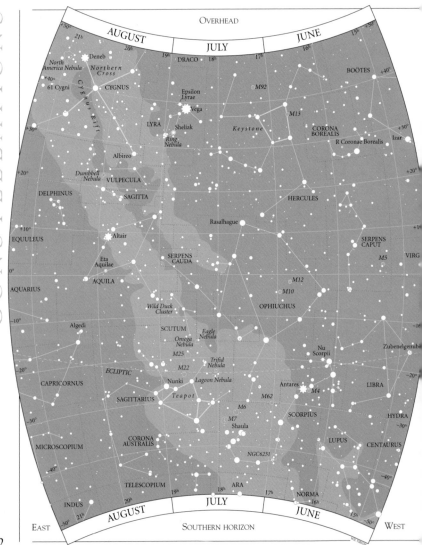

OVERHEAD

AUGUST

JULY

JUNE

+50° 21ʰ 20ʰ 19ʰ DRACO 18ʰ 17ʰ 16ʰ 15ʰ +50°

North America Nebula

Deneb

Northern Cross

BOÖTES +40°

61 Cygni

CYGNUS

M92

Cygnus Rift

+30° Epsilon Lyrae M13 CORONA BOREALIS +30°

LYRA Vega Keystone

Sheliak R Coronae Borealis Izar

Albireo Ring Nebula

Dumbbell Nebula +20° VULPECULA +20°

DELPHINUS SAGITTA HERCULES

+10° Rasalhague +10°

EQUULEUS Altair SERPENS CAPUT

VIRG

Eta Aquilae M5

0° SERPENS CAUDA

AQUILA

AQUARIUS M12

M10

-10° OPHIUCHUS -16

Algedi Wild Duck Cluster

SCUTUM Eagle Nebula Zubenelgenubi

Omega Nebula

-20° M25 LIBRA -20°

CAPRICORNUS ECLIPTIC M22 Trifid Nebula Nu Scorpii

Nunki Lagoon Nebula Antares M4 HYDRA

SAGITTARIUS Teapot M62 -30° MICROSCOPIUM -30°

M6 SCORPIUS

M7 Shaula LUPUS CENTAURUS

CORONA AUSTRALIS

-40° NGC6231 -40°

TELESCOPIUM

INDUS 21ʰ 20ʰ 19ʰ 18ʰ ARA 17ʰ NORMA 16ʰ 13ʰ

-50° AUGUST JULY JUNE -50°

EAST SOUTHERN HORIZON WEST

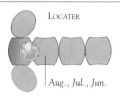

LOCATER

Aug., Jul., Jun.

JUNE TO AUGUST HIGHLIGHTS

The Milky Way dominates the view, along with the Summer Triangle of Deneb, Vega, and Altair. Cygnus points along the galaxy, while the dark band between Cygnus and Serpens—the Cygnus Rift—hides the stars beyond. Look for arrow-shaped Sagitta and Scutum—near them is a bright patch of the Milky Way. To the south, the distinctive patterns of Scorpius and Sagittarius lie on either side of the Milky Way.

DUMBBELL NEBULA

Below Cygnus lies a small, faint planetary nebula. It is visible through binoculars, although its colors do not show up. It gets its name from its brightest parts, which show up looking like a dumbbell in small telescopes.

Dumbbell Nebula is the remains of a star that died thousands of years ago

WILD DUCK CLUSTER

This open star cluster, which is at the top of Scutum, is just visible with the naked eye. When viewed through a pair of binoculars, its stars are in a V-shape that looks like a flight of ducks—hence its name.

KEY ON PAGE 346

MAP DATA

• Three bright stars from different constellations—Deneb in Cygnus, Vega in Lyra, and Altair in Aquila—make up the Summer Triangle.

• Albireo is a double star that marks the head of Cygnus, the swan. In high-powered binoculars, its two stars have contrasting yellow and blue colors.

• The Eagle Nebula, just below Serpens Cauda, is visible as a hazy spot of light in binoculars. A medium-sized telescope reveals a dark shape within the nebula, which in photographs looks like an eagle flapping its wings.

CONSTELLATIONS

353

NORTHERN HEMISPHERE STAR MAPS, DECEMBER TO MAY

In winter, constellations and stars—including the brightest constellation, Orion, and the brightest star, Sirius—are the main attractions because the Milky Way is faint. Most of the visible stars, as well as several star nurseries such as the Orion Nebula, are in the Local Arm of the galaxy. Star clusters are common, too. By spring, the view shifts to looking sideways out of the Milky Way, and the Virgo cluster is visible.

LOCATER

May, Apr., Mar.

MARCH TO MAY highlights

The constellation Leo is easy to spot, with a curve of stars—called the Sickle—marking its head. More difficult to see is Virgo and the Virgo Cluster of 2,000 galaxies, to the southeast of Leo. Below Virgo is a small constellation with four distinctive stars, Corvus. It is easy to find in the sky, though its stars are not very bright.

BLACK EYE GALAXY

A spiral galaxy just below Coma Berenices, the Black Eye Galaxy has a dark dust lane near its center. Small telescopes just show a little hazy oval of light, but large telescopes make it look like an eye, hence the name.

KEY ON PAGE 346

MAP DATA

• Arcturus, in Boötes, is a red giant and the fourth-brightest star in the sky.

• The M65 and M66 galaxies in Leo are easy to find because they are quite bright and lie between two fairly bright stars. With a telescope, the galaxies look like tiny, hazy spindles.

• Porrima in Virgo is a double star. From 2005 to 2007, the stars will be so close to each other that even with a telescope, they will look like a single star. The next time this occurs will be in 2174.

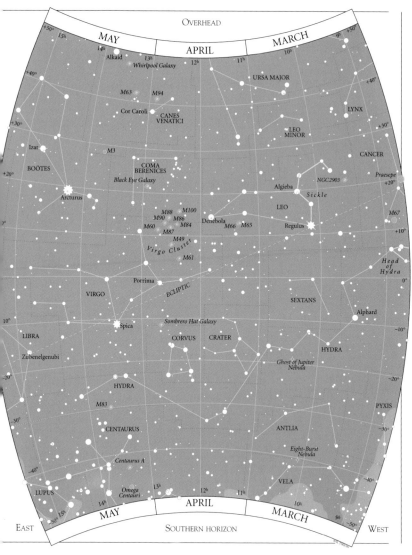

OVERHEAD

MAY
APRIL
MARCH

+50° 15ʰ
14ʰ
Alkaid 13ʰ
Whirlpool Galaxy 12ʰ 11ʰ 10ʰ 9ʰ +50°

+40°
URSA MAJOR +40°

M63 M94

Cor Caroli CANES
VENATICI LYNX

+30°
LEO
MINOR +30°

Izar
M3 CANCER

BOÖTES
COMA
BERENICES Algieba *Sickle* NGC2903 *Praesepe* +20°

+20°
Black Eye Galaxy

Arcturus M88 M100 LEO M67

M90 M86
M60 M84 Denebola M66 M65 Regulus +10°
M87
M49
Virgo Cluster M61 *Head
of
Hydra* 0°

Porrima ECLIPTIC

VIRGO SEXTANS

10° Spica Alphard -10°

LIBRA *Sombrero Hat Galaxy*

Zubenelgenubi CORVUS CRATER HYDRA

-20° *Ghost of Jupiter
Nebula* -20°

HYDRA

M83 PYXIS

CENTAURUS ANTLIA -30°

*Eight-Burst
Nebula*

Centaurus A VELA

-40°
LUPUS *Omega
Centauri* 13ʰ 12ʰ 11ʰ 10ʰ 9ʰ -50°

-50° 15ʰ
14ʰ

EAST MAY APRIL MARCH WEST

SOUTHERN HORIZON

355

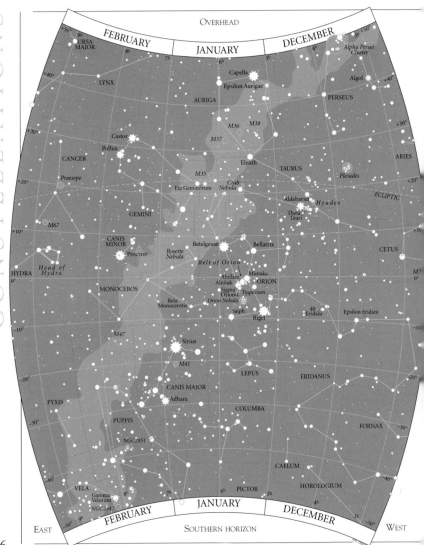

OVERHEAD

FEBRUARY

JANUARY

DECEMBER

+50° 9ʰ
URSA
MAJOR
8ʰ
LYNX
7ʰ
+40°
+40°
6ʰ
Capella
Epsilon Aurigae
AURIGA
5ʰ
4ʰ
3ʰ +50°
Alpha Persei
Cluster
Algol
PERSEUS
+40°

+30°
Castor
Pollux
CANCER
M36 M38
M37
+30°
ARIES

Praesepe
M35
Crab
Nebula
Eta Geminorum
Elnath
TAURUS
Pleiades
+20°
+20°
ECLIPTIC

+10°
M67
GEMINI
Aldebaran Hyades
Theta
Tauri
+10°

CANIS
MINOR
Betelgeuse
Bellatrix
CETUS

HYDRA
Head of
Hydra
0°
Procyon
Rosette
Nebula
Belt of Orion
M7?
0°

MONOCEROS
Alnilam Mintaka
Alnitak ORION
Sigma
Orionis Trapezium
Orion Nebula
40
Eridani
Epsilon Eridani
−10°

Beta
Monocerotis
Saiph
Rigel

M47
Sirius
LEPUS
ERIDANUS
−20°
−20°

PYXIS
M41
CANIS MAJOR
Adhara
COLUMBA
FORNAX
−30°

PUPPIS
NGC2451
CAELUM
HOROLOGIUM
−40°

VELA
Gamma
Velorum
NGC2547
8ʰ 7ʰ 6ʰ 5ʰ
PICTOR
4ʰ 3ʰ
−50° 9ʰ
−30°

FEBRUARY

JANUARY

DECEMBER

EAST

SOUTHERN HORIZON

WEST

LOCATER

Feb., Jan., Dec.

DECEMBER TO FEBRUARY HIGHLIGHTS

Orion is a signpost in the sky. Above it is Auriga, with the M36 and M38 star clusters. The three stars in Orion's Belt point down to Sirius in Canis Major, and up to Aldebaran in Taurus and the Pleiades beyond. Betelgeuse, Sirius, and Procyon (in Canis Minor) form the Winter Triangle. A diagonal through Rigel and Betelgeuse leads to Gemini.

M36 AND M38 CLUSTERS

The brighter of the two open star clusters is M36. Both are visible with the naked eye. Since M36 and M38 appear quite close, they can easily be mistaken for a comet at a casual glance.

M38—a wide area with about 100 stars scattered across it

M36 is a compact cluster of about 60 stars

PRAESEPE

An open star cluster in Cancer, Praesepe—visible with the naked eye on clear and dark nights—is a splendid sight when viewed with binoculars.

M35 CLUSTER

An open star cluster of about 120 stars to the north of Eta Geminorum, M35 is just visible with the naked eye. It is easy to spot with binoculars, which will show some of its brightest stars.

MAP DATA

• The Orion Nebula is the brightest nebula in the sky. It appears as a misty patch to the naked eye, but small telescopes show a group of four stars—the Trapezium—at its center.

KEY ON PAGE 346

CONSTELLATIONS

357

SOUTHERN HEMISPHERE STAR MAPS, SEPTEMBER TO FEBRUARY

The Southern Hemisphere maps show the stars when viewed looking north. Choose the map with the month in which you are observing. This will show the night sky as it appears at 10 p.m. (11 p.m. during daylight saving time), with stars to the west visible earlier and those farther to the east later. Stars near the bottom of the map will be visible on the northern horizon, and those at the top will be almost overhead.

Sept., Oct., Nov.

LOCATER

HELIX NEBULA
The largest, and closest, planetary nebula is the Helix Nebula in Aquarius. It can be seen in a very dark sky, using binoculars or a telescope. The red color shows up only in photographs.

KEY ON PAGE 346

SEPTEMBER TO NOVEMBER HIGHLIGHTS
The brightest star in this part of the sky is Fomalhaut in Piscis Austrinus—the southern fish. The Square of Pegasus is in the northern sky. Use the edges and diagonals of the Square to locate Andromeda, Aquarius, Pisces, and Cetus. The stars in Pisces are all faint.

MAP DATA

• The maps have been designed to overlap. Stars at the edges are repeated on the next map. Stars at the top also appear on the outer edge of the south polar map, and those along the bottom on the north polar map. If joined together, they would form one continuous map.

• Right Ascension, the equivalent of longitude on Earth, is labeled in hours along the top and bottom. Declination, the equivalent of latitude, is labeled in degrees on both edges.

• Triangulum Galaxy, a misty patch the size of a full moon, can be seen with binoculars in a dark night sky.

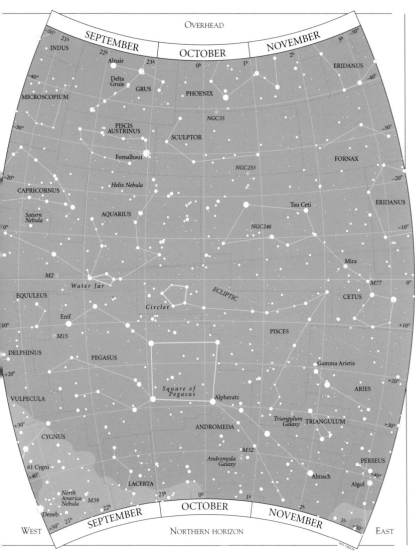

OVERHEAD

SEPTEMBER

OCTOBER

NOVEMBER

−50° 21ʰ
INDUS
22ʰ
Alnair
Delta
Gruis
GRUS
23ʰ
0ʰ
1ʰ
2ʰ
3ʰ −50°
ERIDANUS
−40°
MICROSCOPIUM
PHOENIX
NGC55
−30°
PISCIS
AUSTRINUS
SCULPTOR
Fomalhaut
FORNAX
NGC253
−20°
CAPRICORNUS
Helix Nebula
NGC246
Tau Ceti
ERIDANUS
−10°
Saturn
Nebula
AQUARIUS
0°
M2
Water Jar
Mira
M77
0°
EQUULEUS
Circlet
ECLIPTIC
CETUS
Enif
10°
M15
PISCES
+10°
DELPHINUS
PEGASUS
Gamma Arietis
+20°
VULPECULA
Square of
Pegasus
Alpheratz
ARIES
+20°
Triangulum
Galaxy
TRIANGULUM
+30°
CYGNUS
ANDROMEDA
M32
PERSEUS
61 Cygni
Andromeda
Galaxy
+40°
North
America
Nebula
M39
LACERTA
Almach
Algol
Deneb
21ʰ
22ʰ
23ʰ
0ʰ
1ʰ
2ʰ
3ʰ +50°

SEPTEMBER

OCTOBER

NOVEMBER

WEST

NORTHERN HORIZON

EAST

359

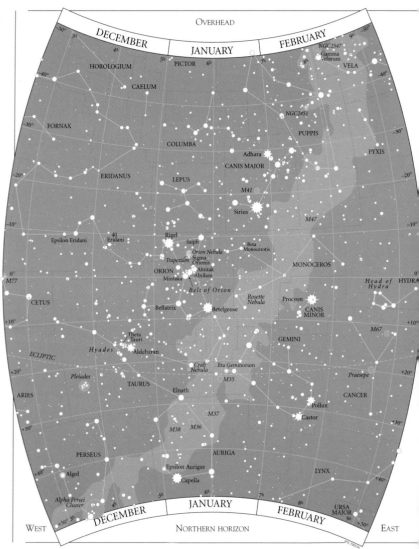

OVERHEAD

DECEMBER   JANUARY   FEBRUARY

−50° 3ʰ   4ʰ   5ʰ PICTOR 6ʰ   7ʰ   8ʰ 9ʰ −50°

NGC2547
Gamma
Velorum
VELA

HOROLOGIUM

−40°   CAELUM   −40°

NGC2451

−30° FORNAX   PUPPIS   −30°

COLUMBA   PYXIS

Adhara
−20° ERIDANUS   CANIS MAJOR   −20°
LEPUS
M41

−10° Epsilon Eridani   M47   −10°
Sirius

40
Eridani   Rigel Saiph
Orion Nebula   Beta
Trapezium Sigma   Monocerotis
Orionis
0° M77   ORION Mintaka Alnitak   MONOCEROS   0°
Alnilam   Head of
CETUS   Hydra HYDRA
Belt of Orion   Rosette
Bellatrix   Nebula Procyon
+10°   Betelgeuse   CANIS   +10°
MINOR
M67
Theta
Tauri   GEMINI
+20° ECLIPTIC Hyades Aldebaran   Crab Eta Geminorum   Praesepe +20°
Nebula
Pleiades   M35
ARIES   TAURUS   CANCER
Elnath   Pollux
+30°   M37   Castor   +30°
M38 M36
PERSEUS   AURIGA
+40° Algol   Epsilon Aurigae   LYNX   +40°
Capella
Alpha Persei   URSA
Cluster   3ʰ 4ʰ   5ʰ 6ʰ   7ʰ 8ʰ MAJOR
+50°   9ʰ +50°
DECEMBER   JANUARY   FEBRUARY

WEST   NORTHERN HORIZON   EAST

Dec., Jan., Feb.

LOCATER

DECEMBER TO FEBRUARY HIGHLIGHTS

Orion acts as a signpost to many other constellations. The three stars of Orion's Belt point northeast to Sirius and Canis Major, and southwest toward Aldebaran in Taurus. Near Aldebaran is a V-shaped cluster of stars called the Hyades. The Pleiades, a little to the west, attract the eye because there are few very bright stars nearby.

M41 is about 2,300 light-years away, and contains about 100 stars

The ancient Greeks observed M41, which is about the same size as a full moon in the sky

MAP DATA

• Sirius is the brightest star in the sky and, at 8.6 light-years away, one of the closest. It is sometimes called the Dog Star because it is in the constellation of Canis Major, the great dog.

• Trapezium is a multiple star in the Orion Nebula, just south of Orion's Belt. The nebula is visible as a misty patch with the naked eye. A telescope shows four stars in the shape of a trapezoid that were recently born and are now illuminating the nebula.

• Betelgeuse is a noticeable orange, while the other stars of Orion are mostly bluish. It is a red giant star, and varies slightly and unpredictably in brightness.

• The Crab Nebula in Taurus gets its name from its clawlike extensions. It is the remains of a brilliant supernova that appeared in 1054. Now all that can be seen with a telescope is a hazy blur.

• Capella, at a distance of 42 light-years, is one of the sky's most famous double stars. Its two components are only about 60 million miles (95 million km) apart and travel around their respective orbits in just 104 days.

M41 CLUSTER

To the south of Sirius lies M41, an open star cluster in Canis Major, just visible with the naked eye. Binoculars show that many of the stars seem to form chains. This is probably because some stars lie almost along the same line of sight as more distant stars. Several of the stars in M41 are red giants, the most luminous of which is 700 times more luminous than the Sun. The cluster is about 26 light-years across, and is estimated to be 190 million years old.

KEY ON PAGE 346

CONSTELLATIONS

CONSTELLATIONS

Southern hemisphere star maps, March to August

In the early part of the year, the sky is rich in galaxies. The great Virgo Cluster of galaxies lies at right angles to the line of the Milky Way, so there is no dust from our own galaxy to obscure the view. During May, the star clouds of the Milky Way start to appear low in the east, and then arch overhead in winter. Nebulas and star clusters are dotted along the Milky Way, many of them visible with binoculars.

Mar., Apr., May

LOCATER

Sombrero Galaxy
A spiral galaxy in Virgo, the Sombrero Galaxy looks like a broad-brimmed Mexican hat in photographs. The dark line visible in a telescope is a dust lane, like the Cygnus Rift in the Milky Way.

Key on page 346

March to May highlights
There are three bright stars in this part of the sky—Arcturus in Boötes, Regulus in Leo, and Spica in Virgo. There are about 2,000 galaxies in Virgo, but only a few are visible in small telescopes. The stars are so sparse at this time of the year that Alphard in Hydra was named "the solitary one" by the Arabs.

MAP DATA

• The center of the Sombrero is stars concentrated in the middle of the galaxy, and the rim is its spiral arm.

• M83 in Hydra is a spiral galaxy, which appears in small telescopes as a round, hazy blur. With large telescopes, the spiral arms become visible.

• M87, an elliptical galaxy, is near the center of the Virgo Cluster. It is one of the largest galaxies known, but is not very spectacular in small telescope, since it lies 50 million light-years away. It looks like a circular hazy spot, brighter in the middle.

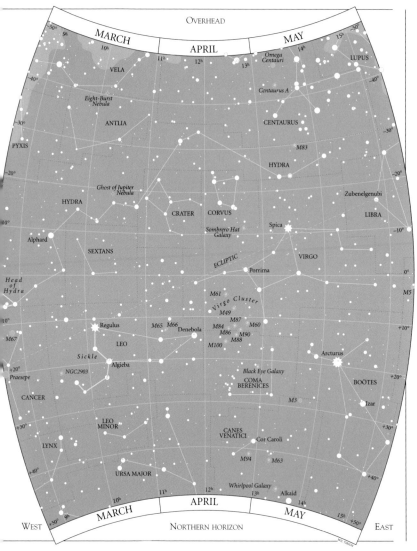

OVERHEAD

MARCH   APRIL   MAY

9h   10h   11h   12h   13h   14h   15h

-50°   -40°   -30°   -20°   -10°   0°   +10°   +20°   +30°   +40°   +50°

VELA

Eight-Burst Nebula

ANTLIA

PYXIS

Omega Centauri

LUPUS

Centaurus A

CENTAURUS

M83

HYDRA

Zubenelgenubi

Ghost of Jupiter Nebula

HYDRA

CRATER   CORVUS

Sombrero Hat Galaxy

Spica

LIBRA

Alphard

SEXTANS

VIRGO

Head of Hydra

ECLIPTIC

Porrima

M61

Virgo Cluster

M49

Regulus   M65   M66   Denebola   M87   M60

M84   M86   M90

M88

M100

LEO

M67

Sickle

NGC2903   Algieba

Arcturus

Praesepe

Black Eye Galaxy

COMA BERENICES

M3

BOÖTES

Izar

CANCER

LEO MINOR

LYNX

CANES VENATICI   Cor Caroli

M94   M63

URSA MAJOR

Whirlpool Galaxy   Alkaid

10h   11h   12h   13h   14h   15h

MARCH   APRIL   MAY

WEST   +50°   NORTHERN HORIZON   +50°   EAST

OVERHEAD

JUNE · JULY · AUGUST

-50° 15ʰ 16ʰ NORMA 17ʰ ARA 18ʰ 19ʰ 20ʰ 21ʰ -50° INDUS

TELESCOPIUM

-40°

CENTAURUS LUPUS NGC6231 CORONA AUSTRALIS MICROSCOPIUM

-30° Shaula M7

HYDRA SCORPIUS M6 SAGITTARIUS

M62 Teapot

CAPRICORNUS

M4 Lagoon Nebula Nunki

LIBRA Antares ECLIPTIC

Nu M22

Scorpii Trifid M25 Algedi

Zubenelgenubi Nebula

Omega

Eagle Nebula

Nebula SCUTUM

OPHIUCHUS AQUARIUS

M10 Wild Duck

M12 Cluster

AQUILA

VIRGO M5 Eta

SERPENS Aquilae

CAPUT SERPENS EQUULEUS

CAUDA Altair

+10°

Rasalhague

HERCULES SAGITTA DELPHINUS

VULPECULA

Dumbbell

+20° Nebula

Albireo

Izar R Coronae Borealis Ring

CORONA Nebula

BOREALIS Keystone Sheliak LYRA

M13 Vega CYGNUS 61 Cygni

M92 Epsilon

Lyrae

BOOTES CYGNUS North America

Northern Nebula

Cross Deneb

16ʰ 17ʰ 18ʰ DRACO 19ʰ 20ʰ 21ʰ

JUNE · JULY · AUGUST

WEST NORTHERN HORIZON EAST

364

Jun., Jul., Aug.

LOCATER

JUNE TO AUGUST HIGHLIGHTS

The center of the Milky Way lies in the direction of Sagittarius, but huge dust clouds block our view of it. Some of the stars of Sagittarius make a teapot shape—a bright part of the Milky Way looks like a wisp of steam coming from its spout. To the west of Sagittarius is Scorpius, with red Antares at the scorpion's heart and a curve of stars marking its tail.

The Lagoon Nebula is one of only two star-forming nebulas faintly visible to the naked eye from mid-northern latitudes

The curving lane of dust, shaped like a lagoon, after which the nebula is named

MAP DATA

• To the naked eye, the M7 open star cluster looks like a bright part of the Milky Way, about twice the size of a full moon. Binoculars or a small telescope show many stars in this and another nearby cluster, M6.

• Sagittarius is a rich viewing area. Not only does the center of the Milky Way lie in this direction, but it contains more bright nebulas and star clusters than any other constellation.

• The dark band in the Milky Way—the Cygnus Rift—is caused by dust clouds lying in front of the stars.

• The Ring Nebula lies between the two stars at the top corners of Lyra, and looks like a tiny doughnut. This planetary nebula is quite bright, but is too small to be seen without a telescope.

LAGOON NEBULA

One of the brightest nebulas in the Milky Way, the Lagoon Nebula is visible to the naked eye. It gets its name because telescopes show a curved dark area within it that looks like a tropical island lagoon. It is 50 light-years across, and was discovered in 1747. It lies 5,200 light-years away.

KEY ON PAGE 346

365

ASTRONOMY TIMELINE

3000BCE STONE ASTRONOMY
Stonehenge, built about this time in southern England, is a giant astronomical calendar with stones aligned to the Sun and possibly the Moon. Many other ancient sites are thought to have astronomical significance, such as the Egyptian pyramids (2600 BCE) and, later, buildings in China and Central and South America (1st century CE).

750BCE LUNAR CYCLE
In Babylon, astronomers discover a 18.6-year cycle in the rising and setting of the Moon. From this they create the first almanacs—tables of movements of the Sun, Moon, and planets for use in astrology. In 6th-century Greece, this knowledge is used to predict eclipses.

380BCE EARTH-CENTERED VIEW Greek
philosopher Plato founds a school of thought that will influence the next 2,000 years. It promotes the idea that everything in the universe moves in harmony, and that the Sun, Moon, and planets move around Earth in perfect circles.

270BCE SUN-CENTERED VIEW
Aristarchus of Samos proposes an alternative to the geocentric (Earth-centered) universe. His heliocentric model places the Sun at its center, with Earth as just one planet orbiting around it. However, few people at the time take the theory seriously. They argued that if Earth is moving through space, then why do the stars not move through the sky?

164BCE HALLEY'S COMET The earliest recorded
sighting of Halley's comet is made by Babylonian astronomers. Their records of the comet's movements allow 20th-century astronomers to predict accurately how the comet's orbit changes over the centuries.

150CE STAR CATALOG
Ptolemy publishes his star catalog, listing 48 constellations, and endorses the Earth-centered view of the universe. His views go unquestioned for nearly 1,500 years, and are passed down to Arabic and medieval European astronomers in his book *The Almagest*.

928 ASTROLABE The earliest surviving astrolabe—an
instrument that shows the position of stars and planets—is made by Islamic craftsmen. Astrolabes are the most advanced instruments of their time. The precise measurement of the positions of stars and planets allows Arab astronomers to compile the most detailed almanacs and star atlases yet.

1054 SUPERNOVA Chinese astronomers record the
sudden appearance of a bright star. Native American rock carvings also show the brilliant star close to the Moon. This star is the Crab supernova exploding.

1543 COPERNICAN SYSTEM Nicolaus Copernicus publishes his theory that Earth goes around the Sun, in contradiction of the Church's teachings. However, he complicates his theory by retaining Plato's perfect circular orbits of the planets.

1577 TYCHO'S COMET A brilliant comet is observed by Tycho Brahe, who proves that it is traveling beyond Earth's atmosphere and, therefore, provides the first evidence that the heavens can change.

1608 FIRST TELESCOPE Dutch spectacle-maker Hans Lippershey (1570–1619) invents the refracting telescope. The invention spreads rapidly across Europe, as scientists make their own instruments. Their discoveries begin a revolution in astronomy.

1609 KEPLER'S LAWS Johannes Kepler publishes his *New Astronomy*. In this and later works, he announces his three laws of planetary motion, replacing the circular orbits of Plato with elliptical ones. Almanacs based on his laws prove to be highly accurate.

1610 OBSERVATIONS Galileo Galilei publishes the findings of his observations with the telescope he built. These include spots on the Sun, craters on the Moon, and four satellites orbiting Jupiter. Proving that not everything orbits Planet Earth, he promotes the Copernican view of a Sun-centered universe.

1663 REFLECTOR Scottish astronomer James Gregory (1638–75) builds a reflecting telescope, using mirrors instead of lenses, to allow a larger aperture and reduce light loss. Within five years, Isaac Newton improves the design, creating the Newtonian telescope; other variations soon follow.

1687 THEORY OF GRAVITY Isaac Newton publishes his *Principia Mathematica*, establishing the theory of gravitation and laws of motion. The *Principia Mathematica* explains Kepler's laws of planetary motion and allows astronomers to understand the forces acting between the Sun, the planets, and their moons.

1705 HALLEY'S COMET Edmond Halley calculates that the comets recorded at 76-year intervals from 1456 to 1682 are one and the same. He predicts that the comet will return again in 1758. When it reappears as expected, the comet is named in his honor.

1750 SOUTHERN SKIES French astronomer Nicolas de Lacaille (1713–62) sails to southern oceans and begins work compiling a catalog of more than 10,000 stars in the southern sky. Lacaille's star catalog is the first comprehensive one of the southern sky.

ASTRONOMY TIMELINE

1781 URANUS Amateur astronomer William Herschel discovers the planet Uranus, although he at first mistakes it for a comet. Uranus is the first planet to be discovered beyond Saturn (the most distant of the planets known since ancient times).

1784 MESSIER CATALOG Charles Messier publishes his catalog of star clusters and nebulas. Messier draws up the list to prevent these objects from being identified as comets. However, it soon becomes a standard reference for the study of star clusters and nebulas, and is still in use today.

1800 INFRARED RADIATION William Herschel splits sunlight through a prism and, with a thermometer, measures the energy given out by different colors; this is the first study of a star's spectrum. He notices a sudden increase in energy beyond the red end of the spectrum, discovering invisible infrared (heat) radiation and laying the foundations for spectroscopy.

1801 ASTEROIDS Italian astronomer Giuseppe Piazzi (1746–1826) discovers what appears to be a new planet orbiting between Mars and Jupiter, and names it Ceres. William Herschel proves it is a very small object—199 miles (320 km) in diameter—and not a planet. He proposes the name "asteroid," and soon other similar bodies are being found. We now know

that Ceres is 579 miles (932 km) in diameter—but still too small to be a planet.

1814 FRAUNHOFER LINES Joseph von Fraunhofer builds the first accurate spectrometer and uses it to study the spectrum of the Sun's light. He discovers and maps hundreds of fine dark lines crossing the solar spectrum. In 1859, these lines are linked to chemical elements in the Sun's atmosphere. Spectroscopy becomes the method for studying what the stars are made of.

1838 STELLAR PARALLAX Friedrich Bessel successfully uses the method of stellar parallax (the effect of Earth's annual movement around the Sun) to calculate the distance to 61 Cygni: the first star other than the Sun to have its distance measured. Bessel has pioneered the truly accurate measurement of stellar positions, and the parallax technique establishes a framework for measuring the scale of the universe.

1843 SUNSPOT CYCLE German amateur astronomer Heinrich Schwabe (1789–1875), who had studied the Sun for 17 years, observes a regular cycle in sunspot numbers—the first clue to the Sun's internal structure.

1845 LARGE TELESCOPES Irish astronomer the Earl of Rosse completes the first of the world's great telescopes, with a 71-in (180-cm) mirror. He uses it to study and draw the structure of nebulas, and within a few months discovers the spiral structure of the Whirlpool Galaxy.

1845 ASTROPHOTOGRAPHY French physicists Jean Foucault (1819–68) and Armand Fizeau (1819–96) take the first detailed photographs of the Sun's surface through a telescope—the birth of scientific astrophotography. Within five years, astronomers produce the first detailed photographs of the Moon. Early film is not sensitive enough to image stars.

1846 NEPTUNE A new planet, called Neptune, is identified by German astronomer Johann Gottfried Galle (1812–1910). He had been searching in the position suggested by Urbain Le Verrier. Le Verrier had calculated the position and size of the planet from the effects of its gravitational pull on the orbit of Uranus. An English mathematician, John Couch Adams (1819–92), also made a similar calculation a year earlier.

1868 SUN'S COMPOSITION Astronomers notice a new bright emission line in the spectrum of the Sun's atmosphere during an eclipse. The emission line is caused by an element giving out light, and British astronomer Norman Lockyer (1836–1920) concludes that it is an element unknown on Earth. He calls it helium, which is from the Greek word for the Sun. Nearly 30 years later, helium is found on Earth.

1872 SPECTRA OF STARS American astronomer Henry Draper (1837–82) takes the first photograph of the spectrum of a star (Vega), showing absorption lines that reveal its chemical makeup. Astronomers begin to see that spectroscopy is the key to understanding how stars evolve. William Huggins uses absorption lines to measure the red shifts of stars—the first indication of how fast stars move.

1901 SPECTRAL CATALOG A comprehensive survey of stars, the Henry Draper Catalog, is published. In the catalog, Annie Jump Cannon proposes a sequence of classifying stars by the absorption lines in their spectra that is still in use today.

1906 STAR MAGNITUDE Ejnar Hertzsprung establishes the standard for measuring the true brightness of a star (its absolute magnitude). He shows that there is a relationship between color and absolute magnitude for 90 percent of the stars in the Milky Way Galaxy. In 1913, Henry Russell publishes a diagram that shows this relationship.

1916 BLACK HOLES German physicist Karl Schwarzschild (1873–1916) uses Albert Einstein's Theory of General Relativity to lay the groundwork for black hole theory. He suggests that if any star collapses below a certain size, its gravity will be so strong that no form of radiation will escape from it.

ASTRONOMY TIMELINE

1923 GALAXIES Edwin Hubble discovers a Cepheid variable star in the Andromeda Nebula and proves that Andromeda and other nebulas are galaxies far beyond our own. By 1925, he produces a classification system for galaxies.

1929 HUBBLE'S LAW Edwin Hubble discovers that the universe is expanding and that the farther away a galaxy is, the faster it is moving away from us. Two years later, Georges Lemaître suggests that the expansion can be traced back to an initial "Big Bang."

1930 DWARF STARS By applying new ideas from subatomic physics, Subrahmanyan Chandrasekhar predicts that the atoms in a white dwarf star of more than 1.44 solar masses will disintegrate, causing the star to collapse violently. In 1933, Walter Baade and Fritz Zwicky describe the neutron star that results from this collapse, causing a supernova explosion.

1930 PLUTO Clyde Tombaugh discovers the planet Pluto at the Lowell Observatory in Flagstaff, Arizona. The planet is so faint and slow-moving that he has to compare photos taken several nights apart.

1932 RADIO ASTRONOMY Karl Jansky detects the first radio waves coming from space. In 1942, radio waves from the Sun are detected. Seven years later, radio astronomers identify the first distant sources—the Crab Nebula and the galaxies Centaurus A and M87.

1938 STELLAR ENERGY German physicist Hans Bethe explains how stars generate energy. He outlines a series of nuclear fusion reactions that turn hydrogen into helium and release enormous amounts of energy in a star's core. These reactions use the star's hydrogen very slowly, allowing it to burn for billions of years.

1944 V-2 ROCKET A team of German scientists, led by Wernher von Braun, develops the V-2, the first rocket-powered ballistic missile. Scientists and engineers from von Braun's team are captured at the end of World War II and are drafted into the American and Russian rocket programs.

1948 HALE TELESCOPE The largest telescope in the world, with a 200-in (5.08-m) mirror, is completed at Palomar Mountain in California. At that time, the telescope pushes single-mirror telescope technology to its limits—larger mirrors tend to bend under their own weight.

1957 SPACECRAFT Russia launches the first satellite, Sputnik 1, into orbit, beginning the Space Age. The United States launches its first satellite, Explorer 1, four months later.

1923–1969

1959 MOON PROBES Russia and the US both launch space probes to the Moon, but NASA's Pioneer probes all fail. The Russian Luna program is more successful. Luna 2 crash-lands on the Moon's surface in September, and Luna 3 returns the first pictures of the Moon's far side in October.

1961 HUMANS IN SPACE Russia again takes the lead in the space race as, in April, Yuri Gagarin becomes the first person to orbit Earth. Gagarin made one orbit in his Vostok 1 rocket, before successfully reentering Earth's atmosphere. NASA astronaut Alan Shepard becomes the first American in space a month later, but does not go into orbit. John Glenn achieves this in early 1962.

1962 PLANETARY PROBE Mariner 2 becomes the first space probe to reach another planet, flying past Venus in December. NASA follows this with the successful Mariner 4 mission to Mars in 1965, and both the US and Russia send many more probes to planets through the rest of the 1960s and 1970s.

1963 QUASARS Dutch-American astronomer Maarten Schmidt measures the spectra of quasars, the mysterious starlike radio sources discovered in 1960. He establishes that quasars are active galaxies, and among the most distant objects in the universe.

1965 BIG BANG Arno Penzias and Robert Wilson announce the discovery of a weak radio signal coming from all parts of the sky. Scientists work out that this must be emitted by an object at a temperature of −454°F (−270°C). Soon it is recognized as the remnant of the very hot radiation from the Big Bang that created the universe 14 billion years ago.

1966 LUNAR LANDINGS The Russian Luna 9 probe makes the first successful soft landing on the Moon in January, while the US lands the far more complex Surveyor 1 in May. The Surveyor missions, which are followups to NASA's Ranger series of crash landers, scout sites for possible crewed landings.

1967 PULSARS Jocelyn Bell Burnell and Antony Hewish detect the first pulsar, an object emitting regular pulses of radio waves. Pulsars are eventually recognized as rapidly spinning neutron stars with intense magnetic fields— the remains of a supernova explosion.

1969 APOLLO 11 The United States wins the race for the Moon, as Neil Armstrong and Edwin (Buzz) Aldrin step onto the lunar surface on July 21. The astronauts spent over 21 hours on the Moon, conducting scientific experiments and planting an American flag. Apollo 11 is followed by five further landing missions, three carrying a sophisticated Lunar Rover vehicle.

ASTRONOMY TIMELINE

1970 X-RAY ASTRONOMY The Uhuru satellite, designed to map the sky at X-ray wavelengths, is launched by NASA. The existence of X-rays from the Sun and a few other stars has already been found using rocket-launched experiments, but Uhuru charts more than 300 X-ray sources, including several possible black holes.

1971 SPACE STATIONS Russia launches its first space station, Salyut 1, into orbit. It is followed by a series of stations, culminating with Mir in 1986. A permanent platform in orbit allows cosmonauts to carry out serious research and to set a series of new duration records for spaceflight.

1975 PLANETARY VISIT The Russian probe Venera 9 lands on the surface of Venus and sends back the first pictures of its surface. The first probe to land on another planet, Venera 7 in 1970, had no camera. Both break down within an hour in the hostile atmosphere.

1977 VOYAGERS NASA launches the two Voyager space probes to the outer planets. The Voyagers return scientific data and pictures from Jupiter and Saturn and, before leaving the solar system, Voyager 2 becomes the first probe to visit Uranus and Neptune.

1981 SPACE SHUTTLE Columbia, the first of NASA's reusable Space Shuttles, makes its maiden flight. The Shuttle carries large payloads to various orbits, provides crew rotation for the International Space Station, and conducts servicing missions to the Hubble Space Telescope.

1983 INFRARED ASTRONOMY The first infrared astronomy satellite, IRAS, is launched. It must be cooled to extremely low temperatures with liquid helium, and it operates for only 300 days before its supply of helium is exhausted. During this time it completes an infrared survey of 98 percent of the sky.

1986 COMET PROBES The returning Halley's Comet is met by a fleet of five space probes from Russia, Japan, and Europe. The most ambitious is the European Space Agency's Giotto, which flies through the comet's coma and photographs the nucleus itself.

1990 MAGELLAN Launched by NASA, the Magellan probe arrives at Venus and spends three years mapping it with radar. Magellan is the first in a new wave of space probes including Galileo, which reaches Jupiter in 1995, and Cassini, which reaches Saturn in 2004.

1990 SPACE TELESCOPE The Hubble Space Telescope, the first large optical telescope in orbit, is launched using the Space Shuttle, but astronomers soon discover it is crippled by a problem with its mirror. A complex repair mission in 1993 allows the telescope to start producing spectacular images of distant stars, nebulas, and galaxies.

1992 COSMIC RIPPLES The Cosmic Background Explorer (COBE) satellite produces a detailed map of the background radiation remaining from the Big Bang. The map shows "ripples," caused by slight variations in the density of the early universe—the seeds of galaxies and galaxy clusters.

1992 KECK TELESCOPE The 33-ft (10-m) Keck Telescope on Mauna Kea, Hawaii, is completed. The first of a revolutionary new wave of telescopes, the Keck's main mirror is made of 36 six-sided segments, with computers to control their alignment. New optical telescopes also make use of interferometry—improving resolution by combining images from separate telescopes.

1998 INTERNATIONAL SPACE STATION Construction work on a huge new space station begins. A joint venture between many countries, including Russia, Japan, and the US, the space station can house up to seven astronauts in orbit at any one time and acts as a platform for microgravity research, astronomy, and further exploration of the solar system. It is due to be completed in 2010.

2004 ORBITING MISSION Space probe Cassini arrives at Saturn. The probe was designed to make 74 orbits of Saturn and numerous flybys

of its moons. Cassini also carried a mini-probe called Huygens, which is exploring Titan, Saturn's largest moon. The Huygens probe has shown that Titan's surface is similar to Earth's, with evidence of lakes and rain clouds.

2004 MARS ROVERS The planetary rovers Spirit and Opportunity land on Mars and begin to explore the surface. As well as providing useful data on rocks and soil from the surface of the planet, the rovers send back evidence to NASA headquarters that water once flowed on Mars.

2004 ROSETTA COMET ORBIT Launched by the European Space Agency, Rosetta will be the first space probe to orbit a comet, one of the most difficult maneuvers ever attempted. The probe will study Comet Churyumov-Gerasimenko for over three years and carries a separate craft that will land on the surface of the comet's nucleus. Rosetta is due to reach the comet in May 2014.

2005 MARS RECONNAISSANCE ORBITER (MRO) Launched from Cape Canaveral in August 2005, the MRO, at 4,650 lb (2,100 kg), is the most massive spacecraft to be sent to the Red Planet. It is a weather satellite designed to tell us if the global cooling that Mars suffered could happen to Earth. Observations by MRO will also support future Mars missions by examining potential landing sites.

BIOGRAPHIES

EDWIN "BUZZ" ALDRIN
born 1930

American astronaut who piloted the Lunar Module of Apollo 11 and, on July 21, 1969, became the second person to walk on the Moon. Aldrin is an engineer by training. In November 1966, he made a record 5-hour spacewalk during the Gemini 12 mission.

ARISTARCHUS OF SAMOS
about 320–250 BCE

Greek astronomer who used geometry to measure the distance between the Sun and Moon. He calculated that the Sun was 20 times farther away than the Moon (it is actually 400 times farther), and suggested that Earth must travel around the Sun, as the Sun was seven times bigger than Earth (it is actually 109 times bigger). The idea gained ground over 18 centuries later.

NEIL ARMSTRONG
born 1930

American Air Force test pilot who, as commander of Apollo 11, was the first person to walk on the Moon on July 21, 1969. As he stepped onto the Moon, he said, "That's one small step for a man, one giant leap for mankind." After leaving NASA, he became a university professor.

WALTER BAADE
1893–1960

Emigrated to the United States from Germany in 1931. In 1943, he discovered that the universe contained two types of stars—very old ones containing few metals, and newer ones rich in metals. This also applied to the Cepheid variable stars, whose properties are used to calculate the size of the universe, which was then found to be twice as big as previously thought.

FRIEDRICH BESSEL
1784–1846

German astronomer who became the first director of the observatory in Königsberg in 1813. He concentrated on measuring the exact positions of stars. In 1838, he used parallax to measure the distance of the star 61 Cygni (10.3 light-years). This was the first star to have its distance measured by parallax, and helped establish a scale for the universe.

TYCHO BRAHE
1546–1601

Danish astronomer who accurately measured the positions of stars and planets. Between 1572 and 1573, he recorded a supernova in Cassiopeia, proving that the sky could change. He measured the distance to the great comet of 1577, showing that it was farther away than the Moon and had an elongated orbit, which passed the planets. Johannes Kepler, his assistant, used his results to calculate the orbits of the planets.

WERNHER VON BRAUN
1912–77

German rocket engineer who developed the V-2 missile and the Saturn V Moon launcher. His work on rocket engines in the 1930s led to his appointment as technical director of a rocket establishment, where he developed the V-2—a liquid-fueled rocket weapon—during World War II. Between 1942 and 1945, more than 5,000 V-2s were built. After the war, he was selected for work in New Mexico. There he designed the Redstone rocket, which put Explorer 1—the first US satellite—into orbit in 1958, and in 1961 launched Alan Shepard on the first Mercury suborbital mission. In 1960, von Braun was put in charge of the Marshall Space Flight Center in Alabama, where he developed the Saturn rockets that were used to send humans to the Moon in the Apollo program.

JOCELYN BELL BURNELL
born 1943

British astronomer who, as a research student at Cambridge, discovered pulsars. On August 6, 1967, while observing the rapid variations in signals from radio sources and looking for quasars, she discovered an unusual radio signal consisting of a rapid series of pulses that occurred precisely every 1.337 seconds. This turned out to be a pulsating neutron star (a pulsar).

ANNIE JUMP CANNON
1863–1941

American astronomer who classified the spectra of more than 300,000 stars into a temperature sequence. She joined the staff of Harvard College Observatory in 1896 and stayed there until she retired in 1940. Her work was the foundation stone of the Henry Draper Catalog of stellar spectra.

GIOVANNI CASSINI
1625–1712

Italian astronomer who was the first to understand the nature of Saturn's rings. He suggested that they were not solid but made up of individual rocks. He discovered four of Saturn's satellites and a gap in its rings. He helped build and run the Paris Observatory, where he measured the distance between Earth and Mars and used this to calculate the Sun–Earth distance.

SUBRAHMANYAN
CHANDRASEKHAR
1910–95

Indian-born astrophysicist who studied astronomy in Madras and England before moving to the United States in 1936. He received the 1983 Nobel Prize for Physics for his work on dying stars. Chandrasekhar realized that a white dwarf star with more than 1.4 times the Sun's mass could not stop shrinking, and would become a neutron star or a black hole.

ARTHUR C. CLARKE
born 1917

British science fiction writer who, in 1945, suggested that a satellite in geostationary orbit—23,924 miles (35,800 km) above Earth—could be used to transmit TV and telephone signals between Europe and North America. Though the technology was unavailable at the time, geostationary satellites are now commonplace.

NICOLAUS COPERNICUS
1473–1543

Polish astronomer, doctor, and priest who suggested that the Sun and not Earth was at the center of our planetary system. He studied mathematics and the classics in Poland, and law and astronomy in Italy. He returned to Poland in 1506 to become a canon at Frauenberg Cathedral, a post he held until he died. His duties were light and he devoted most of his time to astronomy. By about 1513, he had realized that Earth was not at the center of the universe or even of the solar system. Earth, which went around the Sun, was not special but was merely one of a collection of planets. He was aware that his idea went against the teachings of the church, and his book *De Revolutionibus Orbium Coelestrium* was not published until he was on his deathbed.

FRANK DRAKE
born 1930

American radio astronomer who, in 1960, pioneered the use of radio telescopes to listen for signals from extraterrestrial life. In 1974, using the Arecibo radio telescope in Puerto Rico, this project was continued.

ARTHUR EDDINGTON
1882–1944

English astronomer who showed how the physical characteristics inside a star could be calculated from its surface features. He devised a model of a star's interior, discovered the relationship between a star's mass and its luminosity, stressed that nuclear fusion produced stellar energy, and measured how much a ray of light is bent by a gravitational field.

ALBERT EINSTEIN
1879–1955

German-born American theoretical physicist whose theory of general relativity explains the evolution of the expanding universe. He received the Nobel Prize for Physics in 1921 for explaining how light is radiated in packets of energy called quanta, but he is best remembered for his theories of relativity. Einstein found that mass (m) was equivalent to energy (E) according to his now famous equation $E = mc^2$.

ERATOSTHENES OF CYRENE
about 273–192 BCE

Greek scholar who calculated the size of Earth. Born in north Africa, he was educated in Athens and then became the tutor to the son of King Ptolemy III of Egypt. A skilled geographer, he calculated the curvature of Earth by measuring the length of the shadow the Sun cast, at two places 590 miles (950 km) apart. From this he estimated Earth's circumference to be 28,895 miles (46,500 km). It is actually 24,903 miles (40,075 km) at the equator.

EUDOXUS OF CNIDUS
about 408–355 BCE

Greek astronomer and mathematician who constructed a model of the solar system, with Earth at its center and the planets moving around Earth. The planets were in spheres, nested inside each other, with the axis of each sphere attached to the surrounding sphere. This model was replaced after a few centuries, since it did not account for everyday changes in the distances between Earth and other planets.

JOHN FLAMSTEED
1646–1719

Britain's first Astronomer Royal, he was in charge of the Royal Observatory at Greenwich. Using a mural arc and a sextant with telescopic sights in conjunction with the new, accurate clocks that ran for a year, he produced a new catalog of 3,000 stars, 15 times more accurate than earlier ones. He also made detailed studies of the shape of the orbits of both the Moon and Earth.

JOSEPH VON FRAUNHOFER
1787–1826

A Bavarian glass- and lens-maker, he noticed that the Sun's spectrum was crossed by numerous fine, dark lines. He measured the wavelengths of 324 of the 574 lines that he could see, which are now known as Fraunhofer lines.

YURI GAGARIN
1934–68

Russian cosmonaut who, on April 12, 1961, became the first person to fly in space. The flight on the Vostok 1 spaceship lasted one orbit of Earth. The spaceship reached a height of 214 miles (344 km) and Gagarin was airborne for 108 minutes. He died in a plane crash while training to return to space.

GALILEO GALILEI
1564–1642

Italian mathematician, physicist, and astronomer, who did much to disprove ancient Greek theories of physics. He discovered that the Sun spun around every 25 days, the Moon was mountainous, Jupiter had four satellites, and Venus showed Moon-like phases. The Venus observations helped prove that the Sun and not Earth was at the center of the solar system. His revolutionary ideas led to trouble with the Church, and late in life he was tried by the Inquisition in Rome and placed under house arrest.

GEORGE GAMOW
1904–68

Ukrainian physicist who defected to the US in 1933. With Ralph Alpher and Hans Bethe, he showed how helium could be produced during the Big Bang, and could then combine with other nuclei to create elements. He predicted that the universe would be filled with radiation left over from the intense temperature of the Big Bang.

JOHN GLENN
born 1921

American astronaut who, in 1962, was the first American to orbit Earth. He made three orbits during a 5-hour flight. After retiring from the space program in 1964, he took up politics, and, in 1974, was elected senator in Ohio. In 1998, he became the world's oldest astronaut when he flew on a Space Shuttle mission.

ROBERT GODDARD
1882–1945

American inventor and rocket engineer who made and launched the world's first liquid-fueled rocket in 1926. In the 1930s, he launched his first stabilized rocket. This had a liquid-fuel motor that used gasoline and liquid oxygen.

ALAN GUTH
born 1947

American particle physicist who devised the theory of inflation in 1979, in which he proposed that just after the Big Bang, the universe expanded from the size of a proton to the size of a grapefruit in a tiny fraction of a second. This both smoothed out space-time and made a universe that looks the same in all directions.

GEORGE HALE
1868–1938

American astronomer who invented the spectroheliograph that revealed details of the Sun's surface. He also discovered that sunspots had magnetic fields, and measured the strengths of these fields. He directed the building of several large telescopes, including Hale's Telescope on Palomar Mountain, California.

EDMOND HALLEY
1656–1742

English astronomer and mathematician who proved that some comets were periodic and predicted that Halley's comet would return to the Sun every 76 years. He was a close friend of Isaac Newton and helped him to prepare his book *Principia Mathematica*. In 1698, he sailed over the Atlantic, measuring the deviation of the magnetic compass. He drew the first map of the southern sky, discovered that stars move, and realized that Earth was very old.

JOHN HARRISON
1693–1776

A British clockmaker who introduced a pendulum that did not change length as its temperature varied, and a ratchet that kept a clock going as it was being wound up. In the early 1730s, he was given money to build a clock that worked accurately when on board a ship at sea. His final precision clocks enabled a ship's longitude to be measured when out of port. Accurate clocks are important in astronomy for measuring the position of stars in the sky.

STEPHEN HAWKING
born 1942

British theoretical physicist who, even though he suffers from motor neurone disease, has spent his life studying the behavior of matter close to a black hole. Astronomers used to think that nothing could escape from a black hole, but Hawking showed that thermal radiation could be emitted. His book *A Brief History of Time* is one of the best-selling science books ever.

CAROLINE HERSCHEL
1750–1848

German astronomer who came to England in 1772 to collaborate with her brother William. She discovered eight comets between 1786 and 1797. In 1787, the British king granted her a salary to continue as assistant to her brother. She is remembered especially for her catalog of 2,500 nebulas and star clusters.

WILLIAM HERSCHEL
1738–1822

German-born astronomer who moved to England in 1757. He made superb reflecting telescopes and discovered Uranus in 1781. He discovered hundreds of nebulas and found that the Sun was moving toward the constellation Hercules.

EJNAR HERTZSPRUNG
1873–1967

Danish astronomer who realized that the width of a stellar spectral line was a function of the light-emitting region's pressure, and that stars were of two basic types—dwarfs and giants. In 1906, he noticed that a star's luminosity was related to its surface temperature, which was independently discovered by Henry Russell in 1913. The Hertzsprung-Russell diagram, which plots standard brightness against temperature, is vital to the study of stellar evolution.

ANTONY HEWISH
born 1924

English radio astronomer who studied fluctuations in radio sources, and how the signals from two radio telescopes could be combined to mimic a dish as large as the distance between them. In 1967, he and his student Jocelyn Bell Burnell discovered pulsars. He was awarded the Nobel Prize for Physics in 1974.

BIOGRAPHIES

HIPPARCHUS
about 190–120 BCE

Greek astronomer, who is remembered for inventing an improved theodolite with which he measured the positions of 850 stars. He produced a catalog of these, which was still in use 18 centuries later. He also classified the stars according to how bright they appeared in the sky. This system forms the basis of today's magnitude scale of stellar brightness. Earth's spin axis moves like a spinning top, and Hipparchus measured the rate at which the axis changed position, and the way in which the distance between Earth and the Sun varies throughout the year.

FRED HOYLE
1915–2001

English astrophysicist, who often visited the California Institute of Technology, where he collaborated with William Fowler. In 1957, they showed how elements such as lithium, carbon, oxygen, and iron could be created inside stars. When large stars eventually explode as supernovas, these elements are distributed into space and are recycled in second-generation stars. In 1948, Hoyle, with Thomas Gold and Hermann Bondi, introduced the steady-state theory of the universe. This theory lost ground in 1965 after the discovery of the background radiation—the remnant of the Big Bang.

EDWIN HUBBLE
1889–1953

American astronomer who proved that the universe contained a multitude of galaxies that were moving away from the Milky Way. At the Mount Wilson Observatory in California, he used the new 98-inch (2.5-m) telescope to study nebulas, and identified two types—those in our own galaxy and those beyond it. In 1924, he realized that the distant ones were separate galaxies. He also found that the fainter, more distant galaxies were moving away from ours more quickly. He classified the different types of galaxies but (incorrectly) suggested that one type evolved into another as they aged.

WILLIAM HUGGINS
1824–1910

English astronomer who sold his family drapery business to concentrate on observing the sky. In 1863, he showed that the universe is made of the same elements that exist on Earth. In 1868, he became the first astronomer to use the spectroscope to measure the speed with which stars are moving away from Earth. He also discovered that some nebulas are made of gas.

CHRISTIAAN HUYGENS
1629–95

Dutch scientist who, in 1655, discovered a large satellite of Saturn—Titan. He realized that the bulges on either side of Saturn were a ring of particles in orbit around its equator. The telescope that he produced was the best telescope of his time. He also invented the pendulum clock, and proposed that light was a wave motion.

KARL JANSKY
1905–50

American radio engineer and the father of radio astronomy. He built a rotating radio aerial and receiver in 1932 in order to discover the source of interference in radio signals being used for ship-to-shore communications, and soon realized that the interference came from the constellation of Sagittarius. This is the densest part of the Milky Way, and the radiation was from electrons in its magnetic field.

JOHANNES KEPLER
1571–1630

German astronomer who formulated three laws of planetary orbits—Kepler's laws of motion—using data obtained by Tycho Brahe. He discovered that planets have elliptical orbits and orbit the Sun more slowly the farther away they are from it. His Rudolphine Tables allow astronomers to calculate the past, present, and future positions of planets.

SERGEI KOROLEV
1906–66

Russian engineer and founding member of the Moscow Group for the Study of Rocket Propulsion. He was responsible for the production of the first Russian inter-continental missile and for designing the Sputnik satellite, and the Vostok, Voskhod, and Soyuz crewed spacecraft.

PIERRE SIMON DE LAPLACE
1749–1827

French mathematician and astronomer who spent 13 years, starting in 1773, explaining how variations in the orbits of Jupiter and Saturn could be accounted for within Newton's laws of gravity. In 1796, he proposed that the Sun and solar system were formed out of a gas cloud that rotated faster and faster as it shrank, and threw off rings of material as it got smaller. These rings then formed planets. This theory held until the end of the 19th century.

HENRIETTA LEAVITT
1868–1921

American astronomer who studied Cepheid variable stars and discovered that the cycle of variation was related to their luminosities—the longer the cycle, the more luminous the star. This led to the discovery that the Magellanic Clouds were about 100,000 light-years away and were small galaxies beyond our own galaxy.

GEORGES LEMAÎTRE
1894–1966

Belgian physicist who was a priest who turned to cosmology. In 1931, Lemaître proposed that the universe was once contained in a primeval atom about 30 times the size of the Sun. This exploded into space, scattering material that then condensed to form galaxies and stars. This later developed into the Big Bang theory.

BERNARD LOVELL
born 1913

Director of the Jodrell Bank radio observatory for more than 30 years. He developed airborne radar for nonvisual bombing raids during World War II. After the war, he pioneered radar observations of meteors and instigated the funding for a 249-ft (76-m) radio telescope at Jodrell Bank in time to track the rocket of the first Russian satellite, Sputnik 1.

PERCIVAL LOWELL
1855–1916

American astronomer who set up an observatory in Flagstaff, Arizona. He concentrated on visual and photographic observations of Mars, and was convinced that a system of canals existed there. His prediction of the position of a Planet X in 1905 eventually led to the serendipitous discovery of Pluto in 1930 by Clyde Tombaugh, using Lowell's telescope.

CHARLES MESSIER
1730–1817

French astronomer who was the first to deliberately search for new comets, starting with Halley's comet in 1758–59. He discovered more than 15 new comets and was nicknamed the "comet ferret." He also compiled a list of 103 star clusters, nebulas, and galaxies. This list is still used today.

ISAAC NEWTON
1642–1727

English scientist who explained how gravity keeps the planets in orbit around the Sun, and also invented a reflecting telescope. He was professor of mathematics at the University of Cambridge at the age of 26. He revolutionized the concept of gravity, and his theory brought together Kepler's laws of planetary motion and Galileo's laws of falling bodies. He suggested that gravity applied throughout the universe and not just near the surface of Earth. In the 1660s, he began to study the nature of light and found that white light is made up of a rainbowlike spectrum of colors, which is revealed when the light passes through a prism or a lens. He tried to make a telescope but, because of this effect, the images he saw had colored edges. To overcome this, in 1668 he invented and built a reflecting telescope that used mirrors. His book *Principia Mathematica* was published in 1687.

BIOGRAPHIES

HERMANN OBERTH
1894–1989

One of the founding fathers of astronautics and author of *The Rocket into Interplanetary Space* (1923) and *The Road to Space Travel* (1929). He worked on rocket motors in the 1930s and developed the German V-2 rocket during World War II. He also worked on satellite launchers in the United States.

JAN OORT
1900–92

Dutch astrophysicist who studied the Milky Way using radio waves, and proposed that its galactic center was 30,000 light-years away. He found that the Sun orbited the Milky Way every 200 million years, and that the galaxy's mass was 100 billion times that of the Sun. He also suggested that the Sun was surrounded by a huge reservoir of comets.

ERNST ÖPIK
1893–1985

Estonian astronomer who became director of the Armagh Observatory. In 1932, he proposed that the solar system was surrounded by a cloud of comets—a cloud now named after Jan Oort. Öpik's work on how dust particles burn up as they enter Earth's atmosphere has been applied to the design of devices that protect spacecraft from heat as they reenter the atmosphere.

CECILIA PAYNE-GAPOSCHKIN
1900–79

British-born astronomer who was the first to suggest that hydrogen and helium were the main constituents of the universe. In 1923, she left England to work at Harvard College Observatory. She showed how the temperature of a star is related to its type or spectral class, and that the main sequence stars are made almost entirely of hydrogen and helium. She also identified variable stars while working with her husband, Sergei Gaposchkin. Her study of luminous stars is used today to measure distances to distant galaxies. Awarded the Harvard Chair in Astronomy in 1956, she was the first female professor at Harvard.

ARNO PENZIAS
born 1933

A German refugee who moved to the United States as a child and became a radio engineer in Bell Telephone Laboratories in 1961. In 1965, while trying to trace a source of radio interference, Penzias and Robert Wilson found radio waves that came toward Earth from all directions. The source had a temperature of –454°F (–270°C), and was what remained from the radiation made by the Big Bang. Penzias and Wilson received the 1978 Nobel Prize for Physics.

BIOGRAPHIES

VALERI POLIAKOV
born 1942

Russian doctor and cosmonaut who holds two world records—the most time spent in space and the longest single stay in space. He traveled aboard Soyuz TM-6 to Mir on August 29, 1988, and stayed for 241 days. He returned to Mir on January 8, 1994, and stayed for 438 days. As part of a medical experiment, he had some of his bone marrow removed before the mission so that it could be compared with another sample of bone marrow taken when he returned after months of weightlessness.

PTOLEMY
about 90–168 CE

Egyptian astronomer whose works dominated scientific thought until the 17th century. He thought that Earth was a perfect sphere at the center of the universe, surrounded by seven transparent spheres, each of which carried a moving object. In order of speed across the sky (and supposed distance from Earth), these were the Moon, Mercury, Venus, the Sun, Mars, Jupiter, and Saturn. An eighth sphere contained the stars. He compiled the astronomical ideas of the ancient Greeks in *The Almagest*, which built on the works of Hipparchus and others, added to his own observations. He also noted the latitude and longitude of many places on Earth, and his maps were used by Christopher Columbus.

MARTIN REES
born 1942

England's 15th Astronomer Royal, based at the University of Cambridge. He has concentrated on the study of the centers of active galaxies, and the way in which jets of gas from these galaxies interact with the surrounding interstellar medium. Rees has also written extensively on cosmology and the dark matter in the universe. He has enthusiastically promoted the communication of science to the general public.

HENRY RUSSELL
1877–1957

American astronomer who became professor of astronomy at Princeton in 1905. Russell studied multiple stars and the relationship between their orbits and masses. From his work on stellar distances, he was able to show that there was a main sequence of stars by plotting stellar luminosity against surface temperature on a graph. This came to be known as the Hertzsprung-Russell diagram because Ejnar Hertzsprung had plotted a similar graph in 1906. Russell incorrectly predicted that stars evolved by moving either up or down this sequence. In 1929, he suggested, correctly, that stars consist mainly of hydrogen.

MARTIN RYLE
1918–84

British radio astronomer who produced a catalog of 5,000 radio sources. He perfected a technique of combining signals from different movable radio telescopes to create a high-resolution image of the object emitting radio waves. He mapped regions on the Sun, and distant galaxies that emit radio waves, and showed that galaxies were closer together in the early universe—evidence for the Big Bang. In 1974, Ryle and Antony Hewish were awarded the Nobel Prize for Physics.

CARL SAGAN
1934–96

American astronomer who studied the atmospheres of planets. In the 1960s, he calculated that the surface of Venus was very hot due to a runaway greenhouse effect. He also researched the early atmosphere of Earth and ways in which life could be generated. His television series, *Cosmos*, was viewed around the world in 1980.

ALLAN SANDAGE
born 1926

American astronomer who started as Edwin Hubble's assistant. In 1960, with Tom Matthews, he was the first to optically identify a quasar. In 1965, he discovered the first "radio-quiet" quasars. In fact, only 1 in 200 quasars emits radio waves.

GIOVANNI SCHIAPARELLI
1835–1910

Italian astronomer who worked at the Brera Observatory in Milan from 1860 to 1900. In 1862, he realized that the Perseid meteor shower was produced by the decay of Comet Swift-Tuttle, and that they both had the same orbit. He made detailed observations of Mars and concluded it had channels (*canali*) on its surface, some of which he thought were splitting into two.

BERNHARD SCHMIDT
1879–1935

Estonian engineer who joined the staff of Hamburg Observatory in 1926. Large reflecting telescopes can cover only a very small field of view, so Schmidt devised a telescope for the observatory that used a spherical mirror behind a thin correcting lens to produce a very sharp image over a large field of view. Many Schmidt telescopes have been used for mapping the sky.

HARLOW SHAPLEY
1885–1972

American astronomer who started work as a journalist. While working at Mount Wilson Observatory in California, he used Cepheid variable stars to estimate the distance to globular star clusters, which he used to plot the shape and size of the Milky Way galaxy. He moved to Harvard in 1921 and became famous for his debate with Heber Curtis about whether the universe consisted of one galaxy or a multitude. Shapley showed that galaxies are clustered into groups.

ALAN SHEPARD
1923–98

A United States Navy test pilot who was the first American in space. His suborbital hop on May 5, 1961 took him and his Mercury space capsule 112 miles (180 km) above Earth, before it landed in the Atlantic Ocean 301 miles (485 km) downrange from the launch pad at Cape Canaveral, Florida. He returned to space in early 1971, when he commanded the Apollo 14 Moon mission.

JOSEF SHKLOVSKII
1916–85

Ukrainian astronomer who, in 1953, started the radio astronomy division of Russia's Astronomical Institute. He was among the first to suggest that spiraling electrons trapped in astronomical magnetic fields produced radio waves with a long wavelength called synchrotron radiation.

JILL TARTER
born 1944

American astrophysicist who was the first radio astronomer to start searching full-time for extraterrestrial intelligence in the early 1970s. As the chief scientist of Project Phoenix, she uses a multichannel analyzer that takes the signal from large radio telescopes and then listens to many frequencies at the same time, searching for messages.

VALENTINA TERESHKOVA
born 1937

Russian cosmonaut, formerly a textile worker and amateur parachutist, who was the first woman in space. In June 1963, she made 48 orbits of Earth on the Vostok 6 spacecraft in a 71-hour flight. The next woman flew 19 years later. Tereshkova married Andrian Nikolayev, who was also a cosmonaut, in 1963 and, after having a child, continued to train as a cosmonaut until 1969. Tereshkova went on to become an important member of the Communist Party and a representative in the Soviet government.

CLYDE TOMBAUGH
1906–97

American astronomer who discovered Pluto. He was born in Streator, Illinois, and, in 1929, joined the Lowell Observatory in Arizona as an assistant because he was too poor to go to college. In 1905, Percival Lowell had predicted the position of Planet X. To assist in the search, Tombaugh built a machine that looked at two photographic plates taken of the same area of sky, a few hours apart, to see if anything had moved against the fixed background of stars. On February 18, 1930, he discovered Pluto. Uncertain as to whether Pluto was big enough to disturb the orbit of Uranus, he continued his search for another planet for eight years, but without success.

KONSTANTIN TSIOLKOVSKY
1857–1935

Russian pioneer of the theory of space flight. Sputnik I was launched to commemorate his birth centennial. By 1898, he had produced theories of rocketry but did not have the resources to build a rocket. His book *Exploration of Cosmic Space by Means of Reaction Devices* (1903) contained designs of liquid hydrogen and liquid oxygen rockets, very similar to those in use today. He also showed that multistage rockets would be needed to leave Earth's gravitational field.

URBAIN LE VERRIER
1811–77

French astronomer who proved that the orbits of the planets were stable. He also studied how the orbits of the planets are pulled off course by the gravitational force exerted by adjacent planets, and predicted the position of undiscovered Neptune from its effects on Uranus's orbit. Johann Galle used his predictions to find Neptune.

FRED WHIPPLE
1906–2004

American astronomer who discovered six new comets and suggested, in 1951, that comets were made of snow and dust, the surface of which evaporated as it was heated in the inner solar system. He also studied the orbits of meteors and spacecraft, and the effect of Earth's atmosphere on them.

ROBERT WILSON
born 1936

American physicist who joined Bell Telecommunication Laboratories, and, with Arno Penzias, received the Nobel Prize for Physics in 1978. He worked with Penzias on reducing the radio noise in a horn-shaped radio antenna. In 1965, he discovered radio waves coming in all directions from a source with a temperature of –454°F (–270°C). This was what remained of the hot radiation produced by the Big Bang.

JOHN YOUNG
born 1930

American astronaut who trained as a test pilot in the navy. In 1965, he flew in Gemini 3, the first United States two-man space mission. After flying in Gemini 10, he made 31 lunar orbits in Apollo 10 in 1969, the dress rehearsal for the first Moon landing. He was commander of the Apollo 16 mission in 1972, making three walks on the Moon. In April 1981, he commanded the first Space Shuttle flight.

FRITZ ZWICKY
1898–1974

Swiss astrophysicist who moved to the California Institute of Technology in 1927. He suggested that supernova explosions destroy most of a massive star, leaving only the central core as a neutron star. He calculated that only one supernova would appear every 400 years in a galaxy, and that while the universe was expanding, the clusters were not.

GLOSSARY

Words in *italics* have their own
entries in the glossary.

Absolute zero The lowest
possible temperature (–459°F).

Absorption line A dark line
in a *spectrum*, caused by atoms
absorbing *radiation* of a
certain *wavelength*.

Accretion disk A disk of
material that is spiraling
into a *black hole*.

Active galaxy A *galaxy*, with a
central *black hole*, generating
huge amounts of energy.

Antimatter *Matter* made of
subatomic particles, with equal
and opposite properties to
normal matter.

Aperture The diameter of a
telescope's main mirror or lens.

Aphelion The point in an
object's *orbit* at which it is
farthest from the Sun.

Apogee The farthest point from
Earth reached by the Moon or
an orbiting artificial *satellite*.

Arc second A unit used to
measure the size or separation
of objects in the sky, equal to
1/3,600 degrees.

Astronomical unit (au) The
average distance between the
Sun and Earth—93 million
miles (149.6 million km).

Atom The smallest part of
an element.

Aurora Green and red glow
seen in the sky near the poles,
caused by particles from the
Sun colliding with gases in
Earth's atmosphere.

Background radiation A faint
radio signal emitted by the
entire sky—the remnant of
radiation from the Big Bang.

Barred spiral galaxy A *galaxy*
with spiral arms linked to a
central bulge by a straight bar
of stars and gas.

Binary system A pair of stars in
orbit around their center of mass.

Black hole A collapsed object,
with *gravity* so strong that
nothing—not even *light*—
can escape from it.

Blazar An *active galaxy*, angled
in such a way that we on Earth
see *radiation* coming straight
from its core.

Blue shift A shift in *spectral
lines* toward the blue end of the
spectrum.

Brown dwarf An object that
is smaller than a star but larger
than a planet, and produces
heat but no *light*.

Celestial sphere An imaginary
sphere of sky surrounding Earth,
on which celestial objects
appear to lie.

Cepheid variable A type of
variable star that changes in
luminosity and size, used to
measure distances in space.

Circumpolar star Any star
that does not appear to set, but
instead appears to circle the
celestial pole.

Conjunction The point in
the *orbit* of a planet when it
appears directly in line with the
Sun when viewed from Earth.

Cosmic ray A tiny, fast-
moving, electrically charged
particle coming from space.

Dark matter Invisible matter
thought to make up 97% of
the universe's *mass*.

Deep-sky object A collective
term for *nebulas*, *star clusters*,
and *galaxies*.

Doppler effect The change in
frequency of waves (of sound or
radiation) that reach an observer
when the source is moving.

Dust Microscopic grains of
"soot" from cool stars that
absorb starlight in space.

Eclipse An effect caused by
a celestial object casting its
shadow on another.

Eclipsing binary A pair of
stars in *orbit* around each other,
where each passes in front of
and behind the other as seen
from Earth.

Ecliptic An imaginary line in
the sky along which the Sun
seems to move through the year.

Electromagnetic radiation
Waves of energy, ranging from

gamma rays (shortest *wavelength*) to *radio waves* (longest wavelength) carried by photons that travels through space and matter at the *speed of light*.

Element Any of the basic substances of nature, each with unique properties, that cannot be broken down by chemical reactions.

Elliptical galaxy An oval or round *galaxy* with no spiral arms.

Elliptical orbit An *orbit* in the shape of an elongated circle.

Emission line A bright line in a *spectrum* caused by atoms giving out energy of a certain *wavelength*.

Escape velocity The speed at which one object must travel to escape another's *gravity*.

Extrasolar Beyond the *solar system*.

Extraterrestrial Not belonging to Earth.

Filament A string of galaxy *superclusters* stretching across a huge expanse of space.

Flyby An encounter between a space probe and a planet, comet, or asteroid, in which the probe does not stop to orbit or land.

Frequency The number of waves of *electromagnetic radiation* that pass a point every second.

Galaxy A body consisting of millions of stars, gas, and *dust* held together by *gravity*.

Galaxy cluster A group of *galaxies* held together by *gravity*.

Gamma rays *Electromagnetic radiation* of very short *wavelength* emitted by the most energetic objects in the universe.

Gas giant A large planet, primarily made up of a very deep, dense gaseous atmosphere.

Geostationary orbit An *orbit* 22,320 miles (36,000 km) above the equator, used by geostationary satellites.

Giant star A star in the last stages of its evolution, which has swollen in size, increased in brightness, and changed color. Sun-like stars become red giants; stars with more than 10 times the mass of the Sun become supergiants, which are the most luminous stars in the universe.

Gravitational well Distortion of space and time by the *gravity* of a massive object such as a star.

Gravity Force of attraction between any objects with *mass*.

Greenhouse effect The rise in temperature caused by gases—such as carbon dioxide and methane—trapping heat that a planet's surface would other-wise reflect back into space.

Hertzsprung-Russell diagram A diagram showing how a star's brightness and color are related.

Inflation A period of rapid expansion occurring within less than a second of the Big Bang.

Infrared Heat radiation—a type of *electromagnetic radiation*, with *wavelengths* just longer than visible *light*.

Intergalactic Between *galaxies*.

Interstellar Between stars.

Interstellar medium *Atoms* and molecules in the space between the stars.

Ionosphere The electrically charged region of the Earth's atmosphere between 30 and 375 miles (50 and 600 km) above the surface.

Irregular galaxy A *galaxy* with no obvious shape.

Kuiper Belt An area of the *solar system* extending from Neptune's *orbit* to the *Oort cloud's* inner edge, with millions of icy, cometlike objects.

Lava Molten rock released from the interior of a planet.

Light *Electromagnetic radiation*, with *wavelengths* visible to the human eye.

Light-year A standard unit of astronomical measurement, based on the distance light travels in one year—roughly 5.9 million million miles (9.5 million million km).

Local Arm Also called the Orion Arm—the spiral arm of the *Milky Way* in which the Sun lies.

Local Group The cluster of about 30 galaxies to which the *Milky Way* belongs.

389

Low Earth orbit An orbit about 155 miles (250 km) above Earth's surface, used by the Space Shuttle, space stations, and many *satellites*.

Luminosity The amount of energy given off by a star as *radiation* each second.

Magnetic field The magnetism generated by a planet, star, or *galaxy* that extends into space.

Magnetosphere The bubble around a planet where the *magnetic field* is strong enough to keep out the *solar wind*.

Magnitude The brightness of a celestial object, expressed on a scale of numbers. Apparent magnitude is a measure of brightness as seen from Earth; absolute magnitude is a measure of an object's *luminosity*.

Main sequence The region on the *Hertzsprung-Russell diagram* where most stars lie.

Mare (plural maria) A huge, lava-flooded depression on the Moon's surface.

Mass A measure of the amount of matter in an object.

Microgravity Very low *gravity*, as experienced in *orbit*.

Milky Way The name of the *galaxy* in which we live.

Molecular cloud An *interstellar* cloud made of molecules such as hydrogen and carbon monoxide.

Multiple star Three or more stars held in *orbit* around each other by *gravity*.

Nebula A cloud of gas and *dust* in space, visible when it reflects starlight or blocks out light coming from behind.

Neutrino A *subatomic particle*, of very small mass, produced by *nuclear fusion* in stars.

Neutron star A collapsed star composed mainly of neutrons.

Nova An explosion on the surface of a *white dwarf* star in a *binary system* that has pulled material off its companion star.

Nuclear fusion A combination of *nuclei* of atoms to form heavier ones at very high temperatures and pressures.

Nucleus (plural nuclei) The central part of an *atom*, made up of protons and neutrons, where nearly all its *mass* is contained.

Occultation One celestial object passing in front of another.

Oort cloud A spherical cloud around the Sun and planets, containing billions of comets.

Orbit The path of one object around another, more massive object in space.

Orbital period The time taken for one object to complete its *orbit* around another.

Parallax The shift in a nearby object's position against a more distant background, when seen from two separate points, used to measure distances of stars.

Parsec The distance at which a star or other object has a *parallax* of 1 *arc second*, equivalent to 3.26 *light-years*.

Payload The cargo carried into space by a launch vehicle or on an artificial satellite.

Penumbra The outer, lighter part of a sunspot. Also, the lightest part of a lunar eclipse shadow, where the Moon lies only partially in Earth's shadow.

Phase The relative size of the illuminated portion of a planet or moon, as seen from Earth.

Photosphere A star's visible surface, at which the star becomes transparent, allowing the star's *light* to blaze into space.

Planetary nebula The shell of gas puffed off by a red giant star before it becomes a *white dwarf*.

Polar orbit A *satellite orbit* passing above or close to the Earth's poles.

Pole star The star Polaris, in the constellation Ursa Minor, around which the northern sky appears to rotate.

Protostar A young star that has not yet started *nuclear fusion* in its core.

Pulsar A spinning *neutron star* that beams *radiation* into space.

Quasar A distant *active galaxy* that releases huge amounts of energy from a small central area.

Radar The technique of bouncing *radio waves* off an object to measure its distance.

Radiation Energy released by an object in the form of *electromagnetic radiation*.

Radio galaxy An *active galaxy* that shines at *radio wavelengths*.

Radio waves *Electromagnetic radiation* of very long *wavelength*, produced by gas clouds and energetic objects.

Red shift A shift in *spectral lines* toward the red end of the *spectrum*.

Resolving power A measure of a telescope's ability to distinguish fine detail.

Satellite An object held in *orbit* around another by its *gravity*, such as moons or artificial satellites around a planet, or a small galaxy around a larger one.

Seyfert galaxy A *spiral galaxy* with an unusually bright center—a type of *active galaxy*.

Solar flare A huge explosion above the surface of the Sun, caused as two loops of the Sun's *magnetic field* touch.

Solar system Everything trapped by the Sun's *gravity*, from planets to comets.

Solar wind A stream of high-speed particles blowing away from the Sun.

Spectral analysis The study of *spectral lines* to reveal the composition of a star or *galaxy*, or to find its *red shift*.

Spectral lines Bright or dark lines in the *spectrum* of a body emitting *radiation*.

Spectral type A method of classifying stars according to color and surface temperature.

Spectroscope An instrument used for splitting starlight into a *spectrum* and revealing *spectral lines*.

Spectrum (plural spectra) A band of *radiation* split into different *wavelengths*.

Speed of light A measure of how far a ray of *light* travels in one second—nearly 186,420 miles (300,000 km). Nothing can travel faster than this speed.

Spiral galaxy A galaxy with spiral arms emerging from a smooth central hub.

Star cluster A group of stars held together by *gravity*. Open clusters are loose groups of a few hundred young stars; globular clusters are dense balls with many thousands of old stars.

Starburst galaxy A *galaxy* that has undergone a sudden period of star formation.

Subatomic particle Any particle smaller than an *atom*; primarily, protons, neutrons, and electrons.

Supercluster A group of *galaxy clusters* held together by *gravity*.

Supernova An enormous stellar explosion that happens when a *supergiant* star runs out of fuel, or when a *white dwarf* explodes.

Tidal force A force on the surface of one object caused by a nearby object's *gravity*.

Ultraviolet *Electromagnetic radiation* with a *wavelength* just shorter than visible *light*.

Umbra The inner, darker region of a sunspot. Also, the darkest part of a lunar *eclipse* shadow, where the Moon is completely eclipsed.

Van Allen belts Regions of *radiation* around Earth, where Earth's *magnetic field* traps particles from the *solar wind*.

Variable star A star that changes in brightness. Many variable stars also regularly change size.

Wavelength The distance between the peaks or troughs of electromagnetic waves.

White dwarf The collapsed core of a Sun-like star that has stopped generating energy.

X-rays Radiation with a very short *wavelength*.

Key to Greek Alphabet Symbols	
α alpha	ν nu
β beta	ξ xi
γ gamma	ο omicron
∂ delta	π pi
ε epsilon	ρ rho
ζ zeta	σ sigma
η eta	τ tau
θ theta	υ upsilon
ι iota	φ phi
κ kappa	χ chi
λ lambda	ψ psi
μ mu	ω omega

INDEX

A B

AB Doradus, variable star 145
Abell 2256 galaxy cluster 204
absolute magnitude 138, 139, 142
accretion disks 170
active galaxies 182-83, 217
adaptive optics 223
aerogel 121
aerospike engine 305
Aldebaran, giant star 147, 342,
  343, 356, 360
Alpha Centauri system, 146, 308,
  314, 328
Alpha Regio, Venus 82
altazimuth mount, telescope 221
Amalthea, Jupiter moon 95
Andromeda, constellation 316,
  324, 347, 351, 359
Andromeda Galaxy 176, 203,
  324, 347, 350, 351, 359
annular eclipse 47
antennas, communications
  satellites 264, 265
antimatter 25, 26
engines 309
Antlia, constellation 317, 355,
  363
Aphrodite Terra, Venus 83
Apollo program 63, 286, 290
  Moon landings 68, 69, 276
Apollo-Soyuz link 287
apparent magnitude 142
Apus, constellation 317, 348
Aquarius, constellation 317, 325,
  351, 352, 359, 364
Aquila, constellation 316, 352,
  364
Ara, constellation 317, 348, 352,
  364
Arecibo Radio Telescope 217
Ariane rockets 247, 250, 256
Arianespace 253

Ariel, Uranus moon 105
Aries, constellation 317, 351,
  356, 359, 360
arrays (solar panels) 263
artificial satellites 262
Asteroid Belt 32, 35, 124, 125
asteroids 85, 112, 120, 124-25
astronauts
  living in space 292-93
  working in space 290-91, 294-95
atmosphere
  Earth 54-55, 120, 121
  Jupiter 92-93
  Mars 85
  Mercury 75
  Neptune 106
  Saturn 96
  Sun 44-45
atomic clocks 267
atoms 27, 28, 29
Aureum Chaos, Mars 88-89
Auriga, constellation 317, 347,
  356, 360
auroras 45, 51, 212, 213
Baikonur Cosmodrome 253
barred-spiral galaxies 176, 177
Belt of Orion 150, 356, 360
Betelgeuse, supergiant star 148,
  335, 356, 360, 361
Beta Pictoris, young star 71
Big Bang 15, 22, 24-25
Big Dipper, The, star cluster 149,
  151, 345, 346, 347
binary stars 144, 155
binoculars, using 210, 211
Black Eye Galaxy 354, 355, 363
black holes 139, 170-73, 195
blazars 183
booster rockets 288, 289
Boötes, constellation 316, 347,
  352, 355, 363, 364
bosons 26, 27

brightness of stars 17, 142-43, 144
brown dwarf stars 141

C

Caelum, constellation 317, 348,
  356, 360
Callisto, Jupiter moon 95
Caloris Basin, Mercury 76
Cambridge Optical Aperture
  Synthesis Telescope (COAST)
  223
Camelopardalis, constellation
  317, 347
Cancer, constellation 317, 355,
  356, 360, 363
Canes Venatici, constellation
  316, 347, 355, 363
Canis Major, constellation 317,
  356, 360
Canis Minor, constellation 317,
  356, 360
Canopus, star 326, 327, 348
Capella, double star 347, 356,
  360, 361
Capricornus, constellation 317,
  351, 352, 359, 364
capture theory 35
Carina, constellation 318,
  326, 348
Cartwheel Galaxy 178
Cassini orbiter 99, 102, 279, 303
Cassiopeia, constellation 167,
  318, 347
Cassiopeia A, supernova remnant
  193, 232-33
cataloging stars 152-53
Cat's-Eye Nebula 162, 347
celestial equator 312
celestial sphere 150, 151, 208,
  312, 314
cells, life 57
Centaurus, constellation 318,

328, 348, 352, 355, 363, 364
Cepheid variable stars 17, 145
Cepheus, constellation 318, 347
Cerenkov detector 240
Ceres asteroid 125
Cetus, constellation 318, 351, 356, 359, 360
Chamaeleon, constellation 318, 348
Chandra X-Ray Telescope 245
Chandrasekhar limit 163
charge-coupled device (CCD) 226
Charon, Pluto moon 109, 231
chromosphere, Sun 44
Circinus, constellation 318, 348
circumpolar stars 346
classification of galaxies 177
Clementine space probe
  Moon 65
Clipper Graham (DC-XA) spaceplane 304
clouds
  molecular 134, 189
  interstellar 235
  Jupiter 93
  Neptune 106, 107
  Saturn 96
  Uranus 104
  Venus 81
clusters
  galaxy 18, 19, 202, 204
  star (globular) 133, 158-59
  star (open) 133, 154, 155
COBE 22, 29
coded mask gamma-ray detector 241
Columba, constellation 318, 348, 356, 360
Coma Berenices, constellation 318, 355, 363
Coma Cluster, of galaxies 205
comets 112, 113, 114-17, 120
  exploring 116-17
Comet Hale-Bopp 113, 116
Comet Halley 113, 114, 115
Comet NEAT 118-19

Comet Shoemaker-Levy-9 93, 115, 117
Comet Wild 2 117
communications satellites 263, 264-65
constellations 150-51
  guide 316-23
  names 152, 346
Copernicus Crater, Moon 61, 62
corona, Sun 38, 44, 45
Corona Australis, constellation 318, 348, 352, 364
Corona Borealis, constellation 318, 352, 364
Corvus, constellation 318, 355, 363
cosmic air shower 224
Cosmic Background Explorer Satellite see COBE
cosmic inflation 25
cosmic rays 224
cosmic year 185
cosmonauts 303
Crab Nebula 168, 193, 229, 343, 356, 360, 361
Crater, constellation 319, 355, 363
craters 127
  Mercury 74, 76, 77
  Moon 60, 61, 63, 65
  Venus 79
  see also meteorite impacts
Crux, constellation 318, 329, 349
V404 Cygni black hole 195
Cygnus, constellation 144, 319, 330-1, 347, 351, 352, 359, 364
Cygnus Loop 189
Cygnus Rift 189, 365
Cygnus X-1 black hole 195

D E
declination 350
Deep Space 1 probe 306
Deimos, Mars moon 85
Delphinus, constellation 319, 351, 352, 359, 364
Delta rockets 251

diffraction grating 227
Dione, Saturn moon 102
Discovery Rupes, Mercury 77
distances, measuring 16-17, 146-47
Dog Star see Sirius
Doppler shift 149
Dorado, constellation 319, 332, 348
30 Doradus 200-201
double stars 155
Draco, constellation 319, 333, 347, 352, 364
Dumbbell Nebula 352, 353, 364
dust 114, 189, 213
Eagle Nebula 352, 353, 364
Earth, planet 50-55
  climate change 55
  deforestation, mapping 271
  magnetism 51
  meteors/meteorites 126, 127, 281
  plates 52, 53
  tides 66-67
  wind circulation 55
Earth resources satellites 270-71
eclipses
  Moon 59
  Sun 38, 44, 46-47, 212
ecliptic 211
Einstein's Theory of General Relativity 172
electromagnetic radiation 228
electromagnetic spectrum 228
electromagnetism 24
electronic cameras 226, 230
elliptical galaxies 176, 177, 202, 205
elliptical orbit, satellite 262
Enceladus, Saturn moon 103
Epimetheus, Saturn moon 103
equatorial mount, telescope 221
Equuleus, constellation 319, 351, 352, 359, 364
Eridanus, constellation 319, 348, 351, 356, 359, 360
ERS-1 satellite 270
escape velocity 247

Eta Carinae, variable star 144, 327, 348
Europa, Jupiter moon 95
European Southern Observatory 219, 223
European Space Agency (ESA) 102, 253, 266, 296
event horizon 172
evolution, on Earth 56
experiments in space 69, 296-97
extrasolar planets 70-71

F G

false color in images 231, 271
fireballs 121
flares, Sun 42, 44
flyby probes 274, 278
Fornax, constellation 319, 351, 356, 359, 360
full moon 59, 67
galaxies 12, 14, 23, 153, 76-77
  distant 12, 20-21
  expansion 18, 19
  types 176
Galileo space probe 56, 125
  Jupiter 92, 95, 275
gamma-ray bursters 241
gamma rays 28, 228, 240-41, 245
Ganymede, Jupiter moon 95
Gaspra asteroid 125
Gemini, constellation 319, 356, 360
Gemini Telescope 220
geostationary orbit (GEO) satellites 262, 264
geostationary satellites 264, 269
Giotto probe 115, 117
Global Orbiting Navigation Satellite System (GLONASS) 266
Global Positioning System (GPS) 266, 267
Global Surveyor 283
Globalstar 265
GOES satellite 269
gravitational waves 225
gravitational wells 19, 172, 173
gravity 24, 66, 67

black holes 170, 172
  galaxies 178
  and space probes 274
grazing incidence mirror, telescope 239, 245
Great Dark Spot, Neptune 107
Great Red Spot (GRS), Jupiter 92
greenhouse effect
  Earth 55
  Venus 81
Grus, constellation 319, 351, 359

H I J K

Hale Telescope 214
Hawking radiation 171
heliosphere 49
heliostat 43
helium 22, 23, 27
  stars 130, 131
  Sun 48, 49
Helix Nebula 133, 191, 325, 351, 358, 359
Hercules, constellation 130, 319, 347, 352, 364
Hertzsprung-Russell (H-R) diagram 135, 139, 141
Horologium, constellation 320, 348, 356, 360
Horsehead Nebula 13, 335
Hubble Space Telescope (HST) 244, 260-61
  Neptune 107
  stars and galaxies 14, 20-21, 159
Humboldt Crater, Moon 63
hurricane forecasting 268, 269
Huygens lander
  Saturn/Titan 102, 279, 303
Hyades star cluster 147, 191, 342, 343, 356, 360
Hydra, constellation 320, 352, 355, 356, 360, 363, 364
hydrogen 22, 23, 27
  nuclear fusion 40, 131
  stars 130, 131
  Sun 48, 49
hydrogen-burning stars 139

Hydrus, constellation 320, 348
in-car navigation (GPS) 267
Indus, constellation 320, 348, 351, 352, 359, 364
infrared 229, 234, 271
Infrared Astronomical Satellite (IRAS) 179, 235
infrared telescopes 234-35, 245
Intelsat satellite 267, 302
interstellar exploration 308
interstellar medium 188-89
inverse square law 147
irregular galaxies 176, 203
Io, Jupiter moon 95
ion drive spacecraft 306
International Space Station (ISS) 273, 291, 298-99
interplanetary space probes 306-307
Janus, Saturn moon 102
Jupiter 33, 90-93, 115
  moons 94-95
  ring system 90
  storms 92
Keck Telescope 219, 222, 223
Kennedy Space Center 252
Keyhole Nebula 145
Kitt Peak National Observatory 119, 215
Korolev Crater, Moon 65
Kourov Space Center 253, 256
Kuiper Belt 108, 112

L

L1011 Stargazer launcher 250
Lacerta, constellation 320, 347, 351, 359
Lagoon Nebula 195, 336, 338-39, 352, 364, 365
Lakshmi Planum, Venus 82, 83
landers 276-77, 278
Landsat satellites 270, 271
Large Magellanic Cloud (LMC) 157, 167, 198-99, 332, 348
laser drives 308
last scattering surface 28, 29
launch centers/sites 252-53
  countdown 256-57

launch pad 257
launchers 247, 250-51, 252, 257
Leo, constellation 320, 355, 363
Leo Minor, constellation 320, 355, 363
Leonid meteor shower 120
Lepus, constellation 320, 356, 360
Libra, constellation 320, 352, 355, 363, 364
libration 67
life
 on Earth 50, 56-57
 on Mars, search for 280-81
liftoff, rockets 257
light 28, 48, 143, 226-27
 speed of 14
 stars 71, 140, 141, 148-49
 sunlight 140
light pollution 211
light-years (ly) 14, 146
lithium 26, 27
living in space 292-93
Local Group, galaxy cluster 203, 204
Local Supercluster 205
low Earth orbit (below GEO) satellites 262, 264
luminosity 17, 138, 139, 142
Luna probes 68, 69, 300
 Moon 63, 64, 275, 277
lunar see eclipses, Moon
Lunar Module (LM), Apollo 300
lunar roving vehicle (LRV) 290
Lunokhod 1 and 2 probes 69, 301
Lupus, constellation 320, 348, 352, 355, 363, 364
Lynx, constellation 320, 347, 355, 356, 360, 363
Lyra, constellation 320, 347, 352, 364

M
M15 globular cluster 350, 351
M35, M36 and M38 clusters 356, 357
M41 cluster 360, 361
Magellan orbiter 82

Magellanic Clouds 198-99
Magellanic Stream 199
magnetars 169
magnetic field
 Earth 45
 Jupiter 91
 Mercury 75
 Sun 38, 43
magnetosphere 51, 91
Main Belt see Asteroid Belt
main sequence of stars 139, 141
mapping Milky Way 187
mare/maria, Moon 60, 62, 63
Mare Crisium, Moon 63
Mare Imbrium, Moon 61, 62
Mare Moscoviense, Moon 64
Mare Orientale, Moon 65
Mariner probes 76, 275, 280
Mars, planet 84-85, 88-89, 280-81, 307
 channels/canals 281
 life on, search for 280-81
 missions to 282-83
 polar ice caps 87
 surface 86-87, 230
 water 280, 283
matter 25, 26
Maxwell Montes, Venus 82
Mead Crater, Venus 83
Mensa, constellation 321, 348
Mercury, planet 74-77
Messier catalog (M) 153
meteor radiant 213
meteor showers 120, 121, 212
meteorite impacts (craters) 126-27
 Earth 126, 127, 281
 Mercury 74
 Moon 61, 122
meteorites 121, 122-23, 281
meteoroids 120, 121
meteorology satellites 268-69
meteors 120-21, 126
Meteosat satellite 269
microgravity 296
Microscopium, constellation 321, 348, 351, 352, 359, 364
Milky Way Galaxy 13, 16, 184-85, 202, 209

 center 196-97
 local neighborhood 190-91
 mapping 186-87
 measuring distance 16
 spiral shape 23
 star clusters 133, 154, 158
Mimas, Saturn moon 126
minor members, solar system 112-13
Mir space station 303
Mira stars 145
Miranda, Uranus moon 105
mission control, launch 256
Monoceros, constellation 321, 356, 360
Montes Apenninus, Moon 62
Moon 58-59, 239
 far side 64-65, 67
 landings 68-69, 276
 near side 62-63
 phases 59
 polar regions 63, 65
 surface 60-61
moon buggy 290
moons 32
 Jupiter 94-95
 Mars 85
 Neptune 106
 Saturn 98, 102-103
 Uranus 104, 105
mosaic maps 65
Mouse, pulsar 197
multiple stars 155
Musca, constellation 321, 348

N O
navigation satellites 266-67
nebulas 36-37, 134, 153
negative mass 309
Neptune, planet 33, 106-107
neutrinos 27, 40, 41, 225
neutron spectrometer 230
neutron stars 139, 168-69
neutrons 27
New General Catalog (NGC) 153
new moon 59, 67
newborn stars 71, 134-35, 136-37

NGC 207 galaxy 180-81
NGC 2264 star cluster 154
NGC 4261 star 170
NGC 4603 galaxy 14
NOAA 10 satellite 269
Norma, constellation 321, 348,
    352, 364
North America Nebula 190, 191,
    331, 347, 351, 352, 359, 364
North American Aerospace
    Defense Command (NORAD)
    272, 273
North Star (Polaris) 312
Northern Cross 330, 347,
    352, 364
novas 144
observatories 218-19
observatory telescopes 220-21
observing space 208-209
    good viewing conditions 209
    measuring distances using
        hands 349
Octans, constellation 321, 348
Odyssey probe 230
Olympus Mons, Mars 86
Omega Centauri globular cluster
    159
Omega Nebula 337, 352
Oort cloud, solar system 16, 35,
    112, 113, 116
Ophiuchus, constellation 321,
    352, 364
Opportunity, rover 276, 282
optical telescopes 214-15, 218
orbital maneuvering system
    (OMS) 289
orbiter (spaceplane) 288
orbiter probes 274, 278
orbits 32
    binary stars 155
    comets 113, 114, 117
    Earth 32
    extrasolar planets 70
    Jupiter 32, 91
    Mars 32, 85
    Mercury 32, 75
    Neptune 33, 106
    Pluto 32, 109, 108

satellites 262
Saturn 32
Uranus 32, 105
Venus 32, 78
Orion, constellation 150, 321,
    334-5, 356, 360
    interstellar clouds 235
    observing 211
Orion Arm, Milky Way 190
Orion Nebula 135, 152, 334,
    356, 360
    star nursery 134, 136-37
oxygen cycle, Earth 56
ozone layer, Earth 55

P Q
Pandora, Saturn moon 98
parallax 16, 146, 147
parsecs 146
partial eclipses 46, 59
particles 26, 27
    see also antimatter, matter
Pathfinder lander 278, 282
Pavo, constellation 321, 348
payload, launchers 256
Pegasus, constellation 321,
    351, 359
Pegasus rocket 250
Pelican Nebula 191
penumbra, Moon 59
periodic comets 113, 114
Perseus, constellation 321, 347,
    351, 356, 359, 360
Perseus Arm, Milky Way 192-93
Phobos, Mars moon 85
Phoenix, constellation 321, 348,
    349, 351, 359
photons 25, 27, 28
photosphere, Sun 40, 42, 43, 45
Pictor, constellation 322, 348,
    356, 360
Pioneer probes 80, 274, 275, 301
Pisces, constellation 322, 351,
    359
Pisces Austrinus, constellation
    322, 351, 359
pixels, images 230
planetary nebulas 162-63

planetesimals 35
planets 32, 33, 34, 35, 71
    extrasolar 70-1
planisphere 227
plate tectonics, Earth 52, 53
Pleiades, open star cluster 154,
    342, 343, 356, 360
Pluto, planet 33, 35, 108-109,
    231
polar orbit satellite 262, 269
Polaris, star 312, 347
Praesepe, open star cluster 154,
    355, 356, 357, 360
prism 227
Prometheus, Saturn moon 98
prominences, Sun 38, 42, 44, 48
propellants, rocket 248, 249, 257
proper motion 149
Proton rocket 250
protons 27
protoplanetary disk 135
protoplanets 35, 125
protostars 134, 135
Proxima Centauri, star 146
pulsars 168, 169
Puppis, constellation 322, 348,
    356, 360
Puppis A, supernova remnant 239
Pyxis, constellation 322, 355,
    356, 360, 363
quasars 23, 176, 183

R
radiation
    background, universe 29
    wavelengths 228, 270, 271
radio energy 216
radio galaxies 183, 217
radio lobes, galaxy 182, 197
radio maps 216
radio telescopes 187, 216-17, 218
radio waves 169, 193, 264, 265
Ranger probes 63, 69
red giant stars 132, 139, 141,
    160-61, 162
Red Planet see Mars
redshift 19, 149
reflector telescopes 214, 220, 221

refractor telescopes 214, 215, 220
Reticulum, constellation 322, 348
reusable spacecraft 247
Rho Ophiuchi Nebula 190, 191
Rigel, star 142, 356, 360
right ascension 350
ring systems, planetary 33
    Jupiter 90
    Neptune 106
    Saturn 96, 98-101
    Uranus 104
rockets 246-47, 250-51
    countdown 256-57
    engine 246
    fuels 248-49
Rosat X-ray telescope 239
Rosetta orbiter/lander 303
Roton rocket 305
RR Lyrae stars 159

S

Sagitta, constellation 322, 352,
    364
Sagittarius, constellation 184,
    322, 336-37, 348, 352, 364
Sagittarius A*, black hole 196,
    197
Sagittarius A West 197
Sagittarius Arm, Milky Way
    194-95
satellite constellations 265
satellite footprint 264
satellites 262-63, 273
Saturn 33, 96-97, 231
    moons 98, 102-103
    rings 96, 98-101
Saturn V rocket 68
Scorpius, constellation 322,
    340-41, 348, 352, 364
Sculptor, constellation 322,
    351, 359
Scutum, constellation 322,
    352, 364
Serpens, constellation 322,
    352, 364
Sextans, constellation 323,
    355, 363
Seyfert galaxies 183

shepherd moons, Saturn 98
shock waves, supernova 34
shooting stars 120
single-stage-to-orbit (SSTO)
    spacecraft 304
singularity 172
Sirius, star 142, 356, 360, 361
sky map, gamma ray 241
Skylab 296
Small Magellanic Cloud (SMC)
    198-99, 348
snow 114
SOFIA, flying observatory 219
Sojourner, rover 282
solar atmosphere 237
solar cells 263
solar eclipse see eclipse, Sun
solar energy 48-49
solar mass 131, 138
solar nebula 34
solar oscillations 41
solar panels 263
solar system 23, 32-33, 112
    birth 34-5
solar telescopes 43, 215
solar wind 45, 49
Sombrero Galaxy 355, 362, 363
Southern Cross 348, 349
Southern Pleiades 327, 349
space 230-1
    distorting 172, 173
    expansion 18
    images of 230-31
    observing 208-209
    temperature 22
space colonies 307
space debris 272-73
space endurance record 303
space food 293
space junk 272
space launchers 250-51
space missions 300-303
space probes 274-75, 278-79, 306
Space Shuttle 288-89, 302
    launch site 252, 254-55
    liftoff 248
    living on 292-93
space stations 291, 292, 298-99

space toilet 293
space tourism 305
spaceflight, history of 286-87
Spacelab 296, 297
spaceplanes 304-305
spacesuits 292, 299
spacewalk 287
spaghettification 173
spectral analysis 143
spectral types (stars) 140
spectrohelioscope 215
spectrometers 19
spectroscopy 227
spectrum 140, 143, 149, 227
spin stabilization satellite 263
spiral galaxies 176, 237
Spirit, rover 276, 282
Sputnik, satellite 253, 286
Square of Pegasus 350, 351, 359
star maps 151
    Northern Hemisphere 350-57
    northern sky 312-13
    polar 346-49
    Southern Hemisphere 358-65
    southern sky 314-15
star trails 208
starbirth, Milky Way 190
starburst galaxies 178, 179, 237
Stardust space probe 117
stargazing 210-11
starlight 148, 228
stars 12, 130-31, 148-49
    chemical elements 140
    classification 140-41
    color 140
    life cycle 132-33
    light 140
    magnitudes/brightness 138,
        142-43
    mass 138, 140
    measuring 131
    movement 149
    names 153
    pairs of 145
    sizes 131, 139
    temperature 140, 143
    twinkle 261
    types 138, 140

wobble 71
starships 308-309
stellar classification 140-41
stellar winds 161
storms
  Mars 87
  Jupiter 92
  Saturn 97
strong force 24
subatomic particles 26, 27
Sudbury Observatory 41
Summer Triangle 353
Sun 32, 38-39, 132, 231
  atmosphere 44-45
  Baily's Beads 47
  diamond ring 47
  formation 34
  inside 40-41
  nearest star 146
  nuclear reactions 38, 40
  rotation speed 43
  safety when looking at 39, 47
  surface 39, 42-43
sunspots 38, 42, 43
superclusters, galaxy 204-205
supergiant stars 139, 141,
  160, 161
  exploding 166
Supernova 1987A 167, 332
supernovas 17, 34, 166-67
  remnants 167, 232-33, 239
Surveyor probes 63, 69
synchrotron radiation 193

T U V

Tarantula Nebula 156-57, 159,
  199, 332, 348
Taurus, constellation 323, 342-43,
  356, 360
telemetry 262
telescopes 19, 214, 220, 244-45
  mirrors 220, 222-23, 239, 244
  mountings 221
Telescopium, constellation 323,
  348, 352, 364
thematic mapper, satellite 270
tides, Earth 66-67
Titan, Saturn moon 103

Toby Jug Nebula 161
total eclipses 44, 46, 59
TRACE spacecraft 231
transit of Mercury 77
Trapezium star cluster 134, 335,
  356, 360, 361
Triangulum, constellation 323,
  351, 359
Triangulum Australe,
  constellation 323, 348
Triangulum Galaxy 202, 351,
  358, 359
Trifid Nebula 195, 337, 352, 364
Triton, Neptune moon 107
Tucana, constellation 323, 348
47 Tucanae, globular cluster 158,
  159, 348
Tycho supernova remnant 167
ultraviolet (UV) radiation 236
Ulysses probe 49
umbra, Moon 46, 59
Umbriel, Uranus moon 105
universe 12, 22-23, 26-27
  distances 14, 16-17
  expansion 18-19, 22
  size 14, 16-17
  temperature 23
  three-dimensional maps 16
  transparency 28
Uranus, planet 33, 104-105
Ursa Major, constellation 323,
  344-5, 347, 355, 356, 360, 363
Ursa Minor, constellation 323,
  346, 347
Van Allen belts 51
Van de Graaff crater, Moon 64
variable stars 144-45
Vela, constellation 239, 323, 348,
  355, 356, 360, 363
Vela, supernova 167
Venera space probes 80, 277
Venturestar (X-33) spaceplane
  304
Venus 78-79
  atmosphere 80-81
  surface 82-83
Very Large Array (VLA) radio
  telescope 216

Very Large Telescope (VLT) 223
Viking lander craft 276, 277, 278
Viking Orbiter 87
Virgo, constellation 323, 352,
  355, 363, 364
Virgo galaxy cluster 204, 205,
  355, 363
virtual particle pairs 25
visible light 228, 229
Volans, constellation 323, 348
volcanoes
  Mars 86
  Venus 78
Vostok I spaceship 286, 300
Voyager spacecraft 91, 99, 104,
  106, 274, 278, 308
Vulpecula, constellation 323,
  351, 352, 359, 364

W Y

warp drive 309
water
  Earth 50
  Mars 280, 283
water ice 77, 115
wavelengths
  light 143, 149
  measuring 270, 271
  radiation 228-29
  ultraviolet 236
weak force 24
weather satellites 268, 269
weightlessness 292, 294-95, 296
Whirlpool Galaxy 179, 347, 355,
  363
white dwarf stars 131, 139, 141,
  162, 163, 165
Wild Duck cluster 352, 353, 364
WIMPs 26, 27
wobbling stars 71
working in space 290-91, 294-95
X-34 prototype spaceplane 305
X-ray telescopes 239, 245
X-rays 228, 229, 238-39
young stars 190

ACKNOWLEDGMENTS

Dorling Kindersley would like to thank Julie Ferris for editorial support; Merle Read for proof-reading; Lynn Bresler for the index; Christine Heilman for Americanization; and Hoa Luc for editorial assistance.

Picture credits

The publisher would like to thank the following for their kind permission to reproduce their photographs:

Abbreviations key: t-top, b-bottom, r-right, l-left, c-center, a-above, f-far

Anglo Australian Observatory: 19 (crb), 144-145, 154 (bl), 161 (bl), 166-167, 189 (tr), 191 (tl), 203 (tc), 205 (tr), 261 (tr) David Malin 17 (crb), 183 (cla), 202 (bl), Malin/Pasachoff 193 (tl), Royal Observatory Edinburgh 167 (cra), 188-189, 204-205; akg-images: 376 (br), 377 (br), 378 (cl), Erich Lessing 376 (cl), 384 (c); Bryan And Cherry Alexander Photography: 123 (cbl); Associated press: 253 (tr); www.bridgeman.co.uk: 381 (bl); Cambridge University Library: 219 (c); Central Press Photos Ltd: 382 (cl); Ciel et Espace: 218 (bl), 218-219, 219 (tr), Serge Brunier 6 (bc); Colorific!: 116 (bl); Corbis: 5 (br), 50-51 (b), 68-69 (b), 102 (tr), 263 (crb), 267 (bl), 272 (bl), Bettmann 286 (cr), European Southern Observatory 223 (tl), Hulton-Deutsch Collection 287 (cl), Kipa 309 (crb), Roger Ressmeyer 46 (br), 219 (tr), 307 (tl), William Taufic 143 (br); Dr. Thomas Dame: Centre for Astrophysics/Smithsonian Institution 187 (tr); Empics Ltd: Fiona Hanson 376 (tc); European Space Agency: 245 (c, bl), 296 (clb), 302 (cr), 303 (bl, cr), B. Paris 256 (cb), CNES 257 (tl, c), CNES/CSG 257 (r), D. Ducros 102 (b), 253 (tl), ESTEC 270-271 (c), 271 (tc), NES/CSG 256 (tr); European Southern Observatory: 133 (tr), 146 (cl), 158-159, Meylan 5, 228 (tr), 277 (tl); Mary Evans Picture Library: 375 (cr), 378 (br), 379 (tr); Vivian Fifield,: 378 (bl); Galaxy Picture Library: 62 (b), 64 (br), 81 (cr), 85 (cl), 87 (tr), 91 (cr), 117 (crb), 135

(ca, cl, cr), 140 (cr), 147 (cr), 154 (br), 159 (bc), 189 (br), 191 (cr), 209 (br), 211 (tl, tc), 254 (cl), 325 (crb), 347 (c), 348 (c), 349 (c, clb, cla), 353 (cl, cr), 354 (cl), 357 (cb, cla, clb), 358 (cl), 361 (cra), 362 (clb), 365 (c), Eric Hutton 335 (tc), Gordon Garradd 79 (tl), 326 (br), 327 (tl), 332 (cra), 334 (cl), 341 (br); M. Stecker 2 (bl), 191 (crb), 324 (tr), 327 (br), 331 (tr) 335 (br, tl), 337 (bl, tl, cr), 341 (tl), Nick Szyanex & Ian King 331 (bl) 342 (br) 345 (br), R. Scagell 126 (crb), 329 (tl), 330 (cl), 336 (br), 340 (crb), 343 (br), 345 (tl), Terry Platt 345 (tc), Trevor Searle & Phil Hodgins 345 (bl); 2005 Garmin Ltd. or its subsidiaries: Photo courtesy of Garmin: 267 (tr); Gemini Observatory/Association of Universities for Research in Astronomy: 214 (bl); Genesis Space Photo Library: 229 (tr), 251 (cr); Getty Images: 383 (cl), 385 (tc), Evening Standard Collection 379 (br), Hulton Archive 375 (tl), 376 (cr), 382 (cr); Harvard University Art Museums: 383 (tr); Hencoup Enterprises: 43 (c), 240 (tr), 384 (tr), 386 (cr), Royer 199 (br); Hughes Space & Communications: 251 (tr); FLPA - Images of Nature: 212 (tr); Ernest Orlando Lawrence: Berkeley National Laboratory 41 (tr); Courtesy of Lockheed Martin Aeronautics Company, Palmdale: 250 (cra, cr); Lunar and Planetary Institute: 82 (c); Lund Observatory: 185 (tl); Mullard Radio Astronomy Observatory: University of Cambridge 148 (bl); NASA: 5 (clb), 13 (tr), 14 (c), 45 (tr), 48 (cr, bl), 62 (c), 63 (crb), 64 (c), 79 (cl), 90-91, 95 (cb), 103 (clb, cbl), 107 (tr), 108-109, 117 (cb), 122 (bl), 125 (cr), 126 (cl), 167 (tc), 184 (tr), 223 (br), 227 (cr), 228 (b), 237 (cr), 244 (tr, c), 245 (t), 273 (tr, cr), 276 (b), 286 (cra), 287 (cr), 290 (cl, br, tl), 292 (bl, br), 293 (cla, clb), 296 (br), 297 (br), 299 (br, tr), 300 (cr, tr), 301 (br, cl, tr), 303 (tl), 305 (clb, cr, tl), 306 (cr) 307 (br), Brad Whitmore/STScI 178-179, Egret 183 (bl), Ford/Ferraresa 170 (bl), GSFC 237 (br, fbr), JPL 22 (bl), 38 (tr), 69 (tl), 82 (cb), 98 (bc), 130 (tr), 176 (tr), 177 (tl), 229 (br), 247 (cl), 274 (tr), 276 (tr), KSC 249 (br), 252 (clb), Palomar Observatory 227 (cla), W.M. Keck Observatory 227 (tr); NOAA:

269 (cb); NSSDC/GSFC/NASA: 65 (tc, c, b), 74 (bl), 76 (c), 77 (bc), 83 (cr); Orbital Sciences Corporation: 250 (bl); Patrick Air Force Base: 251 (ca, bl); Max Planck Institute of Radioastronomy: 234 (cl), 239 (cl, br), 241 (tc), ROSAT 204 (bl); planetary.org: 99 (cr); popperfoto.com: 273 (bl); Royal Astronomical Society: 281 (tr), 381 (br); Royal Greenwich Observatory: 224-225, 235 (cl), Dr. Seth Shostak 235 (tl), Simon Tulloch 224 (clb); Royal Observatory Edinburgh: 233 (tl), David Malin/Anglo-Australian Observatory 154-155, 191 (tr), 193 (cr) 374 (br); Satellite Visualisation Software, created by Geometry Center, University of Minnesota: 265 (cr). Science & Society Picture Library: 380 (br). Science Photo Library: 29 (tr), 41 (c), 42 (br), 43 (tr), 44 (c), 55 (c), 60, 79 (br), 262 (b), 380 (tr), 387 (tc), A. Barrington Brown 380, Alex Bartel 216 (tr), Celestial Image Co. 205 (br), Chris Butler 71 (tr), CNES 1987 Distribution Spot Image 271 (bc), D. Golimowski, S. Durrance & M. Clampin 71 (br), D.L. DePoy & N.A. Sharp/NOAO 197 (br), Damien Lovegrove 263 (tr), David A. Hardy 112 (br), 220-221, David Ducros 298 (cb), David Nunuk 5 (tc), 44-45, 47 (br), David P.Anderson SMU/NASA 83 (cb), David Parker 126 (br), Dennis Milon 120 (bl), Dr Leon Golub 45 (cb), Dr Michael J. Ledlow 74-75 (t), Dr. John C. Good 179 (bl), Dr. Luke Dodd 198 (bl), Dr. Seth Shostak 272-273, Earth Satellite Corporation 271(cr), ESA/CE/Eurocontrol 266 (bl), 266-267, European Space Agency 115 (cl), F. Yusef-Zadeh/NRAO/AUI/NSF 197 (cla), Francois Gohier 234 (tr), Fred Espenak 77 (tr), 187 (bl), 209 (t), Hank Morgan 383 (br), Hasler & Pierce NASA GSFC 269 (tl), Joe Tucciarone 124 (bc), John Chumack 233 (cr), 343 (tl), John Sanford 63 (tr), 150 (tr), Julian Baum 280 (bl), 282 (cr), 309 (tl), Luke Dodd 148-149, McDonnell Douglas Aerospace 304 (tr), NASA 2 (cla), 44 (tr), 61 (bl), 78 (tl, crb, bc), 81 (tl), 83 (tr), 90 (tr), 92 (cb, bl), 94 (cr), 94-95 (x2), 95 (tl, tr), 99 (tl), 102-103, 103 (br), 106 (bc), 229 (cl), 237 (tr), 248 (c), 268 (cr), 268-269, 269 (br), 270 (cl), 280-281, 281(br), 282-283, 283 (tr), 287 (bl, tr), 291(tl, b), 297 (bl), 299 (cra), 374 (tl), NASA/ESA/STScI 5 (br), 93 (br), 162-163, 189 (c), NASA/JPL 233 (fcr), NOAO 114 (tr), 199 (tl), Novosti 0 (bl), 286 (cb), NRAO/AUI/NSF 179 (cr), 193 (bl), 197 (tr, clb),

Pekka Parviainen 116-117, 213 (tl), Phillippe Plailly/Eurelios 267 (cr), Royal Observatory Edinburgh 195 (bl), Royal Observatory Edinburgh/AATB 152 (tr), 198-199, Starlight 208 (tr), STARSEM 246 (tr), Tony Hallas 202 (tr, cl), US Geological Survey 84 (bl), 86 (bl), 87 (cr); SETI Institute/Seth Shostak: 386 (bl); spaceimage.com: 270 (bc); Carole Stott: 121 (tr); Stsci/aura/nasa: 26 (br), 97 (tl), 159 (tr), 168 (br), 178 (bl), 183 (tl, clb), 261 (br), Association of Universities for Research in Astronomy Inc. 25 (tr), Hubble Space Telescope 134 (b), J. Hester & P. Scowen (Arizona State University) 27 (bl), W.N. Colley and E. Turner (Princeton University)/J.A. Tyson (Bell Laboratories, Lucent Technologies) 26 (t); Institute for Cosmic Ray Research, University of Tokyo: 221 (tr); University of California: HCO/Lick Observatory 144 (cl, fcl).

All other images © Dorling Kindersley.
For further information, see www.dkimages.com